*Modulation Systems and Noise*

*John J. Downing*

# MODULATION SYSTEMS AND NOISE

PRENTICE-HALL, INC., Englewood Cliffs, N. J.

# Preface

This book attempts to satisfy a need which has become apparent to the author through his having both taught and practiced "communication systems engineering." The need is to treat concisely the ordinary problems of the performance of familiar communication systems within the context of statistical concepts and random-noise representations, which only within the past five years have achieved widespread circulation among the radio engineering community. Most of the results presented herein have appeared much earlier elsewhere and are well known, though they are to varying degrees misinterpreted by practicing engineers who seek to apply them. This situation stems from the partly intuitive bases of the earlier derivations and from their multiplicity of authorship, varied exposition, and scattered publication. Now, with the availability of concise and reasonably rigorous mathematical models of random noise, it is timely to rederive the familiar formulas from this objective foundation and present this information in book form. Although the class of topics thus to be treated falls short of current theoretical research, it includes a large proportion of the matters upon which the author has been called to deliver a useful clarification.

Among those subjects which might properly fall within the scope of this book we do not, however, treat quantitatively the transitional signal-to-noise ratio situation and subthreshold performance, nor the various nonlinear transformations of random processes which occur in most demodulators; these considerations are both disproportionately complex mathematically and limited in practical applicability. Nor, in this context, do we dwell upon propagation effects such as fading and multipath and means (such as diversity reception) of combatting them; on coding theory, signal design, or wideband signalling techniques; on adaptive and time-varying reception methods; on information theory (in the Shannon sense); or on a host of other significant topics. This book is not a treatise, nor even an "introduction" in the awesome sense accomplished by Middleton (I); its purpose is limited to the unified exposition of classical modulation theory and the presentation of analytical tools of circumscribed applicability in this context.

The book is divided into three major parts. The first, concerning mathematical models and analysis techniques, culminates in Chapter 3 in a résumé of the representations of narrow-band noise processes that are of especial utility in communication systems analysis; this material draws heavily on the classic work of Rice (I, II). In the first two chapters, the author feels it appropriate to render a thumbnail sketch of probability theory and of correlation and spectral analysis. This material is not, however, intended as a substitute for the more complete basic works of Cramér, Davenport and Root, Bendat, Yaglom, and others; rather it is included for convenient reference for both reader and author.

The second part, on modulated sinusoids and noise, is in a sense the motivation for writing this book. Chapter 4 treats linear (amplitude) modulation, and particularly synchronous single- and double-sideband suppressed-carrier systems with the aim of developing maximum conceptual understanding and engineering information with minimum mathematical obfuscation, using the noise models of Chapter 3. A brief discussion of the superiority of synchronous linear-modulation techniques under adverse propagation conditions is included. Chapter 5 similarly treats exponential-modulation (FM and PM) systems. The threshold problem, a prominent one in FM, is treated qualitatively (it is quite difficult and unclear mathematically) and an unambiguous presentation is made of the threshold characteristics of conventional wideband FM systems.

The third part treats multiplex and discrete systems, drawing wherever possible on results obtained in previous chapters. Chapter 6 treats frequency-division multiplexing through analysis of the two most common media: SSSC-FM and FM-FM. Chapter 7 considers time-division multiplexing and specifically explores three pulse-transmission techniques: amplitude (PAM), time (PDM), and coded (PCM). Naturally, the variety of multiple-modulation frequency- and time-division multiplexing schemes is far too numerous to permit treating every one explicitly; however, the above choices were made both to include the most widely used techniques and to illustrate generally applicable analysis methods.

The final two chapters of Part 3 might well have become "Part 4"; the reason they did not is that Chapter 8 on coherent binary signalling yet falls within the domain of multiplex and discrete systems. However, introduced here is the germ of system-optimization notions, treated through the matched filter and the analysis of coherent and differentially coherent phase-reversal binary signalling, both of which techniques enjoy successful practical application. At this point, the author could not resist appending Chapter 9, a semiphilosophical discourse on systems optimization and an elementary exposition of the elegant discipline of statistical decision theory. Although actually outside the scope of this book, the results of Chapter 9 nevertheless confirm the optimality of the coherent binary techniques treated in Chapter 8, in the sense therein implied. Thus, and as a springboard for the reader into deeper material, the author rationalizes the inclusion of Chapter 9.

An effort has been made throughout this book to maintain contact with the physical reality of the problems treated, and to avoid lengthy mathematical tangents. Nevertheless, a fairly active mathematical background is presumed of the reader—approximately the equivalent of a two-semester undergraduate course in advanced calculus and theory of functions of a complex variable, beyond the usual elementary training in calculus. Some exposure to Fourier analysis methods and elementary probability theory will also prove helpful. This level of mathematical facility does not, however, necessarily imply familiarity with even the ordinary communication-engineering problems considered.

Compilation of a bibliography at times assumes the proportions of a "random process," and the author makes no claim to have been even partially exhaustive. The reader is hereby guided to the monumental bibliographies compiled by Stumpers (III) and Chessin and to those in Elias *et al.* and Zadeh. Nevertheless, the author feels that the bibliography is an important component of a tutorial book and has therefore attempted to provide a cross section of pertinent references of four kinds:

1. Basic mathematical background.
2. "Classic" papers and publications.
3. Significant papers paralleling the book material.
4. Papers and publications which consider or extend topics which are merely mentioned in the book or are treated in elementary or qualitative fashion.

Not all of the listed references are explicitly cited in the text, and for this reason the pertinent references are given at the end of each chapter, as well as compiled in the Bibliography. The sources used are those which would primarily attract the communication engineer's attention; in the interest of accessibility they are, with rare exception, of American origin. Undoubtedly, therefore, many important contributions will appear to have been overlooked; however, the references cited in those given herein will generally prove fertile ground for further pursuit of a particular topic.

The author gratefully acknowledges the encouragement lent by numerous professional colleagues, from whom he has learned much. Special thanks are due to Dr. Forrest F. Fulton, Jr., for critically reviewing the complete manuscript and suggesting many significant improvements. The author is also indebted to Dr. Thomas Kailath, for seconding the conviction that a book of this kind should be written. Finally, most special gratitude to Cam and Eve, for enduring the apparently endlessly protracted gestation period of this book.

J. J. Downing
Palo Alto, California

# Table of Contents

NOTATION                                                                xiii

*Part 1*  *Mathematical Models*                                           1

PROBABILITY                                                                3

1.1  Basic concepts, 3
1.2  The binomial distribution, 5
1.3  Joint and conditional probability, 6
1.4  Statistical independence, 7
1.5  Averages, 9
CHAPTER   1.6  Random processes, 11
ONE       1.7  Stationarity, 12
1.8  Derived distributions, 13
1.9  Characteristic functions and sum distributions, 14
1.10 The Gaussian distribution and the central limit theorem, 16
1.11 The Chebyshev inequality, 20

CORRELATION AND SPECTRAL ANALYSIS                                         22

2.1  Linear regression and correlation coefficient, 22
2.2  Autocovariance function, 25
CHAPTER   2.3  Spectral analysis, 31
TWO       2.4  Properties of transforms, 39
2.5  Relations among covariance functions, 48

ix

**NARROW-BAND NOISE REPRESENTATIONS**     **51**

CHAPTER
THREE

3.1 Quadrature-carrier representation, 51
3.2 Envelope-and-phase representation, 53
3.3 Relationships between representations, 53
3.4 Sine wave plus narrow-band Gaussian noise, 56
3.5 Envelope, phase, and frequency noise, 59

*Part 2*    *Modulated Sinusoids and Noise*     **63**

**AMPLITUDE (LINEAR) MODULATION**     **65**

CHAPTER
FOUR

4.1 Linear modulation, 65
4.2 Synchronous demodulation, 68
4.3 Envelope demodulation, 69
4.4 Suppressed-carrier techniques, 71
4.5 Unstable transmission media, 82

**ANGLE (EXPONENTIAL) MODULATION**     **86**

CHAPTER
FIVE

5.1 Exponential modulation, 86
5.2 Noise in FM, 93
5.3 Threshold effects in FM, 102
5.4 Interference in FM systems, 106
5.5 Concluding remarks, 109

*Part 3*    *Multiplex and Discrete Systems*     **113**

**FREQUENCY-DIVISION MULTIPLEXING**     **115**

CHAPTER
SIX

6.1 SSSC-FM, 116
6.2 FM-FM, 121

**TIME-DIVISION MULTIPLEXING**     **133**

CHAPTER
SEVEN

7.1 Sampling, 136
7.2 Interpolation, 137
7.3 Practical considerations, 140
7.4 Representative analog TDM systems, 149
7.5 Digital message representation, 164

**COHERENT DIGITAL SIGNALLING**     **177**

CHAPTER
EIGHT

8.1 The matched filter, 177
8.2 Correlation detection, 180
8.3 Coherent binary signalling, 180
8.4 Coherent phase-reversal keying, 182
8.5 Differentially coherent phase-reversal keying, 184

OPTIMUM SIGNAL DETECTION AND DECISION THEORY  189

CHAPTER
NINE

9.1   Nature of the problem, 190
9.2   Optimization techniques, 192
9.3   Discussion of optimization methods, 197
9.4   Conclusion, 198

BIBLIOGRAPHY  200

INDEX  211

# Notation

| Symbol | Chapter | Use |
|---|---|---|
| $a$ | 2, 3 | Arbitrary constant |
| | 2 | Vertical intercept of regression line |
| | 5 | Ratio of interfering-to-desired carrier amplitudes |
| $a_k, a_n$ | 7 | Fourier series coefficients |
| $a_n$ | 8 | Series coefficient |
| $a_0$ | 7 | Bessel filter parameter |
| $a(\tau)$ | 8 | Arbitrary function |
| $A$ | 2–8 | Amplitude of sinusoid |
| | 7 | Magnitude of Bessel filter transfer function |
| | 7 | Error threshold in PCM |
| $A_D$ | 4 | Amplitude of DSSC wave |
| $A_S$ | 4 | Amplitude of SSSC wave |
| AM | | Amplitude modulation |
| $b$ | 2 | Slope of regression line |
| | 2 | Arbitrary constant |
| $b_n$ | 2 | Power of a discrete spectral component |
| $B$ | 5, 6, 7 | One-half IF bandwidth |
| $B_a$ | 5 | Audio bandwidth |
| $B_i$ | 6 | $i$th subchannel bandwidth in FDM |
| $B_{IF}$ | 5, 6, 7 | IF bandwidth |
| $B_m$ | 4, 5, 6 | Message bandwidth; baseband filter bandwidth |
| $B'_m$ | 5 | Effective noise bandwidth of baseband filter |

| Symbol | Chapter | Use |
|---|---|---|
| $B_n$ | 7 | Effective noise bandwidth of Bessel filter |
| $c$ | 1 | Arbitrary constant |
| $c_n$ | 2, 4 | Fourier series coefficient |
| $C$ | 7 | RF carrier power |
| $C_0$ | 6 | Modulation parameter in FM-FM |
| $C(js)$ | 1 | Characteristic function of a probability distribution |
| CPRK | 8 | Coherent phase-reversal keying |
| $d$ | 7 | Pulse duration in PAM |
| $D$ | 5 | Deviation ratio: $D = f_D/B_m$ |
| $D_i$ | 6 | Carrier deviation ratio due to $i$th subcarrier in FM-FM: $D_i = f_{Di}/f_i$ |
| $D_m$ | 6 | Subcarrier deviation ratio in FM-FM: $D_m = (\Delta f)_i/B_m$ |
| $D_0$ | 5 | Deviation ratio: $D_0 = f_D/f_0$ |
| DCPRK | | Differentially coherent phase-reversal keying |
| DSSC | | Double-sideband suppressed-carrier |
| $\epsilon$ | 1 | Belonging to |
| $\mathbf{e}$ | 1 | Value of a random waveform |
| $\overline{e^2}$ | 7 | Equivalent analog error variance in PCM |
| $E$ | 8 | Signal energy |
| $E_{(*)}(t)$ | | Waveform for subscript $(*)$ conditions |
| $\overline{E^2_{\min}}$ | 7 | Minimum relative interpolation error power |
| $f$ | | Frequency: cps |
| $f, f(t)$ | 1, 2 | Random variable |
| $f_b$ | 7 | Bit rate in PCM |
| $f_D$ | 5, 6, 7 | Peak frequency deviation of RF carrier in FM |
| $\overline{f_D^2}$ | 6 | Mean-square frequency deviation of RF carrier in FDM-FM |
| $f_{Di}$ | 6 | Peak frequency deviation of RF carrier due to $i$th subcarrier in FM-FM |
| $f_i$ | 6 | Center frequency of $i$th subchannel in FDM |
| $f_0$ | 2 | Fundamental frequency of a periodic function |
| | 5, 7 | Half-power filter, message spectrum, bandwidth |
| $f_p$ | 7 | Pulse repetition frequency in TDM |
| $f_s$ | 7 | Sampling frequency in TDM |
| $F$ | 2 | Frequency interval |

| Symbol | Chapter | Use |
|---|---|---|
| FDM | | Frequency-division multiplex |
| FM | | Frequency modulation |
| $g, g(t)$ | 1, 2 | Random variable |
| $g(\tau)$ | 8 | Arbitrary time function |
| $G_{(*)}(f)$ | | Power spectral density for subscript $(*)$ quantity |
| $h(t)$ | 2 | Filter impulse response |
| $h(\tau)$ | 8 | Optimum filter impulse response |
| $i$ | 1 | Probability space index |
| | 5 | Subchannel index in FDM |
| $I_0(*)$ | 3 | Modified Bessel function of first kind: $I_0(*) = J_0(j*)$ |
| IF | | Intermediate frequency |
| $j$ | | Complex operator: $j^2 = -1$ |
| $|J|$ | 3 | Jacobian determinant |
| $J_{(*)}$ | 3, 5, 7 | Bessel function of first kind and order $(*)$ |
| $k$ | 1, 2 | Arbitrary constant |
| | 5, 7 | Number of poles of baseband filter, message spectrum |
| | 7, 9 | Summation index |
| $k^2$ | 4, 5, 6, 7 | One-sided IF noise power spectral density $(f \geq 0)$ |
| $K$ | 6 | Modulation parameter in SSSC-FM: $K = K_i/f_i$ |
| $K_b$ | 5 | Constant for FM demodulator output noise spectrum |
| $K_D$ | 6 | Constant percentage-of-subcarrier-frequency deviation in FM-FM |
| $K_i$ | 6 | Weighting factor for $i$th message channel in SSSC-FM |
| $L$ | 7 | Number of links in cascade in PCM |
| $m$ | 2, 4, 8 | Summation index |
| $m_{fg}$ | 2 | Unnormalized correlation coefficient |
| $m(t)$ | 4, 5, 6, 7 | Message waveform |
| $m_i(t)$ | 6 | $i$th message waveform in SSSC-FM |

| Symbol | Chapter | Use |
|---|---|---|
| $m^{\#}(t)$ | 7 | Sampled message waveform |
| $M$ | 1 | Number of trials |
| $n$ | 1, 2, 3, 4, 5, 7, 8 | Moment index; summation index |
| $n(t)$ | 8, 9 | Noise waveform |
| $n_i$ | 8 | In-phase noise component |
| $n_q$ | 8 | Quadrature noise component |
| $N$ | 1 | Number of random variables |
|  | 7 | Number of poles of a Bessel filter |
|  | 7 | Number of bits in a binary word |
|  | 8 | Noise power |
| $N(t)$ | 4 | Noise waveform |
| $N(m, \sigma)$ | 7, 8 | Normal random variable having mean $m$ and standard deviation $\sigma$ |
| $N_{(*)}$ | 4–8 | Noise power for subscript $(*)$ conditions |
| $N_0$ | 8, 9 | Two-sided noise power spectral density $(-\infty \leq f \leq \infty)$ |
| $\mathcal{N}(*)$ | 8 | Normal probability function |
| $p$ | 6 | Peaking factor in FM-FM |
|  | 7 | Summation index |
| $p(*)$ |  | Probability density function |
| $p(t)$ | 7 | Generic pulse shape in TDM |
| $P(*)$ |  | Probability; probability distribution function |
| $P_b$ | 7, 8 | Binary error probability in PCM |
| $P_e$ | 7 | Interpolation error power |
| $P_m$ | 7 | Message power |
| $P_{SBD}$ | 4 | Sideband power in DSSC |
| $P_{SBS}$ | 4 | Sideband power in SSSC |
| PAM |  | Pulse-amplitude modulation |
| PCM |  | Pulse-code modulation |
| PDM |  | Pulse-duration modulation |
| $q$ | 7 | Summation index |
|  | 7 | Quantizing error |
| $Q(*)$ | 1 | Complementary probability distribution function: $Q(*) = 1 - P(*)$ |
| $Q$ | 7 | Width of a digital quantizing increment |
| $Q_b$ | 7 | Binary success probability in PCM |
| $r$ | 2 | Dummy variable |

| Symbol | Chapter | Use |
|--------|---------|-----|
| | 5 | Frequency difference between desired and interfering carriers |
| | 6 | Modulation parameter in FM-FM |
| $r(t)$ | 8 | Reference signal |
| $R$ | 8 | Signal-to-noise ratio |
| $R_{(*)}(\tau)$ | 2, 5 | Autocovariance function of subscript $(*)$ quantity |
| $RF$ | | Radio frequency |
| $s$ | 1 | Argument of characteristic function |
| | 2 | Dummy variable |
| $s(t)$ | 7 | Sampling function |
| | 8, 9 | Signal waveform |
| | 9 | Desired system output |
| $S$ | 8 | Signal power |
| $S_{(*)}$ | | Signal or message power for subscript $(*)$ conditions |
| $(S/N)$ | | Signal-to-noise power ratio |
| SSSC | | Single-sideband suppressed-carrier |
| $t$ | | Time |
| $t_0$ | 7 | Group delay parameter of Bessel filter |
| $T$ | 1, 2 | Time interval; period of periodic function |
| | 7 | Sampling period |
| | 8, 9 | Signal duration |
| $T_b$ | 7 | Bit duration in PCM |
| $T_m$ | 7 | Mean pulse duration in PDM |
| $T_n$ | 7 | Minimum pulse duration in PDM |
| $T_p$ | 7 | Pulse repetition period in TDM |
| $T_r$ | 7 | Rise time of Bessel filter |
| $T_x$ | 7 | Maximum pulse duration in PDM |
| TDM | | Time-division multiplex |
| $u$ | 1, 2 | Dummy variable |
| | 7 | Normalized real-frequency variable |
| $u(t)$ | 7 | Interpolation-generating function |
| $U$ | 1 | Normalized power |
| $U(t)$ | 2 | Unit step function |
| $U(f)$ | 7 | Fourier transform of $u(t)$ |
| $v$ | 1, 2 | Dummy variable |

| Symbol | Chapter | Use |
|--------|---------|-----|
| $V, V(t)$ | 3, 4 | Envelope function |
| $W$ | 7, 9 | Bandwidth |
| $x$ | 1 | Value of random variable |
| | 8 | Dummy variable |
| $x(t)$ | 2 | Time function |
| | 3, 4, 5 | Sample function of gaussian noise process |
| | 9 | System input waveform |
| $x_{cn}, x_{sn}$ | 3 | Fourier coefficients of noise expansion |
| $x_c(t)$ | 3, 4, 5 | In-phase noise component |
| $x_s(t)$ | 3, 4, 5 | Quadrature noise component |
| $X$ | 1 | A random variable |
| $X(f)$ | 2 | Fourier transform of $x(t)$ |
| $y$ | 1 | Value of a random variable |
| | 7 | Dummy variable |
| $y(t)$ | 2, 8 | Time function |
| | 3 | Waveform of sine wave-plus-narrow-band-gaussian-noise |
| $y_c(t)$ | 3 | In-phase component of $y(t)$ |
| $y_s(t)$ | 3 | Quadrature component of $y(t)$ |
| $Y$ | 1 | Sum random variable |
| $Y(f)$ | 2 | Fourier transform of $y(t)$ |
| | 3, 5, 9 | Filter transfer function |
| $Y_a(f)$ | 7 | Aperture operator |
| $z$ | 2 | Dummy variable |
| $z(t)$ | 9 | System output waveform |
| $\alpha$ | 8 | Arbitrary constant |
| $\beta$ | 5 | Bandwidth ratio: $\beta = B_{IF}/f_D$ |
| $\gamma$ | 5 | Fraction of unmodulated carrier amplitude |
| | 6 | Intermediate constant in FM-FM |
| | 7 | Ratio of sampling to break frequency in TDM: $\gamma = f_s/f_0$ |
| $\Gamma(*)$ | 5 | Gamma function: $\Gamma(*) = (* - 1)!$ |
| $\delta(*)$ | 2, 8 | Dirac delta-function |

| Symbol | Chapter | Use |
|--------|---------|-----|
| $\Delta$ | 2 | Mean-square regression error |
| $\Delta f(t)$ | 7 | Instantaneous cyclic frequency deviation |
| $\Delta t$ | 2, 5 | Time increment |
| $(\Delta f)_i$ | 6 | Peak frequency deviation of $i$th subcarrier in FM-FM |
| $\epsilon$ | 8, 9 | Arbitrary number |
| $\eta$ | 2 | Standardized random variable |
| $\theta$ | 2, 8 | Phase angle |
| $\theta(f)$ | 7 | Phase characteristic of filter |
| $\theta(t)$ | 3, 5 | Phase of sine wave-plus-noise relative to carrier |
| $\theta'(t)$ | 3, 5 | Instantaneous radian frequency deviation |
| $\Theta$ | 5 | Peak phase deviation |
| $\lambda$ | 7 | Slope of pulse trailing edge in PDM |
| | 8 | Reciprocal of maximum output signal-to-noise ratio |
| $\Lambda$ | 9 | Likelihood ratio |
| $\mu$ | 8 | Dummy variable |
| $\mu(t)$ | 4 | Harmonic conjugate of message waveform $m(t)$ |
| $\nu$ | 6, 7 | Number of message channel multiplexed |
| $\nu_q$ | 7 | Number of quantizing levels in PCM |
| $\xi$ | 1 | Remainder term |
| $\rho$ | 2, 8 | Normalized correlation coefficient |
| $\rho(\tau)$ | 2 | (Normalized) autocorrelation function |
| $\sigma_{(*)}$ | | Standard deviation of subscript quantity $(*)$ |
| $\sigma^2_{(*)}$ | | Variance of subscript quantity $(*)$ |
| $\tau$ | 2, 3 | Time difference |
| | 5, 8, 9 | Dummy time variable |
| | 7 | Delay |
| $\varphi(*)$ | 1 | Arbitrary function |
| $\phi$ | 3, 5 | Phase angle |
| $\phi(t)$ | 3, 4 | Phase function of random variable |
| $\Phi$ | 1 | Standardized sum of random variables |

| Symbol | Chapter | Use |
|--------|---------|-----|
| $\chi$ | 2 | Standardized random variable |
| $\psi$ | 1 | Functional relationship between two random variables |
| | 3 | Phase function of sine wave-plus-noise |
| $\omega$ | | Radian frequency |
| $\omega_c$ | 3, 4, 5, 8 | Radian carrier frequency |
| $\omega_i$ | 3 | Instantaneous radian frequency |
| $\omega_m, \omega_1$ | 4, 5 | Radian frequency of sinusoidal message |
| $\omega_0$ | 3 | Fundamental radian frequency |
| $\Omega$ | 3 | Radian bandwidth of narrow-band random process |

# PART 1 _Mathematical Models_

It is virtually axiomatic that the analysis of communication techniques and the design of links to fulfill specified mission objectives depend on the detailed characteristics of the messages to be conveyed, and similarly upon knowledge of the perturbations to which the channel is subjected. The term "characteristics," however, does not imply instant-by-instant specifiability of a message waveform, except in certain special cases usually associated with performance standardization and test procedures. Indeed, the message must be unpredictable in this sense if it is to impart _information_, or new knowledge, to the ultimate user; were the message completely predictable, no communication link would be necessary. This is not merely a philosophical abstraction; it is one of the ground rules under which the communications engineer must operate. Even more evident is the fact that extraneous link disturbances cannot be foretold in precise detail. The term _noise_, in fact, carries the semantic connotation of unpredictability.

Although the characterizations of the

input messages and of the channel perturbations are not predictable in detail, their behavior nevertheless is often sufficiently regular, in some average sense, to permit a successful communication system design to be based on knowledge only of their statistical properties. Typical statistical quantities of interest are the probabilities of occurrence of various excursions, and of the distribution of power in the frequency domain. As a natural consequence of such statistical descriptions of essentially random parameters, it follows that system performance criteria are also commonly given in basically statistical terms. Thus the system designer usually strives to minimize the mean-squared error or total "noise power," or to reduce the probability of occurrence of a specified type of error.

In the first part of this book, therefore, it is appropriate to review some statistical principles and some concepts of statistical communication theory. More importantly, our objective is to develop several quite straightforward mathematical models for the type of random noise that is most frequently encountered in ordinary communication systems, and to make clear the origin and significance of these models in such a way that their application to the calculation of system performance becomes as natural as thinking in terms of decibels. The subsequent parts of this book, wherein the performance characteristics of a number of basic modulation techniques are explored, presume that the author has been successful in so indoctrinating the reader.

# Chapter One

# Probability

## 1.1 BASIC CONCEPTS

Since the unpredictability of messages and the random behavior
of noise preclude complete knowledge concerning every detail of
communication system operation, it is generally necessary to
adopt statistical devices to serve as an index of the over-all
situation. The *probability distribution function* and the related
*probability density function* are such quantities; they are defined
with respect to a *random variable*. In this first chapter we shall
briefly review these and other probabilistic concepts which are
useful in communication systems analysis.

The probability distribution function $P_f(x)$ is defined as the
probability that the random variable $f$ is less than or equal to
$x$. Symbolically,

$$P_f(x) = \text{probability that } f \leq x$$
$$= P[f \leq x]; \quad 0 \leq P_f(x) \leq 1. \quad (1.1)$$

The notation $0 \leq P_f(x) \leq 1$ represents the total range of probability,
from complete impossibility to complete certainty of occurrence.
Correspondingly, the probability $Q_f(x)$ that $f$ is greater than $x$ is
given by

$$Q_f(x) = \text{probability that } f > x$$
$$= 1 - P_f(x). \quad (1.2)$$

The probability density function $p_f(x)$ is defined as the derivative of the distribution function $P_f(x)$; thus

$$p_f(x) = \frac{dP_f(x)}{dx}. \tag{1.3}$$

It is more common to find (1.3) written in integral form; that is, since

$$dP_f(u) = p_f(u)\, du \tag{1.4}$$

then

$$P_f(x) = \int_{-\infty}^{x} dP_f(u) = \int_{-\infty}^{x} p_f(u)\, du. \tag{1.5}$$

In writing (1.4) we used a dummy variable $u$ for integration purposes in (1.5).

It is readily seen, using (1.2), that the probability that $f$ lies in some narrow range $dx$ is given by

$$P[x < f \le x + dx] = 1 - P[f \le x \quad \text{OR} \quad f > x + dx]. \tag{1.6a}$$

Since $f \le x$ and $f > x + dx$ are *mutually exclusive*, or *disjoint* events, i.e., the sum of their individual probabilities yields the probability of one OR the other happening, then (1.6a) becomes, using (1.1) and (1.2),

$$\begin{aligned}
P[x < f \le x + dx] &= 1 - P_f(x) - [1 - P_f(x + dx)] \\
&= P_f(x + dx) - P_f(x). \tag{1.6b}
\end{aligned}$$

However, in the limit $dx \to 0$, the RHS of (1.6b) is simply $dP_f(x)$, so that from (1.4) we have

$$P[x < f \le x + dx] = p_f(x)\, dx. \tag{1.7}$$

Equation (1.7) shows an easily visualized property of the probability density function. Specifically, for a random variable $f$ which is *continuous in distribution*, $p_f(x)$ is analogous to the familiar *histogram* ("bar graph") for a random variable which is *discrete in distribution.*

Communication engineers commonly refer to the distinction between continuous or discrete in distribution by the terms *analog* and *digital*, respectively. Thus an analog signal (random variable) may assume *any* value within its total excursion range, whereas a digital signal is restricted to occur *only* at certain definite values within this range. It is important not to confuse these statistical properties with whether the signal is continuously varying or is sampled with respect to time history. For example, a pulse-amplitude modulation (PAM) signal is continuous in distribution by virtue of being analog, but is discrete in time because of the sampling process.

It remains to discuss what is meant by a random variable. Certainly, anyone who has observed thermal noise on an oscilloscope feels intuitive mastery of this concept. However, we should also discuss it somewhat more explicitly. The contemporary definition of a random variable gives it as a mathematical function constructed in one-to-one correspondence with the points of a *probability space*; an example will clarify this notion. Let us choose, as a probability space, the classic situation involving the outcome of the throw of a "fair" die; each of the six faces, 1 through 6, is equally likely to turn up, with probability $\frac{1}{6}$. Thus a probability space is a set of points, or events $(i)$, with associated probabilities $P_i$, such that $\sum_{i\epsilon(i)} P_i = 1$. Now, we might define as a random variable on this probability space the function $f(i) = i$; $1 \leq i \leq 6$. In other words, our random variable might simply equal the number of pips on the die face that turns up. Similarly, we might define as random variables the functions $f(i) = i^2$, or $f(i) = e^i$; each would provide a perfectly valid basis for constructing a gambling game. These random variables, however, are completely explicit mathematical functions defined on the chosen probability space, and each has a probability distribution function.

## 1.2   THE BINOMIAL DISTRIBUTION

Much of the analysis involved, for example, in network traffic routing is of a combinatorial character. Although we shall not be concerned with such problems to any great extent, it is appropriate to introduce the notions involved through a well-known example: the *binomial distribution*.

Consider an experiment involving the toss of a biased coin, which has probability $P$ of landing heads, and probability $Q = 1 - P$ of tails. We wish to determine the probability that exactly $n$ heads will turn up after $M$ trials, and consequently that $M - n$ tails will also have appeared.[†] The outcome of each toss of the coin is independent of that of all other trials, and since the net probability of several independent events' all happening is the product of the individual event probabilities, then the probability of any particular sequence of $n$ heads' and $M - n$ tails' occurring in $M$ trials is $P^n Q^{M-n}$. However, there are a number of ways in which $n$ heads and $M - n$ tails can appear; for example the two sequences

THTTHTTTHH,   HTTHHTTHTT

[†] Here we are dealing with a probability space of $2^M$ points, or *particular* sequences of heads and tails.

both contain 4 heads and 6 tails out of 10 trials. Specifically, there are

$$\binom{M}{n} = \frac{M!}{n!(M-n)!} \qquad (1.8)$$

different ways in which $n$ heads can appear in $M$ trials; the notation $\binom{M}{n}$ represents the *binomial coefficient* giving the number of ways in which $M$ things can be taken $n$ at a time, without regard to order. Thus the total probability $p(n; M)$ of obtaining exactly $n$ heads (and $M - n$ tails) in $M$ trials is

$$p(n; M) = \binom{M}{n} P^n Q^{M-n}. \qquad (1.9)$$

Equation (1.9) is the probability density function for the random variable describing the proportion of heads and tails obtained after a number of tosses of the coin. Thus the corresponding distribution function, i. e., the probability $P(n \leq N; M)$ that, *at most*, $N$ heads will turn up in $M$ trials, is given by

$$P(n \leq N; M) = \sum_{n=0}^{N} p(n; M)$$

$$= \sum_{n=0}^{N} \binom{M}{n} P^n Q^{M-n}. \qquad (1.10)$$

Equation (1.10) is commonly known as the binomial distribution, since

$$P(n \leq M; M) = \sum_{n=0}^{M} \binom{M}{n} P^n Q^{M-n}$$

$$= (P + Q)^M = 1. \qquad (1.11)$$

## 1.3   JOINT AND CONDITIONAL PROBABILITY

The basic concepts of probability extend, of course, to situations in which more than one random variable is defined on a common probability space. Consider, for example, two random variables $f$ and $g$, and their associated probability distribution functions $P_f(x)$ and $P_g(y)$. Now we may also define a new quantity $P_{f,g}(x,y)$ as the probability that $f \leq x$ and $g \leq y$ *simultaneously*; thus $P_{f,g}(x,y)$ is known as the *joint probability distribution function* of the random variables $f$ and $g$. Similarly, the *joint probability density function* of $f$ and $g$ is defined as the derivative of the joint distribution function

$$p_{f,g}(x,y) = \frac{\partial^2 P_{f,g}(x,y)}{\partial x \, \partial y}. \tag{1.12}$$

A closely related concept is that of *conditional probability*. Let it be known that the random variable $g = y$, and let it be required to determine the probability that $f \leq x$, given this information. We denote this probability by $P_f[x \,|\, g = y]$, or more compactly by $P_f(x \,|\, g)$; this quantity is the *conditional probability distribution function* of $f$ given $g = y$. Similarly we have the *conditional probability density function*

$$p_f(x \,|\, g) = \frac{dP_f(x \,|\, g)}{dx}. \tag{1.13}$$

It should be evident from the above definitions that the joint and conditional probability density functions of $f$ and $g$ are related by

$$p_{f,g}(x,y) = p_g(y) p_f(x \,|\, g) \tag{1.14}$$

$$= p_f(x) p_g(y \,|\, f). \tag{1.15}$$

However, it is not possible to write similar relationships for the joint and conditional probability distribution functions as they are defined. Note that the relationships (1.14) and (1.15) are symmetrical on the RHS with respect to $f, g$ and $x, y$; this essentially is *Bayes' rule*. These definitions of and relationships between joint and conditional probabilities can be extended to any number of random variables $X_1, \ldots, X_n$; thus, for example,

$$P(X_1 \leq x_1, \ldots, X_n \leq x_n) = P_{X_1, \ldots, X_n}(x_1, \ldots, x_n) \tag{1.16}$$

and

$$p_{X_1, \ldots, X_n}(x_1, \ldots, x_n) = \frac{\partial^n P_{X_1, \ldots, X_n}(x_1, \ldots, x_n)}{\partial x_1, \ldots, \partial x_n}. \tag{1.17}$$

## 1.4   STATISTICAL INDEPENDENCE

A concept of central importance in probability theory is that of *statistical independence*. Two random variables $f$ and $g$ are statistically independent if statistical information about $f$ provides no such information about $g$, and vice versa. This condition can be formulated mathematically in terms of the joint and conditional probabilities; specifically, it is clear that if $f$ and $g$ are statistically independent, then we have

$$p_f(x \,|\, g) = p_f(x), \tag{1.18a}$$

$$p_g(y \,|\, f) = p_g(y), \tag{1.18b}$$

and similarly for the distribution functions. Thus we can give a concise definition of statistical independence: for the random variables $f$ and $g$ to be statistically independent it is necessary and sufficient that the joint probabilities satisfy

$$p_{f,g}(x, y) = p_f(x)\,p_g(y) \tag{1.19a}$$

or

$$P_{f,g}(x, y) = P_f(x)\,P_g(y). \tag{1.19b}$$

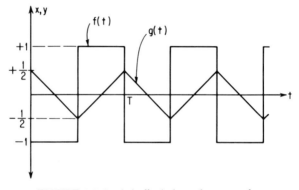

FIGURE 1.1 Statistically independent waveforms.

It may be well to distinguish, by means of an example, between the concept of statistical independence and that of functional independence in an algebraic sense. Consider Fig. 1.1, which shows square and triangular waves $f(t)$ and $g(t)$, respectively, having the same period. The explicit waveforms $f(t)$ and $g(t)$ may also be regarded as random variables $f$ and $g$ with respect to an observation made at a specific time $t_1$, by assuming that the time origin is a random variable uniformly distributed on the interval $(0, T)$. Here, our probability space is the set of points comprising the interval $0 \le t < T$, and the random variables $f$ and $g$ are explicitly defined thereon. It is evident that $f(t) = dg(t)/dt$, and hence that $f$ and $g$ are functionally related in a completely deterministic way. However, we shall show that $f$ and $g$, as random variables, are statistically independent. The probability distribution function for $g$ is easily developed by considering the fraction of a cycle during which $g(t) \le y$, and is given by

$$\begin{aligned}
P_g(y) &= 0, & y &\le -\tfrac{1}{2}; \\
P_g(y) &= y, & -\tfrac{1}{2} &< y \le \tfrac{1}{2}; \\
P_g(y) &= 1, & y &> \tfrac{1}{2}.
\end{aligned} \tag{1.20}$$

Furthermore, it is not necessary in developing (1.20) to consider whether $f(t)$ is positive or negative. Similarly, irrespective of the behavior of $g(t)$, we have for $f(t)$

$$
\begin{aligned}
P_f(x) &= 0, & x &\leq -1; \\
P_f(x) &= \tfrac{1}{2}, & -1 &< x \leq 1; \\
P_f(x) &= 1, & x &> 1.
\end{aligned}
\tag{1.21}
$$

Thus statistical information concerning $f$ (or $g$) yields none concerning $g$ (or $f$), and $f(t)$ and $g(t)$ are therefore statistically independent random variables. This example emphasizes our observation that a random variable need not be "random" in an intuitive sense (the semantic inconsistency of this universal terminology is unfortunate), and further shows that statistical independence does not necessarily imply independence in a functional context. Henceforth, by the term "independence" we denote the property of statistical independence.

## 1.5  AVERAGES

As implied in the foregoing article, the concept of probability is often identified with the fraction of the time that some specified event occurs, or some particular condition exists. This is especially the case in communication systems analysis, where we deal primarily with quantities that are represented as functions of time. The

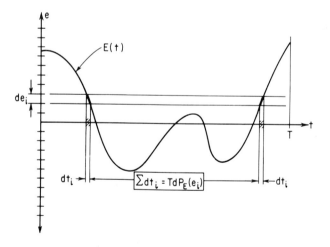

FIGURE 1.2 Fraction-of-time observation.

equivalence of temporal behavior to a statistical description falls under the general heading of *ergodicity;* we shall attempt to clarify this concept first through a discussion of *averages.*

Let the waveform $E(t)$ of, say, an audio voltage be represented during the interval $T$ by a record such as shown in Fig. 1.2. Further, let the amplitude range be divided into small increments $d\mathbf{e}_i$, and an empirical statistical density function $dP_E(\mathbf{e}_i)$ be constructed representing the fraction of the interval $T$ during which the instantaneous signal magnitude falls in each increment. Now, the power $U$ (in 1 ohm resistance[†]) of the audio waveform is defined as the average of $E^2(t)$, that is,

$$U = \frac{1}{T} \int_0^T E^2(t)\, dt. \tag{1.22}$$

However, it is evident that the signal power can also be approximated by

$$U \cong \sum_{\text{all } i} \mathbf{e}_i^2\, dP_E(\mathbf{e}_i), \tag{1.23a}$$

where the increments $d\mathbf{e}_i$ are presumed small enough so that the instantaneous voltage $E(t)$ may be considered constant, equal to $\mathbf{e}_i$, within any increment. In the limit $d\mathbf{e}_i \to 0$, (1.23a) then becomes

$$U = \int_{-\infty}^{\infty} \mathbf{e}^2\, dP_E(\mathbf{e}) \tag{1.23b}$$

$$= \int_{-\infty}^{\infty} \mathbf{e}^2 p_E(\mathbf{e})\, d\mathbf{e}, \tag{1.23c}$$

where we use the definition (1.4) of the probability density function in writing (1.23c). Thus we have from (1.22) and (1.23c)

$$\frac{1}{T} \int_0^T E^2(t)\, dt = \int_{-\infty}^{\infty} \mathbf{e}^2 p_E(\mathbf{e})\, d\mathbf{e}. \tag{1.24}$$

It is not difficult to appreciate that (1.24) generalizes to any single-valued function $\varphi[E(t)]$, so that the equivalence of time and statistical averages is expressed by the *empirical ergodicity condition*[‡]

$$\frac{1}{T} \int_0^T \varphi[E(t)]\, dt = \int_{-\infty}^{\infty} \varphi(\mathbf{e}) p_E(\mathbf{e})\, d\mathbf{e}, \tag{1.25}$$

where $p_E(\mathbf{e})$ is the empirical density function.

In technical literature, an average may variously be referred to

---

† We shall always assume 1 ohm resistance in speaking of "power."

‡ This procedure is justifiable in hindsight by the *law of large numbers*, according to which the counterpart of an empirical distribution does generally converge to an appropriate mathematical probability. See Cramér, chap. 13, Yaglom, sec 4.

as *average, mean, expectation,* or *expected value of* ..., and denoted, for say the average of $X$, by $\bar{X}$, $\tilde{X}$, $E[X]$, $\langle X \rangle$, or $m_X$; frequently $\bar{X}$ is restricted to mean a time average, and the other notations to mean statistical averages. In this book, however, the question of ergodicity will seldom be a fundamental issue, and the bar notation $\bar{X}$ will be used uniformly to denote an average, whether time or statistical.

The special average $\overline{X^n}$ is known as the *nth moment* of the random variable $X$, and the quantity $\overline{(X - \bar{X})^n}$ is called the *nth central moment.* An important special case of the latter, to which we shall make frequent reference, is the *variance* of $X$, denoted by $\sigma_X^2$; here we have

$$\sigma_X^2 = \overline{(X - \bar{X})^2} = \overline{X^2} - (\bar{X})^2. \tag{1.26}$$

The quantity $\sigma_X$ itself is known as the *standard deviation* of $X$.

## 1.6   RANDOM PROCESSES†

As with the random variable, a *random process* is defined as a mathematical function. Specifically, a random process is a function of two variables $f(t, u)$, where $u$ extends the dimensionality of the probability space, for example to several people rolling dice simultaneously and repeatedly, and $t$ represents a parameter, usually regarded as time. One of the basic concepts of probability theory involves the determination of the relative frequency of occurrence of a given outcome in a large number of repetitions of the defining experiment. The notion of repetition suggests performing the experiment over and over again; however, the important accomplishment is not carrying out experiments in time succession, but rather performing a large number of experiments. This requirement could be satisfied as well by simultaneously performing a large number of identically prepared experiments as by repeatedly carrying out a single one. A random process embraces this concept for a situation where each experiment continues with time, and is thus a set of random variables indexed by $t$ such that for each value of $t$, $f(t, u)$ is a random variable in $u$. Alternately, we could observe that for each fixed value of $u$ in the probability space, $f(t, u)$ is a *sample function* of the process; the totality of such sample functions, known as the *ensemble*, defines the process.

† A detailed discussion of this topic is beyond the scope of this book. See Doob, chaps. I and II, Yaglom, sec. 1.

One might then inquire concerning the relationship between ensemble statistics and averages for the random process [taken over a set $(u)$ of identical experiments with fixed $t$], and fraction-of-time distributions and time averages of the sample functions (taken along $t$ with fixed $u$). Although a random process need not necessarily exhibit such a relationship, it is true of those processes which are *ergodic*, that almost all of the sample functions have the same statistics and averages, and that these coincide with the ensemble statistics and averages.

It may be worthwhile to offer a brief interpretation of the concept of ergodicity in the present context. The essential point to be emphasized is that, within the physical structure of a communication system, there does not exist a duality of measurement domains, i.e., time averages and ensemble or statistical averages. The probability distributions used as mathematical models in communication system analysis are usually derived or postulated on the basis of fraction-of-time or similar notions, and the identity of the statistical moments of such model distributions with the corresponding time averages is a necessary consequence of imposing the empirical ergodicity condition. In essence, the operational utility of a statistical model lies in the extent to which its ensemble parameters can be made accurately to represent experimental distributions and averages, and hence to serve as a basis for inferring other aspects of communication system performance.

## 1.7   STATIONARITY

An important class of random processes is that which exhibits the property of *stationarity*. This means that the probability-space parameters of the random process $f(t, u)$ are invariant under a translation of the time index $t$. Thus, given a set of sample functions of the process, we could equally well estimate its ensemble statistics by simultaneously observing the sample functions at time $t_1$, or at any other time $t_n$. Such random processes are said to possess *strict-sense stationarity*.

It is possible for a random process to be nonstationary in the strict sense, yet to have certain average properties which remain invariant under a shift of the time origin (specifically we refer to the mean, and to the autocovariance function, to be considered in the next chapter). Such random processes are said to possess *wide-sense stationarity*,[†] and it is this property which we shall

† See Doob, chap. II, Yaglom, secs. 2, 7, 8.

imply by the term *stationary*. Obviously, any random process which is stationary in the strict sense is also stationary in the wide sense.

## 1.8   DERIVED DISTRIBUTIONS

Often it is necessary to determine the distribution of a function of a random variable which has known statistics. We shall here consider a one-dimensional case of this problem. Let the original random variable be $f$, and its probability density function be $p_f(u)$. We introduce a new random variable $g$, where $g$ is a monotonic function of $f$, and wish to determine the density function $p_g(v)$ for the random variable $g$, in terms of $p_f(u)$ and functional relationship between $f$ and $g$.

To this end, denote the functional relationship by $f = \psi(g)$. Now, necessarily, the probability $P(g \leq y)$ must be identically equal to the probability $P[f \leq x = \psi(y)]$, because of the deterministic functional relationship between $f$ and $g$. Thus, in terms of the distribution functions

$$P_g(y) = P_f[\psi(y)], \tag{1.27a}$$

or in integral form we have

$$\int_{-\infty}^{y} p_g(v) \, dv = \int_{-\infty}^{\psi(y)} p_f(u) \, du. \tag{1.27b}$$

Now, change the variable in the RHS of (1.27b) to $u = \psi(v)$. Thus $du = \psi'(v) \, dv$ and (1.27b) becomes

$$\int_{-\infty}^{y} p_g(v) \, dv = \int_{-\infty}^{y} p_f[\psi(v)] \psi'(v) \, dv, \tag{1.28}$$

where $\psi'(v) = d\psi(v)/dv$. We may then infer that the probability density function of the random variable $g$ is given by

$$p_g(v) = p_f[\psi(v)] |\psi'(v)|. \tag{1.29}$$

It is necessary to use the absolute value of $\psi'(v)$ in writing (1.29) in order to assure that this expression for $p_g(v)$ is positive, as is required of a probability density function. Similarly, the functional relationship $f = \psi(g)$ must be monotonic and single-valued; otherwise the quantity given by (1.29) is ambiguous, and meaningless as a probability density function.

As an illustration of the foregoing, consider the problem of determining the density function of $g$ if $f = \psi(g) = g^2$, and $p_f(u) = e^{-u}$; $u \geq 0$. Then $\psi(v) = v^2$, and $\psi'(v) = 2v$. Thus from (1.29), the density function of $g$ is $p_g(v) = 2ve^{-v^2}$; $v \geq 0$.

**1.9**   CHARACTERISTIC FUNCTIONS AND SUM DISTRIBUTIONS

A topic of considerable importance in probability theory and its application to communication systems analysis involves the statistics of the sum of two or more statistically independent random variables. It is convenient to develop this subject through the use of *characteristic functions*. The characteristic function $C_X(js)$ of a random variable $X$ is defined as an integral transform of its probability density function; thus[†]

$$C_X(js) = \int_{-\infty}^{\infty} p_X(x) e^{jsx} \, dx \qquad (1.30a)$$

$$= \overline{e^{jsx}}, \qquad (1.30b)$$

where (1.30b) emphasizes that the RHS of (1.30a) is an average.

We digress briefly to point out an often-useful property of the characteristic function: that of moment generation. By expanding the exponential factor in (1.30a) in a Taylor series, and interchanging the order of integration and summation, we obtain

$$C_X(js) = \sum_{n=0}^{\infty} \frac{(js)^n}{n!} \int_{-\infty}^{\infty} x^n p_X(x) \, dx \qquad (1.31a)$$

$$= \sum_{n=0}^{\infty} \frac{(js)^n}{n!} \overline{X^n} \ . \qquad (1.31b)$$

In obtaining (1.31b) we observe that the integral in (1.31a) is simply the $n$th moment of the random variable $X$; thus the various moments of $X$ can be determined by inspection of a Taylor series expansion of $C_X(js)$, as $n!$ times the coefficient of $(js)^n$. Conversely, an expansion for $C_X(js)$ can be written, given the moments of the random variable $X$, and the totality of these moments thus specifies the random variable itself.[‡]

Returning to the topic of sum distributions, let the random variable $Y$ be the sum of a number of independent random variables $X_1, \ldots, X_N$; thus

$$Y = \sum_{n=1}^{N} X_n. \qquad (1.32)$$

The characteristic function of $Y$ is then given by

† This integral transform is essentially the *Fourier transform*, which we shall introduce later in connection with spectral analysis. The transform and its inverse are unique, so that $C_X(js)$ defines $p_X(x)$ and vice versa. See Cramér, chap. 10.

‡ See Cramér, pp. 93, 176.

$$C_Y(js) = \overline{\exp\left(js \sum_{n=1}^{N} x_n\right)}$$

$$= \overline{\prod_{n=1}^{N} e^{jsx_n}}. \tag{1.33}$$

Now, the average of the product of independent random variables is equal to the product of the individual averages, so that (1.33) becomes

$$C_Y(js) = \prod_{n=1}^{N} \overline{e^{jsx_n}} \tag{1.34a}$$

$$= \prod_{n=1}^{N} C_{X_n}(js), \tag{1.34b}$$

where we use (1.30b) in writing (1.34b). We thus find that the characteristic function for the sum of independent random variables is equal to the product of the individual characteristic functions.

We may use the fact expressed by (1.34b) to determine the probability density function of the sum of two independent random variables, in terms of the individual density functions. If $f$ and $g$ are the two random variables, then from (1.34b), $C_{f+g}(js) = C_f(js)C_g(js)$. Now, by the inverse integral transform relationship which is complementary to (1.30a), the probability density function $p_{f+g}(u)$ for the sum of $f$ and $g$ is

$$p_{f+g}(u) = \frac{1}{2\pi} \int_{-\infty}^{\infty} C_{f+g}(js)e^{-jus}\, ds \tag{1.35a}$$

$$= \frac{1}{2\pi} \int_{-\infty}^{\infty} C_f(js)C_g(js)e^{-jus}\, ds. \tag{1.35b}$$

Substituting the integral expression for $C_f(js)$ [see (1.30a)] into (1.35b) and rearranging the order of integration yields

$$p_{f+g}(u) = \int_{-\infty}^{\infty} p_f(x) \left[\frac{1}{2\pi} \int_{-\infty}^{\infty} C_g(js)e^{-js(u-x)}\, ds\right] dx. \tag{1.36}$$

However, the bracketed integral in (1.36) is recognized from (1.35a) as being $p_g(u - x)$, so that we have finally

$$p_{f+g}(u) = \int_{-\infty}^{\infty} p_f(x)p_g(u - x)\, dx. \tag{1.37}$$

The RHS of (1.37) expresses the *convolution* of the probability density functions of $f$ and $g$, an operation which is often found written in the abbreviated form $p_{f+g}(u) = p_f(u) * p_g(u)$. Graphically, the convolution operation (1.37) may be visualized as multiplying a plot of $p_f(x)$ by one of $p_g(-x)$, the latter displaced to the right by an amount $u$ (left by $|u|$ for $u < 0$); then the area bounded by the resultant curve is determined, and its value plotted as a single point contributing to the plot of $p_{f+g}(u)$ vs. $u$. Multiple convolution procedures, of course, apply to determining the probability density function of the sum of more than two random variables; however, these become tedious to execute.

Finally, we observe that, since averaging is a linear—i. e., distributive—operation, the mean of a sum of random variables is the sum of the individual means; thus

$$\bar{Y} = \overline{\sum_{n=1}^{N} X_n} = \sum_{n=1}^{N} \overline{X_n} . \tag{1.38}$$

Similarly, the variance of a sum of *independent* random variables is the sum of the individual variances. Thus, assuming for convenience that $\overline{X_n} = 0$, we have

$$\sigma_Y^2 = \overline{Y^2} = \overline{\left(\sum_{n=1}^{N} X_n\right)^2} \tag{1.39a}$$

$$= \sum_{n=1}^{N} \sum_{m=1}^{N} \overline{X_n X_m} \tag{1.39b}$$

$$= \sum_{n=1}^{N} \overline{X_n^2} = \sum_{n=1}^{N} \sigma_{X_n}^2 . \tag{1.39c}$$

The double summation is a common way of expressing the square of a series; (1.39b) also uses the distributive property of averaging. Equation (1.39c) is obtained by noting that $\overline{X_n X_m} = 0$ for $n \neq m$, if $X_n$ and $X_m$ are independent and have zero means; this property will be further discussed when we consider correlation.

**1.10**   THE GAUSSIAN DISTRIBUTION AND THE CENTRAL LIMIT THEOREM

A random variable $X$ is said to possess a *gaussian* probability distribution (often called a *normal* distribution) if its density function is given by

$$p_X(x) = \frac{1}{\sqrt{2\pi}\,\sigma_X} e^{-(x-\bar{X})^2/2\sigma_X^2}. \tag{1.40}$$

The corresponding distribution function is

$$P_X(x) = \frac{1}{\sqrt{2\pi}\,\sigma_X} \int_{-\infty}^{x} e^{-(u-\bar{X})^2/2\sigma_X^2}\, du. \tag{1.41}$$

The integral (1.41) is nonelementary and cannot be written in closed form; however, it can be expressed both by asymptotic and power series, and is extensively tabulated numerically.[†] The characteristic function for the gaussian distribution is given by

$$C_x(js) = \frac{1}{\sqrt{2\pi}\,\sigma_x} \int_{-\infty}^{\infty} \exp\left[-(x - \bar{X})^2/2\sigma_x^2 + jsx\right] dx \quad (1.42a)$$

$$= \exp\left[js\bar{X} + \tfrac{1}{2}(js)^2\sigma_x^2\right], \quad (1.42b)$$

where the integration is performed using tables of definite integrals.

The importance of the gaussian distribution stems from the fact that a great many random processes in nature are characterized by it. In particular, the thermal noise voltages generated by resistors and the shot noise currents of vacuum tubes and transistors, when regarded as random variables, exhibit essentially gaussian probability distributions. This statistical distribution is therefore of primary importance to the analysis of noise effects in communication systems, and we shall have occasion to deal repeatedly with it.

The gaussian distribution arises historically in connection with the sum of a great many independent sequences of events, or random variables. As a physical example of this situation, the anode current of a vacuum tube is actually the cumulative result of a very large number of current pulses, due to the transport of individual electrons. In this context, the fundamental significance of the gaussian distribution is emphasized by the *central limit theorem*. Loosely speaking, this theorem states that, under rather general conditions, the distribution of the sum of a sufficiently large number of random variables tends to be gaussian, even if the distributions of the individual random variables are not gaussian.[‡]

The proofs which have been given for the central limit theorem revolve about determining suitable restrictions to be placed on the statistics of the constituent random variables, and on the number thereof to be taken, in order that the distribution of their sum approach gaussian within specifiable tolerances. We shall not consider this problem in such depth; however, it is worthwhile to demonstrate this very fundamental statistical theorem for a special (but not trivial) case, wherein each of the random variables sum-

---

[†] National Bureau of Standards, *Tables of Normal Probability Functions*, Table 23, NBS Appl. Math. Series (Washington, D. C.: U. S. Government Printing Office, 1953).

[‡] See Cramér, pp. 213–230.

med has the same distribution, not necessarily gaussian. (The sum of a large number of equal-amplitude sine waves of different frequencies could represent this situation.) Furthermore, the demonstration of this special form of the central limit theorem is a good exercise of the statistical principles which we have reviewed in preceding articles.

Thus let the sum of $N$ independent random variables $X_1, \ldots, X_N$ be denoted by

$$Y = \sum_{n=1}^{N} X_n. \tag{1.43}$$

The mean $\bar{Y}$ and variance $\sigma_Y^2$ of the sum random variable $Y$ are given respectively by

$$\bar{Y} = \sum_{n=1}^{N} \bar{X_n} = N\bar{X} \tag{1.44}$$

and

$$\sigma_Y^2 = \sum_{n=1}^{N} \sigma_{X_n}^2 = N\sigma_X^2, \tag{1.45}$$

where the last forms of (1.44) and (1.45) are a consequence of restricting the distributions of all the $X_n$'s to be identical. Now define a *standardized* random variable $\Phi$ as

$$\Phi = \frac{Y - \bar{Y}}{\sigma_Y}. \tag{1.46}$$

Note that $\bar{\Phi} = 0$ and $\sigma_\Phi^2 = 1$. Then, substituting (1.44) and (1.45) into (1.46) yields

$$\Phi = \frac{1}{\sqrt{N}\,\sigma_X} \sum_{n=1}^{N} (X_n - \bar{X}), \tag{1.47}$$

where we note that all the *deviations* $X_n - \bar{X} = X_n'$ also have the same distribution. Denote the characteristic function of this distribution by $C_{X'}(js)$; thus, from (1.34b) and the fact that $C_{aX}(js) = C_X(jas)$, we have

$$C_\Phi(js) = \left[ C_{X'}\left(\frac{js}{\sqrt{N}\,\sigma_X}\right) \right]^N. \tag{1.48}$$

Now, from the identities

$$\overline{(X_n - \bar{X})} = 0 \tag{1.49}$$

and

$$\overline{(X_n - \bar{X})^2} = \sigma_X^2 \tag{1.50}$$

and the moment-generating property (1.31b) of the characteristic function, we have

$$C_{X'}\left(\frac{js}{\sqrt{N}\,\sigma_X}\right) = 1 + 0 + \frac{1}{2}\left(\frac{js}{\sqrt{N}\,\sigma_X}\right)^2 \sigma_X^2 + \cdots$$

$$= 1 - \frac{s^2}{2N} + \xi(N, s),$$

(1.51)

where, for every value of $s$, the remainder term $\xi(N, s)$ vanishes more rapidly than as $1/N$. Thus, substituting (1.51) into (1.48) yields, in the limit as $N \to \infty$,

$$\lim_{N \to \infty}[C_\Phi(js)] = \lim_{N \to \infty}\left(1 - \frac{s^2}{2N}\right)^N$$

(1.52a)

$$= e^{-s^2/2},$$

(1.52b)

where to obtain (1.52b) we use the identity $\lim_{N \to \infty}(1 + a/N)^N = e^a$.

However, the RHS of (1.52b) is simply the characteristic function of a standardized gaussian random variable [see (1.42b)], and this fact is sufficient to prove that $\Phi$ itself is a standardized gaussian random variable, in the limit as $N \to \infty$. We have thus shown the following version of the central limit theorem:

THEOREM: If $X_1, \ldots, X_N$ are independent random variables all having the same distribution function with mean $\bar{X}$ and variance $\sigma_X^2$, then the distribution function of the standardized sum

$$\Phi = \frac{1}{\sqrt{N}\,\sigma_X}\sum_{n=1}^{N}(X_n - \bar{X})$$

is asymptotically gaussian $(N \to \infty)$, with zero mean and unit variance.

The important point regarding this development of the central limit theorem is that [in writing (1.51)] only the finiteness of the second moment of the common distribution of the constituent independent random variables $X_1, \ldots, X_N$ is required; it is not necessary otherwise to specify the form of the common distribution function of the $X_n$'s. Moreover, it is possible to prove the central limit theorem without stipulating identical distributions for the $X_n$'s, by imposing additional conditions involving central absolute moments of no higher order than the third. Finally, the central limit theorem may be extended to cases where the constituent random variables $X_1, \ldots, X_N$ are not independent. Thus we have an extremely powerful basis for correctly postulating gaussian statistical behavior for a wide variety of natural random processes. Fortunately, the gaussian distribution proves to be unusually tractable mathematically when explicit solutions to noise problems in communication systems must be obtained.

**1.11**   THE CHEBYSHEV† INEQUALITY

For our final result in this introductory review of statistical principles, we shall derive an important inequality which will later prove useful. Thus let $X$ be an arbitrary random variable with a probability density function $p_X(x)$ such that

$$\overline{|X|^2} = \int_{-\infty}^{\infty} |x|^2 p_X(x)\, dx < \infty. \qquad (1.53)$$

Since both $|x|^2$ and $p_X(x)$ are nonnegative, then for any arbitrary positive number $c$ we can write

$$\overline{|X|^2} \geq \int_{|x| \geq c} |x|^2 p_X(x)\, dx \geq c^2 \int_{|x| \geq c} p_X(x)\, dx, \qquad (1.54a)$$

where for the last inequality we note that $|x|^2 \geq c^2$ everywhere in the region of integration $|x| \geq c$. The last integral is simply the the probability $P(|X| \geq c)$, so that (1.54a) yields

$$P(|X| \geq c) \leq \frac{\overline{|X|^2}}{c^2}. \qquad (1.54b)$$

Specifically, by taking $X$ to be the difference between a random variable $f$ and its mean $\bar{f}$, $X = f - \bar{f}$, and writing the arbitrary number $c$ in terms of the standard deviation as $c = k\sigma_f$, we obtain the *Chebyshev inequality*

$$P(|f - \bar{f}| \geq k\sigma_f) \leq \frac{1}{k^2}. \qquad (1.55)$$

The importance of this relationship lies in the completely arbitrary statistical nature of the random variable, except for the requirement for a finite second moment expressed by (1.53). Thus (1.55) allows us to bound the probability of postulated excursions without—as often is the case—knowing, or being required to derive, the distribution function for the random variable involved. However, this generality also means that the bound expressed by (1.55) may not be especially "tight" in specific instances. For example, (1.55) yields

$$p(|f - \bar{f}| \geq 3\sigma_f) \leq \frac{1}{9} = 0.111,$$

whereas if $f$ is normally distributed this probability is actually about 0.003. Conversely, for a distribution which has weights $1/2k^2$

---

† The French transliteration "Tchebycheff" is also often used.

at the points $f = \bar{f} \pm k\sigma_f$, and weight $1 - 1/k^2$ at $f = \bar{f}$, we obtain equality in (1.55):

$$P(|f - \bar{f}| \geq k\sigma_f) = \frac{1}{k^2}.$$

Thus the bound given by (1.55) cannot in general be improved without further restricting the class of distributions considered. A common case in this context is where the density function has only a single maximum, i. e., is *unimodal*, and is symmetrical with respect to the mean (and mode) $\bar{f}$. Here it can be shown that[†]

$$P(|f - \bar{f}| \geq k\sigma_f) \leq \frac{4}{9k^2}, \tag{1.56}$$

thus improving the bound provided by the Chebyshev inequality (1.55) by a factor of 2.25.

### REFERENCES

Bendat, J. S., *Principles and Applications of Random Noise Theory*. Wiley, New York, 1958.

Cramér, H., *Mathematical Methods of Statistics*. Princeton U. P., Princeton, N. J., 1946.

Davenport, W. B., Jr., and W. L. Root, *An Introduction to the Theory of Random Signals and Noise*. McGraw-Hill, New York, 1958.

Doob, J. L., *Stochastic Processes*. Wiley, New York, 1953.

Feller, W., *Probability Theory and Its Applications*. Wiley, New York, 1950.

Lindgren, B. W., *Statistical Theory*. Macmillan, New York, 1962.

Loéve, M., *Probability Theory*. Van Nostrand, Princeton, N. J., 1955.

National Bureau of Standards, *Tables of Normal Probability Functions*. Table 23, NBS Appl. Math. Series. U. S. Govt. Printing Office, Washington D. C., 1953.

Yaglom, A. M. (trans. R. A. Silverman), *An Introduction to the Theory of Stationary Random Functions*. Prentice-Hall, Englewood Cliffs, N. J., 1962.

[†] See Cramér, p. 183.

# Chapter Two

# Correlation and Spectral Analysis

We have deferred to this point the subject of *correlation*, because in communication systems analysis it is often more closely identified with spectral concepts than with basically statistical procedures. However, it is well to introduce the topic of correlation in a statistical context.

## 2.1 LINEAR REGRESSION AND CORRELATION COEFFICIENT

As was inferred in our previous discussion of conditional probability and statistical independence, it is often necessary to determine the dependence, if any, of one random variable on another. The classical way of investigating for a possible relationship between two random variables $f$ and $g$ with respect to a defining experiment is to plot the outcomes of a number of trials of the experiment as points in the $(x, y)$ plane. Such a plot, as shown in Fig. 2.1, is known by the descriptive term *scatter diagram*. If the two random variables $f$ and $g$ are statistically independent, then the sample points plotted fall relatively uniformly throughout the plane. Conversely, if $f$ and $g$ are strongly related, then the sample points will concentrate about a curve which describes the functional dependence between the two random veriables. The simplest type of dependence, and one of considerable importance, is linear.

Suppose that a scatter diagram suggests a strong linear dependence between the random variables $f$ and $g$. It is of interest then to determine the straight line

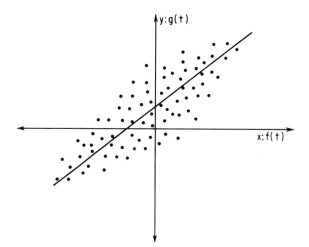

FIGURE 2.1 Scatter diagram.

$$g_p = a + bf, \qquad (2.1)$$

which yields best predicted value of $g$, given a sample value of $f$. A conventional criterion of "best" is minimization of the mean-square difference, $\Delta$, between the true values of $g$ and the predictions $g_p$ given by (2.1):

$$\Delta = \overline{(g - g_p)^2} = \overline{[g - (a + bf)]^2}. \qquad (2.2)$$

With this minimum mean-square error criterion, the line (2.1) is often called the *regression line* of $g$ on $f$.†

We must now determine the values of $a$ and $b$ which define the regression line. Expanding the RHS of (2.2), and equating the derivatives with respect to $a$ and $b$ to zero, yields

$$\frac{\partial \Delta}{\partial a} = -2\bar{g} + 2a + 2b\bar{f} = 0, \qquad (2.3a)$$

$$\frac{\partial \Delta}{\partial b} = -2\overline{fg} + 2a\bar{f} + 2b\overline{f^2} = 0. \qquad (2.3b)$$

Solving (2.3a, b) for $a$ and $b$, we obtain

$$b = \frac{\overline{fg} - \bar{f}\,\bar{g}}{\overline{f^2} - (\bar{f})^2} = \frac{\overline{(f - \bar{f})(g - \bar{g})}}{\sigma_f^2} = \frac{m_{fg}}{\sigma_f^2} \qquad (2.4a)$$

$$a = \bar{g} - \bar{f}\frac{\overline{(f - \bar{f})(g - \bar{g})}}{\sigma_f^2} = \bar{g} - \frac{m_{fg}}{\sigma_f^2}\bar{f}, \qquad (2.4b)$$

† See Cramér, pp. 270–279.

where we introduce the shorthand notation $m_{fg} = \overline{(f - \bar{f})(g - \bar{g})}$. Finally, substituting (2.4a, b) into (2.1) yields, for the desired regression line,

$$g_p = \bar{g} + \frac{m_{fg}}{\sigma_f^2}(f - \bar{f}). \tag{2.5}$$

It is convenient to introduce the standardized random variables $\chi, \eta$,

$$\chi = \frac{f - \bar{f}}{\sigma_f}, \tag{2.6a}$$

$$\eta = \frac{g - \bar{g}}{\sigma_g}, \tag{2.6b}$$

and to define a standardized prediction

$$\eta_p = \frac{g_p - \bar{g}}{\sigma_g}. \tag{2.7}$$

In terms of these, the regression line assumes the simple form

$$\eta_p = \rho_{fg}\chi, \tag{2.8}$$

where $\rho_{fg}$ is the *correlation coefficient* of $f$ and $g$, and is defined by

$$\rho_{fg} = \overline{\chi\eta} = \frac{m_{fg}}{\sigma_f\sigma_g}. \tag{2.9}$$

The correlation coefficient is also often called the *normalized covariance*; geometrically, it is the slope of the regression line which yields the minimum mean-square error estimate of $\eta$ based on a sample value of $\chi$.

The maximum range of $\rho_{fg}$ is $\pm 1$. To show this, let $f$ and $g$ be correlated to the maximum conceivable extent, i.e., $f = \pm g$. Then $\bar{f} = \pm \bar{g}$ and $\sigma_f = \sigma_g$. Furthermore,

$$m_{fg} = \overline{(\pm g \mp \bar{g})(g - \bar{g})} = \pm[\overline{g^2} - (\bar{g})^2] = \pm\sigma_g^2,$$

and (2.9) yields $\rho_{fg} = \pm\sigma_g^2/\sigma_g^2 = \pm 1$.

Conversely, if $\rho_{fg} = 0$, then $f$ and $g$ are said to be *uncorrelated*, or *linearly independent*. If the random variables $f$ and $g$ are *statistically independent*, then the joint moment $\overline{fg}$ factors into $\overline{fg} = \bar{f}\,\bar{g}$; hence [see (2.4a)] $m_{fg} = 0$ and $\rho_{fg} = 0$. Thus statistical independence of two random variables necessarily implies linear independence, or that they are uncorrelated. However, the converse is not true in general. It is important to remember that a *linear* functional relationship is the basis for the concept of correlation; hence two random variables that are uncorrelated are *not necessarily* statistically independent or functionally unrelated in some other way. An important exception, from the standpoint of communication system analysis, is the situation in which $f$ and $g$ are jointly *gaussian*; here, linear independence *does* imply statistical independence.

## 2.2    AUTOCOVARIANCE FUNCTION[†]

Let $f_1$ and $f_2$ be random variables which are identified with the possible values that can be assumed at times $t_1$ and $t_2$, respectively, by the sample functions $f(t)$ of a real random process. The correlation properties of two such random variables constitute one of the key considerations in communication system analysis. Specifically, we introduce the quantity $R_f(t_1, t_2)$, known as the *auto-covariance function* (also *autocorrelation* or simply *covariance* or *correlation*), and defined by

$$R_f(t_1, t_2) = \overline{f_1 f_2}. \tag{2.10}$$

The average written in (2.10) is, in the present context, a statistical one, and dependence on the time instants $t_1$ and $t_2$ is explicitly denoted since the joint probability distribution of $f_1$ and $f_2$ may well be a function of both. However, though the joint density function $p_{f_1, f_2}(u_1, u_2)$ may not be *strictly* stationary, it may be that the autocovariance function depends only on the time *difference* $\tau = t_2 - t_1$; we have previously noted that such processes are stationary in the *wide sense*, and correspondingly we write

$$R_f(t_1, t_1 + \tau) = R_f(\tau). \tag{2.11}$$

The corresponding *normalized* autocovariance function (autocorrelation function) $\rho_f(\tau)$ is

$$\rho_f(\tau) = \frac{R_f(\tau) - (\bar{f})^2}{\sigma_f^2}, \tag{2.12}$$

analogous to the correlation coefficient.

We now state some general properties of the autocovariance function which are useful to remember.[‡] First, on defining $t' = t + \tau$, we have

$$\overline{f(t)f(t + \tau)} = \overline{f(t' - \tau)f(t')}.$$

If now the random process of which $f(t)$ is a sample function

---

† See Yaglom, sec. 3.
‡ See Yaglom, sec. 5.

possesses wide-sense stationarity, the averages are invariant with translation of the time origin, and

$$R_f(\tau) = R_f(-\tau). \tag{2.13}$$

Thus the autocovariance function of a stationary real random process is an even function of $\tau$. Next, it is obvious that

$$R_f(0) = \overline{f^2(t)} = \sigma_f^2 + (\bar{f})^2. \tag{2.14}$$

Thus if $f(t)$ is a voltage or a current, then $R_f(0)$ represents its total power (in 1 ohm). Third, if $f(t)$ is a real function, and since the square of a real function is nonnegative, then $\overline{(f_1 \pm f_2)^2}/R_f(0) \geq 0$. If the process is stationary (wide sense), this inequality yields, on expansion and performing the averages, $|R_f(\tau)|/R_f(0) \leq 1$. Thus for a real stationary random process we have

$$|R_f(\tau)| \leq R_f(0). \tag{2.15}$$

Finally, it is true for nonperiodic processes that $\rho_f(\tau) \to 0$ as $\tau \to \infty$, so that from (2.12)

$$R_f(\infty) = (\bar{f})^2; \tag{2.16}$$

in other words, $R_f(\infty)$ represents the d-c power (in 1 ohm) of a voltage or current $f(t)$.

In order to clarify further the concept of the covariance function, let us give it a formal statistical expression (for real wide-sense stationary random processes), and illustrate this by an example. Thus the statistical average represented by $R_f(\tau)$ is given by

$$R_f(\tau) = \overline{f_1 f_2} = \int_{-\infty}^{\infty} \int_{-\infty}^{\infty} u_1 u_2 p_{f_1, f_2}(u_1, u_2; \tau) \, du_1 \, du_2. \tag{2.17}$$

The important factor here is $p_{f_1, f_2}(u_1, u_2; \tau)$; this is the joint probability density function of two values $f_1 = f(t_1)$ and $f_2 = f(t_2)$ of the function $f(t)$, separated in time by $|t_2 - t_1| = |\tau|$. The total operation represented by (2.17) may be visualized as averaging the product $f(t)f(t \pm \tau)$.[†]

To illustrate how to calculate $R(\tau)$ using (2.17), consider the "boxcar" function shown in Fig. 2.2. At regular intervals $T$, the function $f(t)$ has the option of shifting from 0 (or 1) to 1 (or 0), or staying where it is; the probability of a shift is $\frac{1}{2}$, i. e., over a long interval there will be about as many "1's" as there are

---

† Strictly speaking, (2.17) expresses an average over an ensemble of sample functions $f(t)$. As in Art. 1.4, we implicitly assume a random time origin, uniformly distributed on an appropriate time interval, for each sample function, in order to treat $f(t)$ statistically in the time domain.

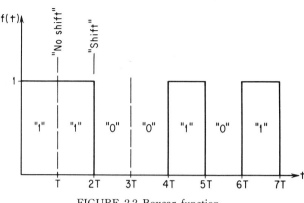

FIGURE 2.2 Boxcar function.

"0's." Viewed as a waveform, this situation would be exemplified by binary pulse-code modulation (PCM).

The first step is to recall (see Art. 1.3) that a joint probability density can be written in terms of the conditional density function; thus

$$p_{f_1, f_2}(u_1, u_2; \tau) = p_{f_1}(u_1) p_{f_2}(u_2; \tau | f_1). \tag{2.18}$$

The first task then is to determine the probability density function $p_{f_1}(u_1)$ for the boxcar function $f(t)$. Since the random variable involved is discrete in distribution, we must digress briefly to introduce the *Dirac delta-function* $\delta(u)$. Specifically, $\delta(u)$ is defined by

$$\delta(u) = 0, \qquad u \neq 0; \tag{2.19a}$$

$$\int_{-\infty}^{\infty} \delta(u) \, du = 1. \tag{2.19b}$$

Geometrically, the delta-function $\delta(u)$ may be visualized as a "spike" of unlimited height and vanishing width, occurring at the origin of its argument $(u)$; the height grows and the width vanishes in a related way so that constant area = 1 is bounded. A rectangle of width $a$ and height $1/a$, for example, becomes a delta-function in the limit $a \to 0$. The delta-function possesses a useful property known as the *sifting property*. This is expressed mathematically by

$$\int_{-\infty}^{\infty} f(u) \, \delta(u - u_0) \, du = f(u_0). \tag{2.20}$$

The function $f(u)$ is essentially constant, equal to $f(u_0)$, over the infinitesimal range of $u$ about $u_0$ for which $\delta(u - u_0)$ is nonzero; the delta-function is zero elsewhere, and since by (2.19b) it bounds unit area, (2.20) follows immediately. The descriptive phrase "sifting property" refers to the ability of a delta-function to extract a specific value of a function $f(u_0)$, as given in (2.20).

To return to the relationship of delta-functions to probability density functions, we observe that the distribution function $P_f(x)$ of a constant random variable $f(t) = A$ is a step of unit magnitude at $x = A$; denote this fact by $P_{f=A}(x) = U(x - A)$. Now, from the properties of the delta-function which we have just discussed, it is evident that the corresponding probability density function of a constant random variable $f(t) = A$ is

$$p_{f=A}(u) = \frac{dU(u - A)}{du} = \delta(u - A). \tag{2.21a}$$

This fact is readily verified by noting from (2.19b) that

$$P_{f=A}(x) = \int_{-\infty}^{x} p_{f=A}(u)\, du = \int_{-\infty}^{x} \delta(u - A)\, du = U(x - A). \tag{2.21b}$$

With this background, we can now write the probability density function $p_{f_1}(u_1)$ for the "boxcar" random variable $f(t)$ as

$$p_{f_1}(u_1) = \tfrac{1}{2}\delta(u_1 - 1) + \tfrac{1}{2}\delta(u_1), \tag{2.22}$$

since with probabilities $\frac{1}{2}$, $f(t_1)$ is either 1 or 0. If now we postulate that $f(t)$ *cannot* shift value, then the conditional probability density function $p_{f_2}(u_2; \tau | f_1)$ becomes

$$p_{f_2}(u_2; 0 | f_1) = \delta(u_2 - u_1), \tag{2.23a}$$

since $f(t_2 = t_1) = f(t_1)$ with probability 1. Similarly, if we postulate that $f(t)$ *must* have the option of shifting value, then we have

$$p_{f_2}(u_2; |\tau| > T | f_1) = p_{f_2}(u_2) = \tfrac{1}{2}\delta(u_2 - 1) + \tfrac{1}{2}\delta(u_2), \tag{2.23b}$$

since with probabilities $\frac{1}{2}$, $f(t_2 > t_1 + T)$ or $f(t_2 < t_1 - T)$ is either 1 or 0, independent of $f(t_1)$.

Now, the probability that in a time interval $|\tau| \leq T$ the random variable $f(t)$ *does* obtain the option of shifting value is

$$P_f(\text{shift option}) = \frac{|\tau|}{T} \tag{2.24a}$$

and the probability that $f(t)$ *cannot* shift value is

$$P_f(\text{no shift option}) = 1 - \frac{|\tau|}{T} = \frac{T - |\tau|}{T}. \tag{2.24b}$$

Thus for $|\tau| \leq T$ we have the conditional density function

$$p_{f_2}(u_2; |\tau| \leq T | f_1) = \frac{T - |\tau|}{T} \delta(u_2 - u_1)$$
$$+ \frac{|\tau|}{T}\left[\frac{1}{2}\delta(u_2 - 1) + \frac{1}{2}\delta(u_2)\right]; \tag{2.25}$$

for $|\tau| > T$, (2.23b) applies.

For values of time translation $|\tau| \leq T$, (2.17) can then be written out as

$$R_f(|\tau| \leq T)$$

$$= \frac{T - |\tau|}{2T} \int_{-\infty}^{\infty} \int_{-\infty}^{\infty} u_1 u_2 [\delta(u_1 - 1) + \delta(u_1)] \delta(u_2 - u_1) \, du_1 \, du_2.$$

(no shift option)　　　　　　　　(2.26)

$$+ \frac{|\tau|}{4T} \int_{-\infty}^{\infty} \int_{-\infty}^{\infty} u_1 u_2 [\delta(u_1 - 1) + \delta(u_1)][\delta(u_2 - 1) + \delta(u_2)] du_1 \, du_2.$$

(shift option)

We perform the first integration with respect to $u_2$ using the sifting property of $\delta(u_2 - u_1)$, and note that the second double integral simply factors, to obtain

$$R_f(|\tau| \leq T)$$

$$= \frac{T - |\tau|}{2T} \int_{-\infty}^{\infty} u_1^2 [\delta(u_1 - 1) + \delta(u_1)] \, du_1 \tag{2.27}$$

$$+ \frac{|\tau|}{4T} \int_{-\infty}^{\infty} u_1 [\delta(u_1 - 1) + \delta(u_1)] du_1 \int_{-\infty}^{\infty} u_2 [\delta(u_2 - 1) + \delta(u_2)] \, du_2.$$

Again using the sifting property (2.20) of the delta-function, all the integrations in (2.27) involving $\delta(u)$ vanish, and all those involving $\delta(u - 1)$ are equal to unity. Thus

$$R_f(|\tau| \leq T) = \frac{T - |\tau|}{2T} + \frac{|\tau|}{4T} = \frac{1}{2} - \frac{|\tau|}{4T}. \tag{2.28a}$$

For $|\tau| > T$ we have, similar to the second integration in (2.26),

$$R_f(|\tau| > T)$$

$$= \frac{1}{4} \int_{-\infty}^{\infty} \int_{-\infty}^{\infty} u_1 u_2 [\delta(u_1 - 1) + \delta(u_1)][\delta(u_2 - 1) + \delta(u_2)] du_1 \, du_2 \tag{2.28b}$$

$$= \frac{1}{4}.$$

Thus from (2.28a, b), the autocovariance function of the "boxcar" function is as shown in Fig. 2.3. With respect to the general properties of the autocovariance function, we see that (2.13) and (2.15) are satisfied. Further, $R_f(0) = \frac{1}{2}$, as obviously should be the case in order to satisfy (2.14). Finally, $R_f(\infty) = \frac{1}{4}$, as is demanded by (2.16).

In Art. 1.5 we expressed, by the empirical ergodicity postulate, the identity of time averages and statistical averages, where the distribution associated with the latter is identified with the fraction of the time that some physical quantity satisfies specified condi-

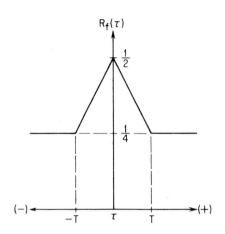

$R_f(\tau)$

$\frac{1}{2}$

$\frac{1}{4}$

$(-)$                                                        $(+)$

$-T$        $\tau$        $T$

FIGURE 2.3 Autocovariance function of
boxcar function.

tions. In Art. 1.6 we introduced the concept of a random process, and inquired concerning a correspondence between statistical or ensemble averages taken "over" the process, and time averages taken "along" its sample functions. Specifically, we noted that if the random process is stationary and *ergodic*, then these statistical and time averages are identical (excluding special cases of zero probability). An exact description of the ergodicity concept is difficult to give in words; however, its essence implies that each sample function of the random process must eventually develop all the patterns of behavior that are exhibited by each other sample function. Thus for a real stationary ergodic random process $f(t, u)$, having a probability density function $p_f(u)$ over the process at any instant $t$, and sample functions $f(t)$, we have

$$\int_{-\infty}^{\infty} \varphi[f(u)]p_f(u)\, du = \lim_{T\to\infty} \frac{1}{2T} \int_{-T}^{T} \varphi[f(t)]\, dt = \overline{\varphi(f)}, \quad (2.29)$$

where $\varphi$ represents any single-valued functional form.

Thus let $\varphi(f_1, f_2) = f_1 f_2 = f(t)f(t + \tau)$, and correspondingly replace $p_f(u)$ by the joint density function $p_{f_1, f_2}(u_1, u_2; \tau)$. Then from (2.17) and (2.29) we obtain

$$R_f(\tau) = \int_{-\infty}^{\infty}\int_{-\infty}^{\infty} u_1 u_2 p_{f_1, f_2}(u_1, u_2; \tau)\, du_1\, du_2$$
$$= \lim_{T\to\infty} \frac{1}{2T} \int_{-T}^{T} f(t)\, f(t + \tau)\, dt. \quad (2.30)$$

The lower line of (2.30) expresses the *time autocovariance function* of a sample function of a real stationary random process, and if the process is ergodic, this is seen to be equal to the statistical or ensemble autocovariance function of the process. As with our use of the bar notation ( ‾ ) to indicate either a time or a statistical average, we shall also not explicitly distinguish between time and statistical covariance functions, using $R(\tau)$ to denote both. Ergodicity is usually implicit in the use of statistical methods in communication systems analysis, as we observed in Art. 1.6.

The latter form of (2.30) yields a clearer insight into the physical nature of the autocovariance function. Specifically, we multiply the waveform $f(t)$ by itself, delayed in time by $\tau$ seconds; then we average the product. The result yields a measure of the extent to which an instantaneous value of the function $f(t)$ is linearly dependent upon an instantaneous sample taken $\tau$ seconds previously. One might intuitively expect this measure of linear dependence or correlation to be determined by how "fast," on the average, the waveform $f(t)$ varies relative to the delay interval $\tau$, and that the longer $\tau$ is with respect to the time taken by $f(t)$ to undergo a substantial excursion, the smaller will be $R_f(\tau)$. These qualitative notions are indeed true, and we shall shortly see that a close relationship exists between the autocovariance function $R_f(\tau)$ and the spectrum of the waveform $f(t)$.

## 2.3   SPECTRAL ANALYSIS

The familiar decomposition of a known waveform into individual frequency components, by means of the Fourier series or the Fourier transform, can to a large extent be applied to stationary random processes, such as are used in communication systems analysis to characterize noise sources. Our primary interest is in the *power spectral density*, which describes the frequency distribution of the power of a process, measured in watts per cps. As noted above, this quantity is closely related to the autocovariance function. We presume of the reader some prior knowledge of Fourier series and transforms, and merely state at the outset some fundamentals for reference purposes.[†]

### Fourier Series

If $x(t)$ is a periodic function of a real variable $t$, commonly regarded as time, and if $x(t)$ is absolutely integrable over the period $T$, that is,

$$\int_0^T |x(t)|\, dt < \infty, \tag{2.31}$$

then $x(t)$ possesses a Fourier series expansion

$$\hat{x}(t) = \sum_{n=-\infty}^{\infty} c_n e^{j2\pi n f_0 t}, \tag{2.32a}$$

[†] See Churchill (I), Wiener (II); also four tutorial papers on the Fourier integral in *IRE Trans. on Circuit Theory*, **CT-2** (September 1955).

where $f_0 = 1/T$ and the Fourier coefficients $c_n$ are given by

$$c_n = \frac{1}{T} \int_0^T x(t)e^{-j2\pi n f_0 t}\, dt. \tag{2.32b}$$

Further, if $x(t)$ is integrable-square over the period $T$, that is,

$$\int_0^T |x(t)|^2\, dt < \infty, \tag{2.33a}$$

then the RHS of (2.32a) converges to $x(t)$ in the sense that

$$\lim_{N \to \infty} \frac{1}{T} \int_0^T |x(t) - \sum_{n=-N}^{N} c_n e^{j2\pi n f_0 t}|^2\, dt = 0. \tag{2.33b}$$

This type of convergence, which states that the mean-squared difference [here between the original function $x(t)$ and its truncated Fourier series representation] vanishes as an unlimited number of terms of the series is included, is known as *convergence-in-the-mean*. We denote this property by

$$x(t) = \underset{N \to \infty}{\mathrm{l.\,i.\,m.}} \sum_{n=-N}^{N} c_n e^{j2\pi n f_0 t}, \tag{2.34}$$

where the notation l. i. m. is read *limit-in-the-mean*.

### Fourier Transform

The Fourier transform is often regarded as an extension of the Fourier series concept to functions of arbitrarily large "periodicity." More precisely, we have the statements

$$x(t) = \int_{-\infty}^{\infty} X(f)e^{j2\pi f t}\, df \tag{2.35a}$$

and

$$\hat{X}(f) = \int_{-\infty}^{\infty} x(t)e^{-j2\pi f t}\, dt. \tag{2.35b}$$

If the integrals (2.35a, b) exist, then one of the basic results of Fourier transform theory[†] states that if $X(f)$ is integrable-square on $-\infty < f < \infty$, then there exists a function $x(t)$, integrable-square on $-\infty < t < \infty$, such that

$$x(t) = \underset{F \to \infty}{\mathrm{l.\,i.\,m.}} \int_{-F}^{F} X(f)e^{j2\pi f t}\, df \tag{2.36a}$$

and

$$X(f) = \underset{T \to \infty}{\mathrm{l.\,i.\,m.}} \int_{-T}^{T} x(t)e^{-j2\pi f t}\, dt. \tag{2.36b}$$

Further, if $X(f)$ is absolutely integrable, then $x(t)$ is given by

---

† Plancherel's theorem; see Wiener (II), ch. I.

(2.35a), and if $x(t)$ is absolutely integrable, then $X(f) = \hat{X}(f)$, as given by (2.35b); we shall thus drop the mathematical formalism of a limit-in-the-mean, and henceforth write the Fourier transform as an identity. It is also common to use the radian frequency $\omega = 2\pi f$; the Fourier transform pair then becomes

$$x(t) = \frac{1}{2\pi} \int_{-\infty}^{\infty} X(\omega)e^{j\omega t}\, d\omega, \tag{2.37a}$$

$$X(\omega) = \int_{-\infty}^{\infty} x(t)e^{-j\omega t}\, dt. \tag{2.37b}$$

We shall, however, adhere to the "symmetrical" form, as in (2.35a, b).

### Parseval's Theorem

The integrable-square condition on $x(t)$ requires that the waveform possess finite energy in the period $T$; this is nearly always satisfied in practice, and we shall tacitly assume this circumstance in future work. The result, then, is *Parseval's theorem*, which states that the average energy (power) of the waveform $x(t)$ is equal to the sum of the powers carried by each frequency component. Thus we have for real periodic functions

$$\frac{1}{T} \int_0^T x^2(t)\, dt = \sum_{n=-\infty}^{\infty} |c_n|^2 \tag{2.38a}$$

and analogously, in terms of energy, for real functions of arbitrarily large "periodicity"

$$\int_{-\infty}^{\infty} x^2(t)\, dt = \int_{-\infty}^{\infty} |X(f)|^2\, df. \tag{2.38b}$$

### Power Spectral Density of a Periodic Function

As mentioned at the outset, our primary interest is in the *power spectral density*. (We shall often refer to this quantity simply as the *power spectrum*; however, some references reserve this latter term for use in a cumulative sense, which we shall explicitly designate by use of the word cumulative where needed.) Let us first calculate the power spectrum of the simplest type of periodic waveform: a sinusoid. Thus, let

$$
\begin{aligned}
x_T(t) &= A \sin (2\pi f_1 t + \theta) \\
&= -j\frac{A}{2} [e^{j(2\pi f_1 t + \theta)} - e^{-j(2\pi f_1 t + \theta)}], \qquad t \leq T; \tag{2.39} \\
&= 0, \qquad t > T.
\end{aligned}
$$

We will ultimately pass to the limit $T \to \infty$. Now define

$$X_T(f) = \int_{-T}^{T} x_T(t) e^{-j2\pi ft} \, dt; \tag{2.40a}$$

on substituting from (2.39) into (2.40a), integrating and combining the result, we have

$$X_T(f) = jA \left[ e^{-j\theta} \frac{\sin 2\pi(f + f_1)T}{2\pi(f + f_1)} - e^{j\theta} \frac{\sin 2\pi(f - f_1)T}{2\pi(f - f_1)} \right]. \tag{2.40b}$$

From the form of the energy equation (2.38b), it is plausible to identify a power spectral density as

$$G_x(f) = \lim_{T \to \infty} \frac{1}{2T} |X_T(f)|^2. \tag{2.41}$$

On substituting from (2.40b) into (2.41) we have

$$G_x(f) = \frac{A^2}{2} \lim_{T \to \infty} \frac{1}{T} \left\{ \left[ \frac{\sin 2\pi(f + f_1)T}{2\pi(f + f_1)} \right]^2 + \left[ \frac{\sin 2\pi(f - f_1)T}{2\pi(f - f_1)} \right]^2 \right.$$
$$\left. - 2 \cos 2\theta \, \frac{\sin 2\pi(f + f_1)T \sin 2\pi(f - f_1)T}{4\pi^2(f + f_1)(f - f_1)} \right\} \tag{2.42a}$$

$$= \frac{A^2}{4} [\delta(f + f_1) + \delta(f - f_1)]. \tag{2.42b}$$

In obtaining (2.42b), we have used the following representations of the delta-function:

$$\lim_{T \to \infty} \frac{\sin^2 Tu}{Tu^2} = \pi\delta(u), \tag{2.43a}$$

$$\lim_{T \to \infty} \frac{\sin Tu}{u} = \pi\delta(u), \tag{2.43b}$$

and noted that $\delta(au) = (1/a)\delta(u)$. The last term in (2.42a) yields the null form

$$\delta(f + f_1)\delta(f - f_1) = 0.$$

By integrating (2.42b) with respect to $f$, we find for the cumulative power spectrum of a sinusoid

$$\int_{-f}^{f} G_x(u) \, du = \frac{A^2}{2} U(f - f_1), \tag{2.44}$$

where $U(\ \ )$ is the unit step function, and we have used a dummy variable $u$ for integration purposes. Thus the total power is $A^2/2$ as it should be, and this is seen to exist entirely at the frequency $f_1$ of the wave. Observe from (2.42b) that power is formally considered to reside at both positive and negative frequencies; this is a mathematical consequence of our use of the Fourier transform.

The delta-function representation of the power spectrum of a constant-frequency sinusoid is analogous to this same representation of the probability density function of a constant random variable. Note that in developing the power spectrum we lose all the information concerning the phase of the original waveform, denoted by $\theta$ in (2.39).

It is easy to appreciate from the Fourier series (2.32a) that the power spectrum of any real periodic (not necessarily sinusoidal) waveform can be written

$$G_x(f) = \sum_{n=-\infty}^{\infty} |c_n|^2 \, \delta(f - nf_0). \tag{2.45}$$

Thus the power spectrum consists of a set of pairs of positive- and negative-frequency impulses corresponding to the constituent frequencies of the periodic waveform $x(t)$; each pair of delta-functions represents the power carried by a particular frequency component. *Discrete spectra* of this type are characteristic of periodic functions.

We can directly calculate the autocovariance function of a real periodic waveform using the Fourier series (2.32a); thus

$$R_x(\tau) = \overline{x(t)x(t+\tau)}$$

$$= \sum_{n=-\infty}^{\infty} \sum_{m=-\infty}^{\infty} \overline{c_n c_m e^{j2\pi(n+m)f_0 t}} e^{j2\pi m f_0 \tau} \tag{2.46a}$$

$$= \sum_{n=-\infty}^{\infty} c_n c_{-n} e^{-j2\pi n f_0 \tau}, \tag{2.46b}$$

where in obtaining (2.46b) we have used the orthogonality condition

$$\overline{e^{j2\pi(n-m)f_0 t}} = \begin{cases} 0, & n \neq m; \\ 1, & n = m. \end{cases} \tag{2.47}$$

Since for real functions [e. g., see (2.39)], $c_{-n} = c_n^*$, where the asterisk denotes the complex conjugate, (2.46b) becomes

$$R_x(\tau) = \sum_{n=-\infty}^{\infty} |c_n|^2 e^{j2\pi n f_0 \tau}. \tag{2.48}$$

Now, taking the Fourier transform of the autocovariance function (2.48) yields

$$\int_{-\infty}^{\infty} R_x(\tau) e^{-j2\pi f \tau} \, d\tau = \sum_{n=-\infty}^{\infty} |c_n|^2 \int_{-\infty}^{\infty} e^{-j2\pi(f-nf_0)\tau} \, d\tau$$

$$= \sum_{n=-\infty}^{\infty} |c_n|^2 \, \delta(f - nf_0) = G_x(f), \tag{2.49}$$

where we have used the delta-function representation

$$\int_{-\infty}^{\infty} e^{-j2\pi ut}\, dt = \delta(u). \tag{2.50}$$

We thus find that for periodic functions, the power spectral density and the autocovariance function are a Fourier transform pair. The power spectrum is therefore completely specified by the auto-covariance function, and vice-versa. It is this Fourier transform-pair relationship between $G_x(f)$ and $R_x(\tau)$ to which we previously alluded. Note from (2.48) that the autocovariance function of a periodic function is itself periodic, with the same period.

### Power Spectrum of a Periodic Random Process

We shall define a stationary random process to be periodic with period $T$ if its autocovariance function is periodic with period $T$. Thus let the process have real sample functions $x(t)$, which can be expanded in a Fourier series in the interval $T$:

$$x(t) = \sum_{n=-\infty}^{\infty} c_n e^{j2\pi n f_0 t}, \tag{2.51a}$$

$$c_n = \frac{1}{T} \int_{0}^{T} x(t) e^{-j2\pi n f_0 t}\, dt, \tag{2.51b}$$

where $f_0 = 1/T$. For each sample function of the process, (2.51b) will in general yield different coefficients $c_n$; thus (2.51b) defines the $c_n$'s as random variables over the ensemble of sample functions comprising the process.

Now it is plausible to define the energy carried by a random process as the *statistical* average, over the ensemble, of the energies carried by the sample functions. Thus

$$\overline{\int_{0}^{T} x^2(t)\, dt} = \overline{\int_{0}^{T} \sum_{n=-\infty}^{\infty} \sum_{m=-\infty}^{\infty} c_n c_m e^{j2\pi(n+m) f_0 t}\, dt}$$

$$= T \sum_{n=-\infty}^{\infty} |c_n|^2 = T \sum_{n=-\infty}^{\infty} b_n. \tag{2.52}$$

The average energy (power) is $\sum_{n=-\infty}^{\infty} b_n$. Thus by analogy to that of a periodic function, we take the power spectral density of a periodic stationary random process as

$$G_x(f) = \sum_{n=-\infty}^{\infty} b_n \delta(f - n f_0), \qquad f_0 = 1/T. \tag{2.53}$$

The autocovariance function is

$$R_x(\tau) = \sum_{n=-\infty}^{\infty} \sum_{m=-\infty}^{\infty} c_n c_m e^{j2\pi(n+m)f_0 t} e^{j2\pi m f_0 \tau}$$

$$= \sum_{n=-\infty}^{\infty} b_n e^{j2\pi n f_0 \tau}. \tag{2.54}$$

Now the Fourier transform of $R_x(\tau)$ is

$$\sum_{n=-\infty}^{\infty} b_n \int_{-\infty}^{\infty} e^{-j2\pi(f-nf_0)\tau}\, d\tau = \sum_{n=-\infty}^{\infty} b_n \delta(f - nf_0) = G_x(f). \tag{2.55}$$

Thus we again observe that the power spectral density and the autocovariance function are a Fourier transform pair, although time averages were used in developing (2.49), and statistical, or ensemble, averages are involved in (2.52)–(2.55).

### Wiener-Kinchine Relation[†]

Because of the apparent generality of the Fourier relationship, we shall henceforth define the power spectral density with respect to the autocovariance function, in accordance with the Wiener-Kinchine relationship; this gives $G_x(f)$ and $R_x(\tau)$ as a Fourier transform pair

$$G_x(f) = \int_{-\infty}^{\infty} R_x(\tau) e^{-j2\pi f\tau}\, d\tau, \tag{2.56a}$$

$$R_x(\tau) = \int_{-\infty}^{\infty} G_x(f) e^{j2\pi f\tau}\, df. \tag{2.56b}$$

We digress briefly to indicate why this definition of the power spectral density is preferable to that expressed by (2.41). Although (2.41) is plausible and useful [as in (2.42a, b)] for determining the power spectrum of an explicit time function, we find it questionable when dealing with a sample function of a random process. An important example involves the gaussian random process. In this context, the shortcoming of the function

$$G_x(f, T) = \frac{1}{2T} |X_T(f)|^2$$

is that although $\lim_{T\to\infty} \overline{G_x(f, T)} = G_x(f)$, where the average is taken over the ensemble, the variance of $G_x(f, T)$ may not vanish. Specifically, it can be shown[‡] for gaussian random processes that

$$\overline{G_x^2(f, T)} \geq 2[\overline{G_x(f, T)}]^2;$$

† See Yaglom, Sec. 8, 9.
‡ See Davenport and Root, pp. 107–108.

thus the variance of $G_x(f, T)$ does not vanish in the limit $T \to \infty$ for any $G_x(f) > 0$, and therefore $\lim_{T \to \infty} G_x(f, T)$ does not converge in the mean to a nonvanishing power spectrum $G_x(f)$, i. e.,

$$\overline{[G_x(f) - \lim_{T \to \infty} G_x(f, T)]^2} \neq 0.$$

The Wiener-Kinchine relation is thus an important one in communication systems analysis, since it permits the power spectral density to be computed from the autocovariance function. Moreover, the autocovariance function is now clearly seen to be a quantity of the most fundamental significance.

### Power Spectrum of an Arbitrary Function

Let us expand our spectral analysis concepts to the unbounded interval $-\infty \leq t \leq \infty$. The energy of a real waveform $x(t)$ given on this interval is

$$\int_{-\infty}^{\infty} x^2(t) \, dt = \int_{-\infty}^{\infty} |X(f)|^2 \, df \qquad (2.57a)$$

and since existence of the Fourier transform $X(f)$ requires that $x(t)$ be integrable-square for $-\infty < t < \infty$, then the average energy (power) is

$$\lim_{T \to \infty} \frac{1}{2T} \int_{-T}^{T} x^2(t) \, dt = 0. \qquad (2.57b)$$

The circumstance represented by (2.57b) is inconvenient from the standpoint of obtaining a meaningful power spectrum. Specifically, (2.57b) requires the power spectral density of a finite-energy waveform defined on the interval $-\infty \leq t \leq \infty$ to be zero at all frequencies, since it must integrate to yield vanishing power. However, one can imagine that the waveform $x(t)$ has and will continue to exist throughout all time; although it has finite energy over any finite interval, the total energy represented may be infinite. We are thus interested in functions which satisfy

$$\lim_{T \to \infty} \frac{1}{2T} \int_{-T}^{T} x^2(t) \, dt < \infty. \qquad (2.58)$$

This class includes those functions which are integrable-square, but unfortunately a function which merely satisfies (2.58) does not in general possess a Fourier transform. We cannot therefore proceed as before, since the Fourier transform needed to replace the Fourier series previously used may well not exist. We appear to be impaled upon the horns of a dilemma.

The escape consists of using the time autocovariance function

$$R_x(\tau) = \lim_{T \to \infty} \frac{1}{2T} \int_{-T}^{T} x(t)x(t + \tau)\, dt. \tag{2.59}$$

We recall from (2.15) that $R_x(\tau) \leq R_x(0)$; thus if (2.58) is satisfied, $x(t)$ possesses an autocovariance function $R_x(\tau)$ which is bounded by $R_x(0)$, and carries total power equal to $R_x(0)$. In accordance with (2.56a) we now define the power spectral density $G_x(f)$ as the Fourier transform of the (time) autocovariance function $R_x(\tau)$; correspondingly (2.56b) completes the Fourier transform-pair relationship between $G_x(f)$ and $R_x(\tau)$. For ergodic stationary random processes, the power spectrum thus defined with respect to the sample functions $x(t)$ of the process is identical to the power spectrum of the process defined over the ensemble of sample functions.

## 2.4   PROPERTIES OF TRANSFORMS

There are several important relations which describe, in the frequency domain, what happens to the transforms of time functions when the latter are combined in various ways, e. g., added, multiplied, etc. These relations state analytically many of the operations encountered in communication systems, e. g., amplification, mixing, modulation, filtering, etc. The relations are readily derived from the defining transform equations

$$X(f) = \int_{-\infty}^{\infty} x(t)e^{-j2\pi ft}\, dt, \tag{2.60a}$$

$$x(t) = \int_{-\infty}^{\infty} X(f)e^{j2\pi ft}\, df, \tag{2.60b}$$

and it is our purpose in this article to demonstrate them. We shall also identify the transform operations with power spectra. Beware, however, that the transform is a complex quantity—i. e., retains phase information—and that it often is identified with the power-spectrum concept through (2.41), which was the topic of some qualification in the preceding article. Where additional restrictions are necessary in this context, we shall develop appropriate relations by direct recourse to the autocovariance function; we assume wide-sense stationarity in every instance, whether or not it is explicitly stipulated.

### Linear Addition

It is readily seen by direct substitution in (2.60a) that the transform of a linear sum is given by

$$ax(t) + by(t) \doteqdot aX(f) + bY(f). \tag{2.61}$$

(Here we introduce some shorthand notation: $\doteqdot$ and the use of corresponding upper- and lower-case letters denotes a transform pair.) Thus linearity and superposition apply in both the time and frequency domains. However, to re-emphasize our introductory caution concerning the relationship of transforms to power spectra, let us develop this same relationship for power spectra. The auto-covariance function of the linear sum is given by

$$\begin{aligned}
R_{ax+by}(\tau) &= \overline{[ax(t) + by(t)][ax(t + \tau) + by(t + \tau)]} \\
&= \overline{a^2 x(t)x(t + \tau)} + \overline{b^2 y(t)y(t + \tau)} \tag{2.62} \\
&\quad + \overline{abx(t)y(t + \tau)} + \overline{abx(t + \tau)y(t)};
\end{aligned}$$

and if $x(t)$ and $y(t + \tau)$ are uncorrelated for all $\tau$, i. e., [see (2.9)] $\rho_{xy} = 0$, and either has zero mean, the latter two terms of (2.62a) vanish. Thus, subject to these conditions, we have

$$R_{ax+by}(\tau) = a^2 R_x(\tau) + b^2 R_y(\tau)$$

and therefore from the Wiener-Kinchine relation and (2.61) that

$$G_{ax+by}(f) = a^2 G_x(f) + b^2 G_y(f). \tag{2.63}$$

Thus, with the stated restrictions, the power spectrum of a sum of functions is the sum of their power spectra, and a function may be regarded as the sum of uncorrelated components, and its power spectrum as the sum of the component power spectra. Amplification is also shown by the foregoing:

$$ax(t) \doteqdot aX(f) \qquad \text{and} \qquad G_{ax}(f) = a^2 G_x(f).$$

### Scale Change

The transform of $x(kt)$ is obtained by changing the variable of integration in (2.60a) from $t$ to $kt$. Thus

$$x(kt) \doteqdot \frac{1}{|k|} \int_{-\infty}^{\infty} x(kt) e^{-j2\pi(f/k)kt} \, d(|k|t)$$

$$\doteqdot \frac{1}{|k|} X\left(\frac{f}{k}\right). \tag{2.64}$$

Time-bandwidth invariance is expressed by (2.64). Expanding a time function $(k < 1)$ compresses its transform in frequency and increases it in amplitude by the same factor. The amplitude increases because more energy is distributed over a smaller bandwidth; for constant energy, multiply both functions by $|k|^{1/2}$. The case $k = -1$ simply reverses the function in time and correspondingly interchanges positive and negative frequencies.

### Delay

Mathematically, the function $x(t)$ may be delayed by writing it $x(t - t_1)$; the delay is $t_1$ seconds. Since $t_1$ is a constant, the corresponding transform can be written

$$x(t - t_1) \doteq \int_{-\infty}^{\infty} x(t - t_1) e^{-j2\pi f(t-t_1)} e^{-j2\pi f t_1} \, d(t - t_1)$$

$$\doteq e^{-j2\pi f t_1} X(f), \tag{2.65}$$

where we treat $(t - t_1)$ as the variable of integration. Thus delaying a function by time $t_1$ adds a linear phase $\theta = -2\pi f t_1$ to the original phase; conversely, a linear phase shift produces a delay of $t_1 = -d\theta/d(2\pi f)$. In case we have wide-sense stationarity, then the autocovariance function is

$$\overline{x(t - t_1) x(t - t_1 + \tau)} = \overline{x(t) x(t + \tau)} = R_x(\tau),$$

and delay does not affect the power spectrum.

### Partition

Any real function $x(t)$ may be resolved into an even part $\frac{1}{2}[x(t) + x(-t)]$ and an odd part $\frac{1}{2}[x(t) - x(-t)]$. The corresponding transforms are obtained by noting from (2.64) that $x(-t) \doteq X(-f)$. Thus, and also invoking (2.61), the transform of the even part of $x(t)$ is $\frac{1}{2}[X(f) + X(-f)]$; this is purely real and contains only even powers or functions of $f$. The transform of the odd part of $x(t)$ is $\frac{1}{2}[X(f) - X(-f)]$, is purely imaginary, and contains only odd powers or functions of $f$. For $x(t)$ real, $X(-f) = X^*(f)$.

### Modulation

The process of modulation involves multiplying a function $x(t)$ by a higher-frequency sinusoid. Using complex notation we denote this in the time domain by $\mathrm{mod}(x) = x(t) e^{j2\pi f_1 t}$; the higher frequency is $f_1$. The corresponding transform is

$$x(t) e^{j2\pi f_1 t} \doteq \int_{-\infty}^{\infty} x(t) e^{-j2\pi (f-f_1)t} \, dt$$

$$\doteq X(f - f_1). \tag{2.66}$$

The autocovariance function for a complex quantity is $\overline{x^*(t)x(t+\tau)}$, so that for $\mathrm{mod}(x)$ we have

$$R_{\mathrm{mod}(x)}(\tau) = \overline{x(t)x(t+\tau)}\, e^{j2\pi f_1\tau} = R_x(\tau)e^{j2\pi f_1\tau}. \qquad (2.67)$$

Then for the power spectrum

$$G_{\mathrm{mod}(x)}(f) = G_x(f - f_1). \qquad (2.68)$$

Thus modulation shifts the center of the spectrum of a low-pass function $x(t)$ from zero frequency to the frequency $f_1$. Real modulation by, say, $\cos 2\pi f_1 t$ produces the time function $\frac{1}{2}x(t)[e^{j2\pi f_1 t} + e^{-j2\pi f_1 t}]$, with the corresponding two-sided transform $\frac{1}{2}[X(f - f_1) + X(f + f_1)]$, and power spectrum

$$\tfrac{1}{2}[G_x(f - f_1) + G_x(f + f_1)].$$

### Multiplication

The transform of the product of two time functions $x(t)$ and $y(t)$ can be obtained by writing

$$x(t)y(t) \doteqdot \int_{-\infty}^{\infty}\int_{-\infty}^{\infty} x(t)Y(s)e^{-j2\pi(f-s)t}\, dt\, ds \qquad (2.69a)$$

$$\doteqdot \int_{-\infty}^{\infty} X(f - s)Y(s)\, ds. \qquad (2.69b)$$

In writing (2.69a) we used the inverse transform (2.60b) to express the function $y(t)$, with the dummy variable of integration $s$; this is a common procedure when manipulating transforms and spectra. Equation (2.69b) follows by integrating with respect to $t$, yielding the transform of $x(t)$ as in (2.60a), with the parameter $(f - s)$ instead of $f$. Equation (2.69b) expresses the *convolution* of the transforms $X(f)$ and $Y(f)$, and is commonly written

$$x(t)y(t) \doteqdot X(f) * Y(f); \qquad (2.69c)$$

a geometrical interpretation of convolution was given in connection with (1.37) of Art. 1.9. For power spectra, we first write the covariance function of the product $x(t)y(t)$,

$$R_{x\cdot y}(\tau) = \overline{x(t)x(t+\tau)y(t)y(t+\tau)}, \qquad (2.70a)$$

and *if $x(t)$ and $y(t)$ are independent*, then the average factors and (2.70a) becomes

$$R_{x\cdot y}(\tau) = \overline{x(t)x(t+\tau)}\,\,\overline{y(t)y(t+\tau)} \qquad (2.70b)$$
$$= R_x(\tau)R_y(\tau).$$

Thus the power spectrum of the product of two *independent* functions is the convolution of their power spectra:

$$G_{x \cdot y}(f) = G_x(f) * G_y(f). \tag{2.71}$$

Multiplication is a more general statement of the modulation property. For example, sampling a waveform is equivalent to multiplying it by a uniform train of unit impulses (remember the sifting property of the delta-function). The spectrum of a sampled waveform then consists of its original spectrum repeated symmetrically about each component of the discrete spectrum of the periodic train of sampling impulses.

### Filtering

In transform terms, filtering is complementary to multiplication. It is well known from circuit theory that the response of a linear electrical network (filter) is given by the convolution of its impulse response with the input waveform. Thus the output $x_0(t)$ is

$$x_0(t) = \int_{-\infty}^{\infty} x(u)h(t-u)\, du, \tag{2.72}$$

where $h(t)$ represents the impulse response of the filter. In case the filter is physically realizable, i. e., cannot anticipate the future, the upper limit of integration in (2.72) may be replaced by $t$. Now by writing [using the inverse transform (2.60b)]

$$x_0(t) = \int_{-\infty}^{\infty} \int_{-\infty}^{\infty} x(u)H(f)e^{j2\pi(t-u)f}\, df\, du, \tag{2.73a}$$

and performing the integration with respect to $u$ first, we obtain

$$x_0(t) = \int_{-\infty}^{\infty} X(f)H(f)e^{j2\pi ft}\, df, \tag{2.73b}$$

which by comparison with (2.60b) shows that

$$x_0(t) \doteqdot X(f)H(f). \tag{2.73c}$$

The quantity $H(f)$ is the frequency transfer function, or complex spectral response of the filter, and is seen to be the transform of its impulse response.

For power spectra, we first use (2.72) to write the autocovariance function of $x_0$ as

$$R_{x_0}(\tau) = \overline{x_0(t)x_0(t+\tau)}$$

$$= \int_{-\infty}^{\infty} \int_{-\infty}^{\infty} x(u)x(v)h(t-u)h(t+\tau-v)\, du\, dv. \tag{2.74a}$$

Now interchange the order of integration and averaging, and note that if $x(t)$ and $h(t)$ are *independent*, the average factors; further, assuming *stationarity* we obtain

$$R_{x_0}(\tau) = \int_{-\infty}^{\infty} \int_{-\infty}^{\infty} R_x(v - u) R_h(v - u - \tau) \, du \, dv. \qquad (2.74b)$$

Let us express (2.74b) as

$$R_{x_0}(\tau, T) = \int_0^{2T} \int_0^{2T} R_x(r - s) R_h(r - s - \tau) \, dr \, ds, \qquad (2.74c)$$

where we introduce the new variables $r = v + T$ and $s = u + T$, and will ultimately pass to the limit $T \to \infty$. Now let $z = r - s$; then the double integral of (2.74c) becomes

$$R_{x_0}(\tau, T) = \int_0^{2T} \int_z^{2T} R_x(z) R_h(z - \tau) \, dr \, dz$$

$$+ \int_{-2T}^{0} \int_0^{(2T+z)} R_x(z) R_h(z - \tau) \, dr \, dz, \qquad (2.74d)$$

which yields, on performing the integration with respect to $r$,

$$R_{x_0}(\tau, T) = 2T \int_{-2T}^{2T} \left(1 - \frac{|z|}{2T}\right) R_x(z) R_h(z - \tau) \, dz$$

$$= 2T \int_{-\infty}^{\infty} R_x(z) R_{h, T}(z - \tau) \, dz. \qquad (2.74e)$$

In the latter form of (2.74e) we have introduced

$$R_{h, T}(z - \tau) = \begin{cases} \left(1 - \frac{|z|}{2T}\right) R_h(z - \tau), & |z| \le 2T; \\ 0, & |z| > 2T. \end{cases}$$

Now as $T \to \infty$, $R_{h, T}(z - \tau) \to R_h(z - \tau)$ and we have the convolution

$$\lim_{T \to \infty} R_{x_0}(\tau, T) = R_{x_0}(\tau) = \lim_{T \to \infty} 2T R_x(z) * R_h(z). \qquad (2.75)$$

Therefore,

$$G_{x_0}(f) = \lim_{T \to \infty} 2T G_x(f) G_h(f), \qquad (2.76a)$$

where $G_h(f)$ is the transform of the autocovariance function $R_h(z)$ of the filter impulse response $h(t)$, i. e., $G_h(f)$ is the power spectral density of $h(t)$. Now, by (2.41),

$$\lim_{T \to \infty} 2T G_h(f) = |H(f)|^2.$$

[There is no problem with a nonvanishing variance here since $h(t)$ is not a sample function of a random process.] Thus the final result is

$$G_{x_0}(f) = G_x(f) |H(f)|^2, \qquad (2.76b)$$

and the power spectrum of the filter output is seen to be the product of the input power spectrum and the "power spectral response" $|H(f)|^2$ of the filter.

### Differentiation

The transform of the derivative $x'(t) = dx(t)/dt$ of the function $x(t)$ is obtained from (2.60a) as follows. We have

$$x'(t) \doteq \int_{-\infty}^{\infty} x'(t) e^{-j2\pi ft} \, dt, \tag{2.77a}$$

and integrating (2.77a) by parts with $dv = x'(t) \, dt$ and $u = e^{-j2\pi ft}$ yields

$$x'(t) \doteq x(t) e^{-j2\pi ft} \Big|_{-\infty}^{\infty} + j2\pi f \int_{-\infty}^{\infty} x(t) e^{-j2\pi ft} \, dt, \tag{2.77b}$$

where the first term in (2.77b) vanishes because we define $x(t)$ for $-\infty < t < \infty$ and presume that $x(\pm\infty) = 0$. The integral in the second term is recognized as $X(f)$, and therefore

$$x'(t) \doteq j2\pi f X(f). \tag{2.77c}$$

The generalization of (2.77c) to the $n$th derivative $x^{(n)}(t) = d^n x(t)/dt^n$ readily follows and is

$$x^{(n)}(t) \doteq (j2\pi f)^n X(f). \tag{2.78}$$

For power spectra, we invoke the fundamental definition of the derivative in order to write the covariance function as

$$R_{x'}(\tau) = \overline{x'(t) x'(t + \tau)}$$

$$= \lim_{\Delta t \to 0} \frac{1}{(\Delta t)^2} \overline{[x(t+\Delta t)-x(t)][x(t+\tau+\Delta t)-x(t+\tau)]}. \tag{2.79a}$$

Expanding (2.79a), we recognize, with *wide-sense stationarity*, that it yields

$$R_{x'}(\tau) = \lim_{\Delta t \to 0} \frac{1}{(\Delta t)^2} [2R_x(\tau) - R_x(\tau + \Delta t) - R_x(\tau - \Delta t)]. \tag{2.79b}$$

Upon passing successively to the limit $\Delta t \to 0$, we then obtain

$$R_{x'}(\tau) = \lim_{\Delta t \to 0} \frac{1}{\Delta t} [-R_x'(\tau) + R_x'(\tau - \Delta t)] \tag{2.80a}$$

$$= -\lim_{\Delta t \to 0} [R_x''(\tau - \Delta t)] = -R_x''(\tau). \tag{2.80b}$$

Then it follows by application of (2.77c) that

$$G_{x'}(f) = -(j2\pi f)^2 G_x(f) = (2\pi f)^2 G_x(f). \tag{2.81}$$

It is readily seen that (2.81) generalizes, for the $n$th derivative, to

$$G_{x^{(n)}}(f) = (2\pi f)^{2n}G_x(f).\qquad(2.82)$$

Thus, differentiating a time function emphasizes the high-frequency content of its spectrum.

### Integration

The transform of the integral of a time function $x(t)$ is obtained as follows; we assume that the function has no average value (d-c component). From (2.60a)

$$\int_{-\infty}^{t} x(u)\,du \doteqdot \int_{-\infty}^{\infty}\int_{-\infty}^{t} x(u)e^{-j2\pi ft}\,du\,dt;\qquad(2.83a)$$

integrating by parts with $dv = e^{-j2\pi ft}\,dt$ and $u = \int_{-\infty}^{t} x(u)\,du$ yields

$$\int_{-\infty}^{t} x(u)\,du \doteqdot -\frac{1}{j2\pi f}e^{-j2\pi ft}\int_{-\infty}^{t} x(u)\,du\Big|_{-\infty}^{\infty}$$

$$+ \frac{1}{j2\pi f}\int_{-\infty}^{\infty} x(t)e^{-j2\pi ft}\,dt.\qquad(2.83b)$$

The first term in (2.83b) vanishes at both limits $t = \pm\infty$, because of the assumed properties of $x(t)$, and the integral in the second term is recognized as $X(f)$. Thus

$$\int_{-\infty}^{t} x(u)\,du \doteqdot \frac{1}{j2\pi f}X(f).\qquad(2.83c)$$

Again, (2.83c) readily generalizes to

$$\underbrace{\int_{-\infty}^{t}\cdots\int_{-\infty}^{u_{n-1}}}_{n} x(u_n)\,du_n\cdots du_1 \doteqdot \frac{1}{(j2\pi f)^n}X(f).\qquad(2.84)$$

The corresponding expression for power spectra is readily obtained using our previous results concerning differentiation, and (2.84). Thus, let $y(t) = x'(t)$, and symbolically write the integral relationship as $x(t) = y^{(-1)}(t)$. Then (2.80b) yields

$$R''_{y^{(-1)}}(\tau) = -R_y(\tau).\qquad(2.85)$$

Then, since

$$R_{y^{(-1)}}(\tau) = \int_{-\infty}^{\tau}\int_{-\infty}^{u_1} R''_{y^{(-1)}}(u_2)\,du_2\,du_1,\qquad(2.86a)$$

and substituting in (2.86a) from (2.85), we obtain

$$R_{y^{(-1)}}(\tau) = -\int_{-\infty}^{\tau}\int_{-\infty}^{u_1} R_y(u_2)\,du_2\,du_1.\qquad(2.86b)$$

Finally, applying (2.84) to the RHS of (2.86b), we see that

$$G_{y^{(-1)}}(f) = \frac{-1}{(j2\pi f)^2}G_y(f) = \frac{1}{(2\pi f)^2}G_y(f).\qquad(2.87)$$

In general, for integration $n$ times, (2.87) becomes

$$G_{y^{(-n)}}(f) = \frac{1}{(2\pi f)^{2n}} G_y(f). \qquad (2.88)$$

Thus, integrating a time function de-emphasizes the high-frequency components of its spectrum.

### Finite-Time Average

We wish, finally, to develop the transform and the power spectrum of the finite-time average of a time function; we shall denote this operation by

$$\overline{x_T(t)} = \frac{1}{T} \int_{t-T}^{t} x(\tau)\, d\tau. \qquad (2.89)$$

Equation (2.89) expresses a "running" average of the function $x(t)$, over an interval $T$. Physically, this is encountered when the function is scanned by an aperture of width $T$, and the transform of (2.89) describes the degradation of resolution which occurs in the output of the scanner; a television camera is an example of this situation. Denoting the transform of $\overline{x_T(t)}$ by $\overline{X_T(f)}$, we have

$$\overline{x_T(t)} \doteqdot \overline{X_T(f)} = \frac{1}{T} \int_{-\infty}^{\infty} e^{-j2\pi f t} \int_{t-T}^{t} x(\tau)\, d\tau\, dt$$

$$= \frac{1}{T} \int_{-\infty}^{\infty} e^{-j2\pi f t} \int_{t-T}^{t} \int_{-\infty}^{\infty} X(u) e^{j2\pi u\tau}\, du\, d\tau\, dt, \qquad (2.90a)$$

where in the latter form of (2.90a), we have used the inverse transform (2.60b) to express $x(t)$. Interchanging the order of integration with respect to $u$ and $\tau$, and performing that with respect to $\tau$ first, yields, after a little manipulation,

$$\overline{X_T(f)} = \int_{-\infty}^{\infty} X(u) \frac{\sin \pi u T}{\pi u T} e^{-j\pi u T} \int_{-\infty}^{\infty} e^{j2\pi(u-f)t}\, dt\, du. \qquad (2.90b)$$

The integral with respect to $t$ is recognized from (2.50) as being the delta-function $\delta(u - f)$. Using the sifting property (2.20) of the delta-function, (2.90b) then yields, for the integration with respect to $u$,

$$\overline{X_T(f)} = X(f) \frac{\sin \pi f T}{\pi f T} e^{-j\pi f T}. \qquad (2.91)$$

Comparing (2.91) with (2.73), we see that taking a running finite-time average is equivalent to passing the time function through a linear filter having the voltage frequency-response function $(\sin \pi f T)/\pi f T$; the exponential factor $e^{-j\pi f T}$ represents a delay of

$T/2$ seconds. The result of (2.91) is often referred to as the *aperture effect*, for reasons which we suggested at the outset. Finally, by reference to (2.76) and the remarks following, it is readily seen that the power spectrum of the averaged function is given by

$$G_{\overline{x_\tau}}(f) = G_x(f)\frac{\sin^2 \pi f T}{(\pi f T)^2}. \tag{2.92}$$

## 2.5   RELATIONS AMONG COVARIANCE FUNCTIONS

In this article we give, without derivation except as noted, several often-useful relationships involving covariance functions:

$$R_{x'}(\tau) = -R_x''(\tau) \qquad\qquad \text{(Art. 2.4)} \qquad (2.93)$$

$$R_{x^{(-1)}}(\tau) = -\int_{-\infty}^{\tau}\int_{-\infty}^{u_1} R_x(u_2)\, du_2\, du_1 \qquad \text{(Art. 2.4)} \qquad (2.94)$$

$$R_{xx'}(\tau) = \overline{x(t)x'(t+\tau)} = -R_x'(\tau). \tag{2.95}$$

From (2.95), since $R_x(\tau) \leqq R_x(0)$, then a function $x(t)$ and its derivative $x'(t)$ are uncorrelated.

If $x(t)$ and $y(t)$ are uncorrelated for all $\tau$ and either has zero mean, then

$$R_{x+y}(\tau) = R_x(\tau) + R_y(\tau). \qquad \text{(Art. 2.4)} \qquad (2.96)$$

If $x(t)$ and $y(t)$ are independent

$$R_{x \cdot y}(\tau) = R_x(\tau)\,R_y(\tau). \qquad \text{(Art. 2.4)} \qquad (2.97)$$

If $x_1$, $x_2$, $x_3$, $x_4$ are jointly *gaussian* and all have zero mean,

$$\overline{x_1 x_2 x_3 x_4} = \overline{(x_1 x_2)}\,\overline{(x_3 x_4)} + \overline{(x_1 x_3)}\,\overline{(x_2 x_4)} + \overline{(x_1 x_4)}\,\overline{(x_2 x_3)}. \tag{2.98}$$

Thus if $x_1 = x_2 = x(t)$ and $x_3 = x_4 = x(t+\tau)$, we get

$$R_{x^2}(\tau) = R_x^2(0) + 2R_x^2(\tau) = \sigma_x^4 + 2R_x^2(\tau), \tag{2.99}$$

and if $x_1 = x_2 = x_3 = x_4 = x(t)$, then

$$\overline{x^4} = 3\sigma_x^4 \tag{2.100}$$

The following result[†] is useful for analyzing the output of certain nonlinear devices in response to a *gaussian* input. Let the input be $x(t)$, and the output be $y(t)$, after a memoryless nonlinear transformation $y = f(x)$; let the corresponding normalized auto-

---

† This is a special form of the result obtained by Price (III).

covariance (autocorrelation) functions be $\rho_x(\tau)$ and $\rho_y(\tau)$. Then

$$\frac{\partial^k \rho_y(\tau)}{\partial \rho_x(\tau)^k} = \overline{f^{(k)}[x(t)]f^{(k)}[x(t+\tau)]} \tag{2.101a}$$

$$= \int_{-\infty}^{\infty}\int_{-\infty}^{\infty} f^{(k)}(x_1)f^{(k)}(x_2)p(x_1, x_2; \tau)\,dx_1\,dx_2 \tag{2.101b}$$

where for brevity we write $x_1 = x(t)$, $x_2 = x(t+\tau)$, and the joint probability density function of the gaussian variates $x_1$ and $x_2$ (assuming zero mean and unity standard deviation) is[†]

$$p(x_1, x_2; \tau) = \frac{1}{2\pi\sqrt{1-\rho_x^2(\tau)}}e^{-[x_1^2+x_2^2-2\rho_x(\tau)x_1x_2]/2[1-\rho_x^2(\tau)]}. \tag{2.102}$$

The utility of (2.101) is especially great when differentiation (one or more, in general, $k$ times) of the nonlinearity $y = f(x)$ yields delta functions; then the sifting property (2.20) makes solution of the integral (2.101b) almost trivial. For example, let the nonlinearity be a "hard" limiter:

$$f(x) = \begin{cases} +1; & x \ge 0, \\ -1; & x < 0. \end{cases} \tag{2.103}$$

Then $f^{(1)}(x) = f'(x) = 2\delta(x)$ and (2.101b) yields

$$\frac{\partial \rho_y(\tau)}{\partial \rho_x(\tau)} = \frac{2}{\pi\sqrt{1-\rho_x^2(\tau)}}. \tag{2.104}$$

Obviously, $\rho_y(\tau) = 0$ when $\rho_x(\tau) = 0$, so that from (2.104) we obtain

$$\rho_y(\tau) = \frac{2}{\pi}\int_0^{\rho_x(\tau)} \frac{d\rho_x(\tau)}{\sqrt{1-\rho_x^2(\tau)}}$$

$$= \frac{2}{\pi}\sin^{-1}[\rho_x(\tau)]; \tag{2.105}$$

this is a well-known result for the hard limiter. We re-emphasize, however, that this technique is valid *only* for gaussian inputs to the nonlinear device under consideration.

### REFERENCES

Bendat, J. S., *Principles and Applications of Random Noise Theory*. Wiley, New York, 1958.

Bennett, W. R.
(I) "Methods of Solving Noise Problems," *Proc. IRE*, **44** (May 1956).

† See Davenport and Root, chap. 8.

Blackman, R. B., and J. W. Tukey, "The Measurement of Power Spectra from the Point of View of Communication Engineering," *Bell Sys. Tech. J.*, **37** (January and March 1958); also Dover, New York.

Churchill, R. V.
(I) *Fourier-series and Boundary-value Problems*. McGraw-Hill, New York, 1941.

Cramér, H., *Mathematical Methods of Statistics*. Princeton U. P., Princeton, N. J., 1946.

Davenport, W. B., Jr., and W. L. Root, *An Introduction to the Theory of Random Signals and Noise*. McGraw-Hill, New York, 1958.

Goldman, S.
(I) *Transformation Calculus and Electrical Transients*. Prentice-Hall, Englewood Cliffs, N. J., 1949.
(II) *Frequency Analysis, Modulation and Noise*. McGraw-Hill, New York, 1948.

*IRE Trans. on Circuit Theory*, **CT-2** (September 1955) (four tutorial papers on the Fourier integral).

Lampard, D. G., "Definitions of 'Bandwidth' and 'Time Duration' of Signals Which are Connected by an Identity," *IRE Trans. on Circuit Theory*, **CT-3** (December 1956).

Price, R.
(III) "A Useful Theorem for Nonlinear Devices Having Gaussian Inputs," *IRE Trans. on Information Theory*, **IT-4** (June 1958).

Wiener, N.
(II) *The Fourier Integral and Certain of Its Applications*. Cambridge U. P., New York, 1933; also Dover, New York.

Yaglom, A. M. (trans. R. A. Silverman), *An Introduction to the Theory of Stationary Random Functions*. Prentice-Hall, Englewood Cliffs, N. J., 1962.

# Chapter Three

# Narrow-Band Noise Representations

Practically all communication systems utilize only a relatively narrow band of frequencies, in the sense that the bandwidth occupied is but a small fraction of the operating frequency upon which it is centered. This leads us naturally to inquire whether there are some special representations for random processes that are particularly applicable to narrow-band situations. There are, in fact, two such methods of representing random processes, which are of special utility in analyzing the effect of noise on communication system performance. We are now in a position to develop these, and shall do so concurrently in the next few articles.

## 3.1 QUADRATURE-CARRIER REPRESENTATION

Let us represent the sample functions $x(t)$ of an ergodic gaussian random process in the interval $0 < t \leq T$ by the Fourier series

$$x(t) = \sum_{n=1}^{\infty} (x_{cn} \cos n\omega_0 t + x_{sn} \sin n\omega_0 t), \tag{3.1}$$

where now we write $\omega_0 = 2\pi/T$, and

$$x_{cn} = \frac{2}{T} \int_0^T x(t) \cos n\omega_0 t \, dt \tag{3.2a}$$

$$x_{sn} = \frac{2}{T} \int_0^T x(t) \sin n\omega_0 t \, dt. \tag{3.2b}$$

We have already noted that $x_{cn}$ and $x_{sn}$ are hereby defined [see (2.51b)] as random variables over the ensemble of sample functions comprising the process. In particular, if the process is gaussian, it can be shown that $x_{cn}$ and $x_{sn}$ are gaussian random variables; further, they become uncorrelated (in a statistical sense) as the expansion interval $T$ increases without limit.[†]
Thus we have

$$\lim_{T \to \infty} \overline{x_{cn} x_{sn}} = 0. \tag{3.3}$$

The radian center frequency $\omega_c$ of the narrow-band random process can be introduced by writing $n\omega_0 = (n\omega_0 - \omega_c) + \omega_c$. Substituting this in (3.1) and expanding the trigonometric factors yields

$$x(t) = x_c(t) \cos \omega_c t - x_s(t) \sin \omega_c t, \tag{3.4}$$

where by definition

$$x_c(t) = \sum_{n=1}^{\infty} [x_{cn} \cos (n\omega_0 - \omega_c)t + x_{sn} \sin (n\omega_0 - \omega_c)t], \tag{3.5a}$$

$$x_s(t) = \sum_{n=1}^{\infty} [x_{cn} \sin (n\omega_0 - \omega_c)t - x_{sn} \cos (n\omega_0 - \omega_c)t]. \tag{3.5b}$$

Since the sample functions $x_c(t)$ and $x_s(t)$ are defined by sums of gaussian random variables, they are themselves gaussian variates, and obviously have zero mean: $\overline{x_c(t)} = \overline{x_s(t)} = 0$. From (3.5a) the mean-square of $x_c(t)$ is

$$\overline{x_c^2(t)} = \frac{1}{2} \sum_{n=1}^{\infty} (\overline{x_{cn}^2} + \overline{x_{sn}^2}), \tag{3.6a}$$

and similarly from (3.5b)

$$\overline{x_s^2(t)} = \frac{1}{2} \sum_{n=1}^{\infty} (\overline{x_{cn}^2} + \overline{x_{sn}^2}). \tag{3.6b}$$

Therefore

$$\overline{x_c^2(t)} = \overline{x_s^2(t)}; \tag{3.7}$$

also, by combining (3.5a) and (3.5b), and using (3.3), we find

$$\lim_{T \to \infty} \overline{x_c(t) x_s(t)} = 0. \tag{3.8}$$

To summarize this development, if the original random process is gaussian, then the coefficients $x_c(t)$ and $x_s(t)$ in (3.4) are inde-

---

[†] See Davenport and Root, Art. 6–4.

pendent gaussian variates,[†] having zero mean and equal variances, in the limit $T \to \infty$.[‡]

If the original random process has bandwidth $\Omega$ (rad/sec) centered at $\omega_c$ (rad/sec), then $x_c(t)$ and $x_s(t)$ each have bandwidth $\Omega$ centered at zero frequency, and may be regarded as low-pass random-noise waveforms having zero mean and positive-frequency bandwidth $\Omega/2$, which respectively double-sideband suppressed-carrier amplitude-modulate the quadrature carriers $\cos \omega_c t$ and $-\sin \omega_c t$. Thus (3.4) is known as the *quadrature-carrier* representation of narrow-band noise. It is a particularly convenient form for calculating the effect of small amounts of noise on communication system performance.

## 3.2   ENVELOPE-AND-PHASE REPRESENTATION

If on an oscilloscope, we observe noise which has been passed through a narrow band-pass filter, we see a sinusoidal-appearing waveform, whose amplitude and phase fluctuate slowly compared to the average period of the wave. This suggests that it is possible to express a sample function of a narrow-band gaussian random process in the form

$$x(t) = V(t) \cos [\omega_c t + \phi(t)]. \tag{3.9}$$

Here, $V(t)$ is the *envelope function* and $\phi(t)$ is the *phase function*. This form is known as the *envelope-and-phase* representation of narrow-band gaussian noise; it is chiefly useful in communication systems analysis when the signal is quite weak compared to the noise.

## 3.3   RELATIONSHIPS BETWEEN REPRESENTATIONS

We have now introduced the two narrow-band representations

---

[†] Henceforth, by the term *variate*, we refer to a sample function of a stationary ergodic random process. We shall often speak directly in statistical terminology with respect to variates, recognizing (see Art. 1.6) that for stationary ergodic processes, the fraction-of-time statistics of the sample functions coincide with the ensemble statistics over the process.

[‡] We note that if the spectrum of the original gaussian random process is symmetrical with respect to the radian center frequency $\omega_c$, then as $T \to \infty$, the cross-variance

$$R_{x_c x_s}(\tau) = \overline{x_c(t) x_s(t+\tau)} = 0$$

for *all* values of $\tau$. See Davenport and Root, Art. 8–5.

of gaussian random noise; let us develop these themes. We can expand (3.9) to yield

$$x(t) = V(t) \cos \omega_c t \cos \phi(t) - V(t) \sin \omega_c t \sin \phi(t). \quad (3.10)$$

By comparison of (3.10) with (3.4), it is evident that

$$x_c(t) = V(t) \cos \phi(t), \quad (3.11a)$$

$$x_s(t) = V(t) \sin \phi(t). \quad (3.11b)$$

Thus the two representations (3.9) and (3.4) are closely related, as can only be expected since they stand for the same random process.

Let us next investigate relationships between the statistics of the quantities involved, when the original process is gaussian. Since the coefficients $x_c(t)$ and $x_s(t)$ of (3.4) are independent gaussian variates, their joint probability density function is the product of their individual probability density functions. Thus [writing $p(x)$ for $p_x(u)$]

$$p(x_c, x_s) = p(x_c) p(x_s)$$

$$= \frac{1}{2\pi \sigma_{x_c} \sigma_{x_s}} e^{-(x_c^2/2\sigma_{x_c}^2 + x_s^2/2\sigma_{x_s}^2)}; \quad (3.12a)$$

from (3.7), however, the variances of $x_c$ and $x_s$ are equal, and both can be denoted by $\sigma^2$. Then (3.12a) becomes

$$p(x_c, x_s) = \frac{1}{2\pi \sigma^2} e^{-(x_c^2 + x_s^2)/2\sigma^2}. \quad (3.12b)$$

Now, the joint probability density function of the envelope function $V(t)$ and the phase function $\phi(t)$ is related to that of the quadrature-carrier coefficients $x_c(t)$ and $x_s(t)$ by

$$p(V, \phi) = \|J\| p[(x_c = V \cos \phi), (x_s = V \sin \phi)]. \quad (3.13)$$

Here $|J|$ is the Jacobian determinant relating polar and Cartesian coordinates, and is given by[†]

$$|J| = \begin{vmatrix} \dfrac{\partial x_c}{\partial V} & \dfrac{\partial x_s}{\partial V} \\ \dfrac{\partial x_c}{\partial \phi} & \dfrac{\partial x_s}{\partial \phi} \end{vmatrix} = \begin{vmatrix} \cos \phi & \sin \phi \\ -V \sin \phi & V \cos \phi \end{vmatrix} = V. \quad (3.14)$$

This is a generalization of the functional transformation discussed in Art. 1.8; the partial derivatives are calculated using (3.11a, b). Thus, combining (3.12b) and (3.14) into (3.13), we obtain

[†] See, for example, Franklin, pp. 60, 128–129.

$$p(V, \phi) = \frac{V}{2\pi\sigma^2} e^{-V^2/2\sigma^2}. \tag{3.15}$$

The probability density function of the envelope function is obtained by integrating $\phi$ out of (3.15); thus

$$p(V) = \int_0^{2\pi} p(V, \phi)\, d\phi = \frac{V}{\sigma^2} e^{-V^2/2\sigma^2}, \qquad V \geq 0. \tag{3.16}$$

Equation (3.16) expresses the *Rayleigh* density function; it is the probability density function of the *envelope* of a gaussian random process, commonly visualized in a narrow-band context.

The probability density function of the phase function is similarly obtained by integrating $V$ out of (3.15); thus

$$p(\phi) = \int_0^\infty p(V, \phi)\, dV = \frac{1}{2\pi}, \qquad 0 \leq \phi \leq 2\pi, \tag{3.17}$$

where the integration is easily performed by changing variable to $u = V^2/2\sigma^2$. Hence, the phase function is uniformly distributed in the interval 0 to $2\pi$, and therefore, for example,

$$\overline{\cos 2\phi(t)} = 0. \tag{3.18}$$

Finally, by comparing (3.15), (3.16), and (3.17), it is evident that

$$p(V, \phi) = p(V)p(\phi), \tag{3.19}$$

and hence that the envelope function $V(t)$ and the phase function $\phi(t)$ represent independent random variates. We caution, however, that the envelope and phase are not independent random processes, in the sense that

$$p(V_1, \phi_1, V_2, \phi_2) \neq p(V_1, V_2)p(\phi_1, \phi_2), \tag{3.20}$$

where the subscripts 1 and 2 refer to time instants $t$ and $t + \tau$, respectively.

The relationships between the variances of the quantities involved in the quadrature-carrier and the envelope-and-phase representations of narrow-band gaussian noise are also of interest. From (3.11a, b) we have

$$\sigma^2 = \overline{x_c^2(t)} = \overline{x_s^2(t)} \tag{3.21a}$$

$$= \overline{V^2(t)\cos^2 \phi(t)} = \overline{V^2(t)\sin^2 \phi(t)} \tag{3.21b}$$

$$= \tfrac{1}{2}\overline{V^2(t)}, \tag{3.21c}$$

where in obtaining (3.21c) we have used the uniform-distribution property of $\phi$, exemplified by (3.18). Also from (3.4)

$$\overline{x^2(t)} = \overline{x_c^2(t) \cos^2 \omega_c t + x_s^2(t) \sin^2 \omega_c t - 2x_c(t)x_s(t) \sin \omega_c t \cos \omega_c t}$$
$$= \tfrac{1}{2}\overline{x_c^2(t)} + \tfrac{1}{2}\overline{x_s^2(t)},$$

and thus, combining (3.22), (3.21a), and (3.21c), we find

$$\overline{x^2(t)} = \overline{x_c^2(t)} = \overline{x_s^2(t)} = \tfrac{1}{2}\overline{V^2(t)}. \tag{3.23}$$

The facts expressed by (3.23) are frequently cause for confusion: that the power of *each* of the coefficients $x_c(t)$ and $x_s(t)$, into which the original sample function $x(t)$ is resolved by (3.4), is *equal* to the power of $x(t)$ itself. However, (3.4) also states that $x(t)$ resolves into $x_c(t)$ and $x_s(t)$ by having the latter double-sideband suppressed-carrier amplitude-modulate quadrature carriers $\cos \omega_c t$ and $-\sin \omega_c t$, respectively. The modulation process is where the apparent excess factor of two is absorbed.

### 3.4  SINE WAVE PLUS NARROW-BAND GAUSSIAN NOISE

In this article we shall derive expressions for the probability density functions of the envelope and phase of the sum of a sine wave and narrow-band gaussian noise. Unfortunately, however, the results are substantially more complicated than those for noise alone, and are therefore less conveniently used in communication systems analysis.

Let a sample function of a stationary narrow-band gaussian random process be represented by $x(t)$, and be resolved into the quadrature-carrier form $x(t) = x_c(t) \cos \omega_c t - x_s(t) \sin \omega_c t$. The sum of a sine wave and this noise will be denoted by

$$y(t) = A \cos(\omega_c t + \phi) + x(t), \tag{3.24}$$

where the amplitude $A$ is constant and the angle $\phi$ is a random variable uniformly distributed between 0 and $2\pi$; $\phi$ is included to express the fact that the phase of the sine wave is independent of the noise process, i.e., of the quadrature-carrier resolution of $x(t)$. We can write (3.24) in the quadrature-carrier form

$$y(t) = y_c(t) \cos \omega_c t - y_s(t) \sin \omega_c t, \tag{3.25}$$

where

$$y_c(t) = A \cos \phi + x_c(t), \tag{3.26a}$$

$$y_s(t) = A \sin \phi + x_s(t). \tag{3.26b}$$

Also, in the envelope-and-phase form we have

$$y(t) = V(t) \cos[\omega_c t + \psi(t)]; \tag{3.27}$$

thus

$$y_c(t) = V(t) \cos \psi(t), \tag{3.28a}$$

$$y_s(t) = V(t) \sin \psi(t), \tag{3.28b}$$

and

$$V^2(t) = y_c^2(t) + y_s^2(t). \tag{3.29}$$

The variates $x_c(t)$ and $x_s(t)$ are, as previously observed, independent and gaussian, with zero mean and equal variances $\sigma_x^2$. Therefore the joint probability density function of $y_c(t)$, $y_s(t)$, and $\phi$ is, using (1.40) and (3.26a, b),

$$p(y_c, y_s, \phi) = \frac{1}{2\pi} \left[ \frac{1}{\sqrt{2\pi}\,\sigma_x} e^{-(y_c - A\cos\phi)^2/2\sigma_x^2} \right] \left[ \frac{1}{\sqrt{2\pi}\,\sigma_x} e^{-(y_s - A\sin\phi)^2/2\sigma_x^2} \right]$$

$$= \frac{1}{4\pi^2\sigma_x^2} e^{-[y_c^2 + y_s^2 + A^2 - 2A(y_c\cos\phi + y_s\sin\phi)]/2\sigma_x^2} \tag{3.30}$$

Hence, using (3.28a, b) and (3.29), the joint probability density function of $V, \psi,$ and $\phi$ is

$$p(V, \psi, \phi) = \frac{V}{4\pi^2\sigma_x^2} e^{-[V^2 + A^2 - 2AV\cos(\psi - \phi)]/2\sigma_x^2}, \tag{3.31}$$

where in obtaining (3.31) the Jacobian determinant $|J| = V$, relating polar and Cartesian coordinates, must also be used [see (3.13) and (3.14)].

The probability density function of $V$ is obtained by integrating $\psi$ and $\phi$ out of (3.31); thus

$$p(V) = \frac{V}{4\pi^2\sigma_x^2} e^{-(V^2 + A^2)/2\sigma_x^2} \int_0^{2\pi} \int_{-\phi}^{2\pi - \phi} e^{(AV/\sigma_x^2)\cos\theta} \, d\theta \, d\phi, \tag{3.32a}$$

where for the integration with respect to $\psi$ we change variable to $\theta = \psi - \phi$. Since the exponential integrand has period $2\pi$ in $\theta$, we may use the fact

$$\int_0^{2\pi} e^{a\cos x} \, dx = 2\pi I_0(a)$$

to obtain

$$p(V) = \frac{V}{\sigma_x^2} I_0\left(\frac{AV}{\sigma_x^2}\right) e^{-(V^2 + A^2)/2\sigma_x^2}, \qquad V \geq 0, \tag{3.32b}$$

where $I_0(a) = J_0(ja)$ is a modified Bessel function. When $A = 0$, (3.32b) reduces to our previous result (3.16) for the envelope of narrow-band gaussian noise.

The probability density function of $\theta = \psi - \phi$, the phase angle of the resultant $y(t)$ relative to the carrier $A \cos(\omega_c t + \phi)$, is obtained by first writing the coordinate relationships

$$\psi = \theta + \phi, \tag{3.33a}$$

$$\phi' = \phi; \tag{3.33b}$$

then the Jacobian determinant is

$$|J| = \begin{vmatrix} \dfrac{\partial \psi}{\partial \theta} & \dfrac{\partial \phi'}{\partial \theta} \\[2mm] \dfrac{\partial \psi}{\partial \phi} & \dfrac{\partial \phi'}{\partial \phi} \end{vmatrix} = \begin{vmatrix} 1 & 0 \\ 1 & 1 \end{vmatrix} = 1 \tag{3.34}$$

and the joint probability density function of $\theta$ and $\phi$ is related to that of $\psi$ and $\phi$ by

$$p(\theta, \phi) = p[(\psi = \theta + \phi), (\phi = \phi)]; \tag{3.35}$$

the density function of $\theta$ is obtained by integrating over $\phi$. Thus

$$p(\theta) = \int_0^{2\pi} p(\theta, \phi) \, d\phi. \tag{3.36}$$

The joint probability density function of $\psi$ and $\phi$ is obtained by integrating $V$ out of (3.31); thus, completing the square, substituting $\theta = \psi - \phi$, and applying (3.36) yields

$$p(\theta) = \frac{1}{4\pi^2 \sigma_x^2} e^{-(A \sin \theta)^2/2\sigma_x^2} \int_0^{2\pi} \int_0^{\infty} V e^{-(V - A \cos \theta)^2/2\sigma_x^2} \, dV \, d\phi, \tag{3.37a}$$

where in (3.36) and (3.37a) we do *not* regard $\theta$ as a function of $\phi$ when integrating with respect to the latter. Then substituting $u = (V - A \cos \theta)/\sigma_x$ and integrating over $\phi$ we have

$$p(\theta) = \frac{1}{2\pi} e^{-(A \sin \theta)^2/2\sigma_x^2} \int_{-(A \cos \theta)/\sigma_x}^{\infty} u e^{-u^2/2} \, du$$
$$+ \frac{A \cos \theta}{2\pi \sigma_x} e^{-(A \sin \theta)^2/2\sigma_x^2} \int_{-(A \cos \theta)/\sigma_x}^{\infty} e^{-u^2/2} \, du. \tag{3.37b}$$

The first integral in (3.37b) is equal to $e^{-(A \cos \theta)^2/2\sigma_x^2}$, and since the integrand of the second is an even function, we have finally, for $0 \le \theta \le 2\pi$,

$$p(\theta) = \frac{1}{2\pi} e^{-A^2/2\sigma_x^2} + \frac{A \cos \theta}{\sqrt{2\pi} \sigma_x} e^{-(A \sin \theta)^2/2\sigma_x^2} \left[ \frac{1}{\sqrt{2\pi}} \int_{-\infty}^{(A \cos \theta)/\sigma_x} e^{-u^2/2} \, du \right]; \tag{3.37c}$$

the integral term in (3.37c) is the normal probability distribution function, and is extensively tabulated. When $A = 0$, (3.37c) reduces to (3.17), as it should.

It is of interest also to examine the approximate forms of (3.32b) and (3.37c) for the case where the sine wave is much stronger than the noise. For large values of the argument, the modified Bessel function has the asymptotic expansion

$$I_0(a) \sim \frac{e^a}{\sqrt{2\pi a}} \left(1 + \frac{1}{8a} + \frac{9}{128a^2} + \cdots \right). \qquad (3.38)$$

Using this, it follows that for $AV \gg \sigma_x^2$, (3.32b) becomes approximately

$$p(V) = \frac{1}{\sigma_x} \sqrt{\frac{V}{2\pi A}} \, e^{-(V-A)^2/2\sigma_x^2}, \qquad V \geq 0. \qquad (3.39)$$

Thus when the amplitude $A$ of the sine wave is large compared to the rms noise $\sigma_x$, and $V \cong A$ (which is the case most of the time), the sum has an approximately gaussian envelope distribution with mean $A$ and variance $\sigma_x^2$. This property is easily visualized by reference to the phasor diagram of Fig. 4.4, used in Part 2 in connection with the analysis of amplitude modulation; remember that $x_s(t)$ [and $x_c(t)$] is a gaussian variate.

An asymptotic expansion for the normal probability distribution function valid for large values of $a$ is given by

$$\frac{1}{\sqrt{2\pi}} \int_{-\infty}^{a} e^{-u^2/2} \, du \sim 1 - \frac{e^{-a^2/2}}{\sqrt{2\pi}a} \left(1 - \frac{1}{a^2} + \frac{1 \cdot 3}{a^4} - \cdots \right). \qquad (3.40)$$

Using this it follows that for $A \cos\theta \gg \sigma_x$, (3.37c) becomes approximately

$$p(\theta) = \frac{A \cos\theta}{\sqrt{2\pi}\sigma_x} \, e^{-(A\sin\theta)^2/2\sigma_x^2}. \qquad (3.41)$$

Thus when the amplitude $A \gg \sigma_x$, and $\theta \ll 1$ (which holds with high probability), the sum of a sine wave and narrow-band gaussian noise has an approximately gaussian distribution of phase deviation, with zero mean and variance $\sigma_x^2/A^2$. This property is similarly evident from Fig. 5.3, used in the analysis of frequency modulation. Further, since the derivative of a gaussian variate is also gaussian, the "instantaneous frequency deviation" of the sum of a sine wave and narrow-band gaussian noise is approximately gaussian under high signal-to-noise ratio conditions.

## 3.5　ENVELOPE, PHASE, AND FREQUENCY NOISE

Let us finally anticipate forthcoming considerations of the role of noise in the demodulation of sinusoidal-carrier communication signals, by formulating explicit and compact expressions for the sum of a sine wave and narrow-band gaussian noise, appropriate to this problem.

Using the quadrature-carrier noise representation, we can write the sum of a sinusoidal carrier and noise as

$$E(t) = A \sin \omega_c t + x_c(t) \cos \omega_c t - x_s(t) \sin \omega_c t$$
$$= [A - x_s(t)] \sin \omega_c t + x_c(t) \cos \omega_c t. \tag{3.42}$$

Transforming this to the envelope-and-phase form we have

$$E(t) = \sqrt{[A - x_s(t)]^2 + x_c^2(t)} \sin [\omega_c t + \theta(t)]. \tag{3.43}$$

It is then evident that an envelope detector will recover the quantity

$$V(t) = \sqrt{[A - x_s(t)]^2 + x_c^2(t)}. \tag{3.44}$$

Similarly, a phase detector will recover the phase function

$$\theta(t) = \tan^{-1}\left[\frac{x_c(t)}{A - x_s(t)}\right]. \tag{3.45}$$

We visualize the wave $E(t)$, expressed as in (3.43), as a rotating vector, or phasor as it is commonly called, having at any instant a phase, or angular displacement from the positive real axis, given by $\omega_c t + \theta(t)$. The actual voltage represented by this phasor is its projection on the vertical axis. Figure 3.1 illustrates

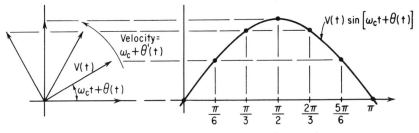

FIGURE 3.1 Phasor representation of sinusoid.

this concept. The frequency of the wave $E(t)$ is then the angular velocity of the rotating phasor, or the time derivative of its instantaneous phase. Thus the instantaneous frequency of $E(t)$ is defined by

$$\omega_i = \frac{d}{dt}[\omega_c t + \theta(t)]$$
$$= \omega_c + \frac{[A - x_s(t)]x_c'(t) + x_c(t)x_s'(t)}{[A - x_s(t)]^2 + x_c^2(t)}, \tag{3.46}$$

where the prime notation denotes differentiation with respect to time, and we have used (3.45) in writing the latter form of (3.46).

The term "instantaneous frequency" has been the subject of some criticism, on the grounds that a wave which represents a pure frequency cannot have changed at any time in the past, nor can it do so at any time in the future. The term "instantaneous frequency," from this standpoint, is thus self-contradictory. However, we shall continue to use this term, with the stipulation that what is meant is the time derivative of the instantaneous phase of $E(t)$, i.e., the instantaneous angular velocity of the rotating phasor.

In frequency modulation, it is common practice to arrange the frequency detector in a balanced form so that its output is zero when the input frequency is constant and equal to the center frequency $\omega_c$ (in rad/sec). Thus the detector output is proportional to the instantaneous frequency deviation

$$\theta'(t) = \frac{[A - x_s(t)]x_c'(t) + x_c(t)x_s'(t)}{[A - x_s(t)]^2 + x_c^2(t)}. \tag{3.47}$$

The explicit formulas (3.44), (3.45), and (3.47) enable the calculation of the post-detection properties of the received noise, using statistical methods which are well known in principle, although quite complicated in the general cases where neither the noise nor the received carrier is assumed small in comparison with the other.[†] Since we are concerned primarily with the solution of ordinary communication problems, we shall for the most part restrict detailed analysis to the high signal-to-noise ratio case.

## REFERENCES

Bendat, J. S., *Principles and Applications of Random Noise Theory.* Wiley, New York, 1958.

Bennett, W. R.
(I) "Methods of Solving Noise Problems," *Proc. IRE,* **44**, (May 1956).

Brown, J. L., "A Property of the Generalized Envelope," *IRE Trans. on Circuit Theory,* **CT-6**, (September 1959).

Davenport, W. B., Jr., and W. L. Root, *An Introduction to the Theory of Random Signals and Noise.* McGraw-Hill, New York, 1958.

Dugundji, J., "Envelopes and Pre-envelopes of Real Waveforms," *IRE Trans. on Information Theory,* **IT-4** (March 1958).

Franklin, P., *Methods of Advanced Calculus.* McGraw-Hill, New York, 1944.

† See, for example, Lawson and Uhlenbeck, chap. 13.

Lawson, J. L., and G. E. Uhlenbeck, *Threshold Signals*, MIT Rad. Lab. Series, Vol. 24. McGraw-Hill, New York, 1950.

Price, R., "A Note on the Envelope and Phase-modulated Components of Narrow-band Gaussian Noise," *IRE Trans. on Information Theory*, **IT-1** (September 1955).

Raemer, H. R., and R. Blyth, "The Probability Density of the Phase Difference of a Narrow-band Gaussian Noise with Sinusoidal Signal," *IRE Trans. on Information Theory*, **IT-7** (October 1961).

Rice, S. O.
(I) "Mathematical Analysis of Random Noise," *Bell Sys. Tech. J.*, **23** (July 1944), and **24** (January 1945). Also in Wax, N., *Selected Papers on Noise and Stochastic Processes*. Dover, New York, 1954.
(II) "Statistical Properties of a Sine-wave Plus Random Noise," *Bell Sys. Tech. J.*, **27** (January 1948).

Yaglom, A. M. (trans. R. A. Silverman), *An Introduction to the Theory of Stationary Random Functions*. Prentice-Hall, Englewood Cliffs, N. J., 1962.

# PART 2  *Modulated Sinusoids and Noise*

In concluding Part 1, we considered in some detail the characteristics of and formulations for the sum of a sine wave and narrow-band gaussian noise. This is a direct consequence of the fact that practically all of the familiar and presently used communication techniques are based on modulating, or changing, some property of a sinusoidal carrier. The almost universal choice of a sinusoid as a communications vehicle stems from the unique and discrete nature of the spectrum of this waveform, in the frequency domain (see Art. 2.3). Thus, simultaneous noninterfering broadcasts by many communication services can be accomplished by assigning each a different carrier frequency; correspondingly, selection of the particular broadcast to be received, and exclusion of the others, is simply effected using frequency-selective tuned circuits. The sine wave, therefore, has survived since the earliest days, as the backbone of communications technology.

If one writes the general sinusoidal wave $E(t) = A \sin (\omega t + \theta)$, then there evidently are two parameters which can be modulated in accordance with the waveform of a message $m(t)$ which it is desired to transmit. These are the amplitude $A$ and the angular argument $\phi = (\omega t + \theta)$. Thus in *amplitude modulation* we vary $A$ to obtain $A(t)$; in *angle modulation* we vary $\phi$ to obtain $\phi(t)$.

There are several formats in which an amplitude-modulation (AM) sinusoidal-carrier signal may ultimately be broadcast, depending on what portions of the basic AM signal spectrum are retained; suppression of the carrier component and of either the upper or lower sideband components is a prominent technique. We shall shortly consider the performance of these methods in detail.

In angle modulation of a sinusoidal carrier we may vary the argument $\phi = (\omega t + \theta)$, by modulating either $\theta$ or $\omega$. In the former instance we have $\phi(t) = [\omega t + \theta(t)]$; this represents *phase modulation* (PM). Alternately, modulating $\omega$ yields *frequency modulation* (FM): $\phi(t) = \{[\omega(t)]t + \theta\}$. These techniques are closely related, and a later chapter in this part will consider them in detail, particularly FM.

In essence, the sinusoidal waveform is an ideal carrier for most communication applications. The study of the performance of its modulated forms in the presence of noise is therefore fundamental in communication systems analysis, and the following part of this book is devoted to the treatment of this important material.

# Chapter Four

# Amplitude (Linear) Modulation

## 4.1 LINEAR MODULATION

The *linear modulation* of a sinusoidal carrier means, by definition, varying its amplitude in accordance with a *linear* function of the message $m(t)$ to be transmitted. Thus in conventional amplitude modulation (AM) we have the wave

$$E(t) = A[1 + m(t)] \sin \omega_c t. \tag{4.1}$$

The constant carrier frequency is denoted by $\omega_c$ (in rad/sec), and the time-varying amplitude $A(t) = A[1 + m(t)]$ is obviously a linear function of the message $m(t)$; it is presumed that $m(t)$ is scaled so that $|m(t)| \leq 1$ practically always. This particular linear function of the message [rather than simply $m(t)$ itself] is chosen to modulate the sinusoidal carrier amplitude, so that the message can be faithfully recovered (except for a trivial d-c component) by a simple envelope detector. Figure 4.1 illustrates amplitude modulation and envelope detection.

The power spectrum of the AM wave of (4.1) is readily seen, by reference to (2.61) and (2.68) of Art. 2.4, to be generated as shown schematically in Fig. 4.2. Formally regarding the message power spectrum $G_m(f)$ to be "two-sided" as shown by Fig. 4.2(a), we find that in AM, upper sideband (USB), and lower sideband (LSB) spectral components are generated by the message, in even-symmetry fashion with respect to the discrete carrier component, as shown by Fig. 4.2(b) for positive frequencies.

65

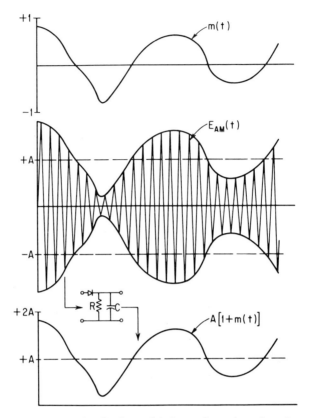

FIGURE 4.1 Amplitude modulation and envelope detection.

The time-domain structure of an AM wave can be simply illustrated by supposing that the message waveform $m(t)$ is, say, an even periodic function of time in an interval $-T/2 \leq t \leq T/2$. Then it can be represented by the Fourier series

$$m(t) = \sum_{n=1}^{\infty} c_n \cos n\omega_0 t \qquad (4.2)$$

where

$$c_n = \int_{-T/2}^{T/2} m(t) \cos n\omega_0 t \, dt, \qquad (4.3)$$

$\omega_0 = 2\pi/T$, and for convenience we let $c_0 = 0$; this in effect postulates that the message has no d-c component. Then from (4.1) and (4.2), the AM wave is given by

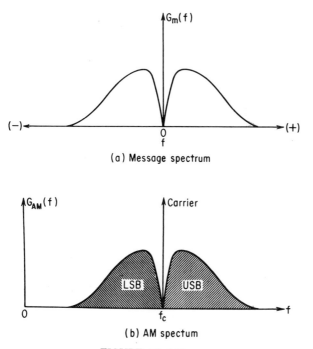

(a) Message spectrum

(b) AM spectum

FIGURE 4.2 AM spectra.

$$E(t) = A \sin \omega_c t + A \sum_{n=1}^{\infty} c_n \sin \omega_c t \cos n\omega_0 t$$

$$= A \sin \omega_c t + \frac{A}{2} \sum_{n=1}^{\infty} c_n [\underbrace{\sin(\omega_c + n\omega_0)t}_{\text{USB}} + \underbrace{\sin(\omega_c - n\omega_0)t}_{\text{LSB}}]. \quad (4.4)$$

In (4.4) we have identified the upper and lower sideband components. In case $m(t)$ is a sinusoid of period $T$, as commonly is the case when testing or evaluating a system, then only $c_1$ survives in (4.2), and (4.4) becomes

$$E(t) = A \sin \omega_c t + \frac{A}{2} c_1 [\sin(\omega_c + \omega_0)t + \sin(\omega_c - \omega_0)t]. \quad (4.5)$$

The phasor diagram corresponding to (4.5) is shown in Fig. 4.3, where we use the carrier phasor (rotating counterclockwise with angular velocity $\omega_c$) as a reference. The upper and lower sideband phasors rotate respectively $\omega_0$ rad/sec faster and slower than the carrier phasor, and are symmetrically phased so that their resultant is always colinear with the carrier. The resultant then varies only

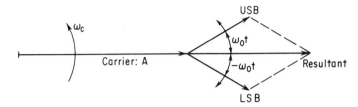

FIGURE 4.3 AM phasor diagram.

in amplitude, and is always in phase with the carrier component. The AM sidebands are thus said to be *coherent* with respect to the carrier.

The preceding material should be largely of a review nature for the reader. Our real concern is to add noise to the modulated carrier, and calculate the effect of this perturbation on communication system performance. Despite the apparent simplicity of AM, this problem, except for one special technique, is quite complicated when arbitrary proportions of signal and noise are allowed. In fact it is not always clear how to define such quantities as "recovered message power" meaningfully.[†] These analytical difficulties arise primarily under conditions of low carrier-to-noise ratio, and since here AM system performance is usually unacceptable in any event, we shall not become involved with them except to give a qualitative indication of general system behavior. We shall, however, treat the small-noise performance of linear modulation systems in considerable detail throughout the remainder of this chapter.

### 4.2  SYNCHRONOUS DEMODULATION

As indicated above, there is one instance in linear modulation which does not suffer the complexity usually attendant upon allowing arbitrary proportions of signal and noise. This is synchronous, or product, demodulation of AM, and we shall consider it first. Using the quadrature-carrier noise representation, the modulated carrier plus noise is given by

$$E_{AM}(t) = \{A[1 + m(t)] - x_s(t)\} \sin \omega_c t + x_c(t) \cos \omega_c t, \quad (4.6)$$

where the message waveform $m(t)$ is assumed to be scaled so

---

† See Blachman (I), where output signal power is defined by the square of the average amplitude of the fundamental-frequency output component.

that its maximum value never exceeds unity. If we now multiply $E(t)$ from (4.6) by a locally generated carrier exactly synchronized in phase with the received carrier, then

$$E_{AM}(t)\sin\omega_c t$$

$$= \{A[1 + m(t)] - x_s(t)\}\sin^2\omega_c t + x_c(t)\cos\omega_c t\sin\omega_c t$$

$$= \{A[1 + m(t)] - x_s(t)\}(\tfrac{1}{2} - \tfrac{1}{2}\cos 2\omega_c t) + \tfrac{1}{2}x_c(t)\sin 2\omega_c t \tag{4.7}$$

is the result. Circuitwise, the multiplication can be carried out using a balanced modulator or an ordinary frequency converter. Passing the wave of (4.7) through a low-pass filter which rejects the double-frequency terms yields

$$E_{lp}(t) = \tfrac{1}{2}A[1 + m(t)] - \tfrac{1}{2}x_s(t). \tag{4.8}$$

Neglecting the d-c term $\tfrac{1}{2}A$, the output message-to-noise power ratio is then

$$(S/N)_{\text{out},AM} = \frac{A^2\overline{m^2(t)}}{\overline{x_s^2(t)}}. \tag{4.9}$$

If we take $m(t) = \sin\omega_m t$ and remember from Art. 3.3 that the input noise power $\overline{x^2(t)} = \overline{x_s^2(t)}$, then the output message-to-noise ratio becomes

$$(S/N)_{\text{out},AM} = A^2/2N_{\text{in}} = (S/N)_{\text{in},AM}, \tag{4.10}$$

where in writing (4.10), we define the input signal power as the unmodulated carrier power $A^2/2$. It is important to note that the message-bearing part of $E_{lp}(t)$ in (4.8) is unaffected by noise. Therefore (4.10) holds for *any* value of input signal-to-noise ratio; an output *strictly proportional* to the original message $m(t)$ is always present, although at low values of $(S/N)_{\text{in}}$ it may be virtually buried in *additive* noise. It is this property of synchronous *AM* demodulation, that the output message appears *unmutilated* and noise *additively* thereto irrespective of the input signal-to noise ratio, that distinguishes it from practically all other demodulation techniques, AM or FM. This is a very unusual property, despite its apparently simple nature; it is common only to stored-reference correlation detection schemes, of which synchronous AM demodulation is an example.

## 4.3  ENVELOPE DEMODULATION

Let us now consider the more conventional envelope detector. Here we have from (3.44)

$$E_{lp}(t) = \sqrt{\{A[1 + m(t)] - x_s(t)\}^2 + x_c^2(t)}. \qquad (4.11)$$

The phasor diagram of signal plus noise for $(S/N)_{in} \gg 1$ is shown in Fig. 4.4. It can be seen that little error results if the envelope is represented by neglecting $x_c(t)$, and thus under high signal-to-noise ratio conditions the output is given closely by

$$E_{lp}(t) \cong A[1 + m(t)] - x_s(t). \qquad (4.12)$$

Except for a scale factor of $\frac{1}{2}$, (4.12) is the same as (4.8). Hence (4.10) also applies to the envelope detector, but with the important qualification that $(S/N)_{in} \gg 1$. In fact, under such high signal-to-noise ratio conditions, the envelope detector is essentially a product demodulator. When the input carrier-to-noise ratio is high, the envelope detector gates, or samples, the input voltage at times controlled by the carrier itself. This is because the d-c back bias voltage stored on the RC diode load permits diode conduction to occur only on the positive peaks of the carrier. Such periodic sampling action is equivalent to product demodulation when a low-pass filter follows the detector.

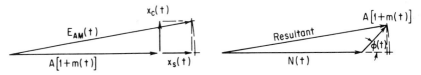

FIGURE 4.4 AM phasor diagram: $(S/N)_{in} \gg 1$.

FIGURE 4.5 AM phasor diagram: $(S/N)_{in} \ll 1$.

A very different picture of the envelope detector emerges, however, when the input carrier-to-noise ratio becomes very low, i. e., $(S/N)_{in} \ll 1$. In this instance it is more convenient to use the envelope-and-phase noise representation. The corresponding phasor diagram for the sum of signal plus noise, now using the noise as a reference, is shown in Fig. 4.5. To the noise phasor $N(t)$ we have added the signal $A[1 + m(t)]$, with the noise phase angle $\phi(t)$ between them. We assume that the signal-to-noise ratio is sufficiently low so that the magnitude of $N(t)$ is practically always much greater than the signal amplitude $A$. Then the quadrature component of the signal with respect to the noise can be neglected and the envelope detector will yield as an output

$$E_{lp}(t) = N(t) + A[1 + m(t)] \cos \phi(t)$$
$$= N(t) + A \cos \phi(t) + Am(t) \cos \phi(t). \qquad (4.13)$$

We see from (4.13) that *no* quantity strictly proportional to the message $m(t)$ appears in the detector output; the last term involves the message multiplied by the cosine of the noise phase angle $\phi(t)$. Since $\phi$ is a random variable uniformly distributed between 0 and $2\pi$, it follows that the detector output does not in fact contain the message waveform $m(t)$ at all; this information is completely lost.

This mutilation of the message accounts for the AM threshold effect. By threshold, we mean a value of input signal-to-noise ratio below which the performance of a system deteriorates very much more rapidly than proportionately to the input signal-to-noise ratio. In AM, however, this effect is a distinct property of noncoherent detectors (envelope, linear rectifier, square-law, etc.), and no threshold occurs if synchronous, or product, demodulation is used.

The intermediate region between high and low carrier-to-noise ratio requires a more involved analysis, the detailed pursuit of which is beyond the scope of this book.[†] Qualitatively, though, we should certainly expect to be well into the threshold region where the probability that the noise envelope $|N(t)|$ exceeds the unmodulated carrier amplitude $A$ is, say, 0.5. Based on the Rayleigh distribution of $|N(t)|$, this corresponds to a carrier-to-noise ratio of $-1.6$ db. Conversely, at $+6.6$ db carrier-to-noise ratio, the same probability is only 0.01, and we should expect to be relatively free of message mutilation and threshold effects. Since in AM, however, the input and output signal-to-noise ratios are equal, and ordinarily a message-to-noise ratio considerably greater than 6.6 db is necessary for satisfactory intelligibility, threshold effects are seldom of great importance in AM.

## 4.4   SUPPRESSED-CARRIER TECHNIQUES

We recall from (4.8) that a d-c term $\frac{1}{2}A$ appeared in the output of synchronously demodulated AM, and that this quantity was discarded since it contributes nothing to recovery of the message $m(t)$. The origin of this d-c component clearly is the presence of a carrier $A \sin \omega_c t$ when the message $m(t) = 0$. We might therefore eliminate this unmodulated carrier component at the outset, and transmit the wave

$$E_D(t) = A_D m(t) \sin \omega_c t. \tag{4.14}$$

[†] See, for example, Grumet, Middleton (IV).

This represents a double-sideband suppressed-carrier (DSSC) wave, and obviously its power is $\frac{1}{2}A^2$ less than that of an ordinary AM wave. DSSC is therefore able to transmit the same message with the same quality with respect to the effect of noise, as can be done with AM, but with a reduction of $\frac{1}{2}A^2$ in transmitted power. The DSSC wave appears as shown in Fig. 4.6. Each time the

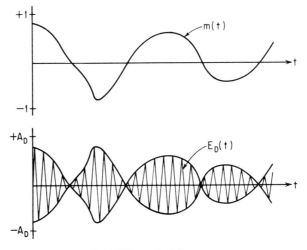

FIGURE 4.6 DSSC wave.

message $m(t)$ passes through zero, the "carrier" reverses phase 180°, and the envelope (an "envelope" by definition is always positive) is the message waveform, full-wave rectified. As we shortly shall see, synchronous demodulation enables distortionless recovery of the message from a suppressed-carrier AM wave.

### DSSC

In the AM case we used the unmodulated carrier power $\frac{1}{2}A^2$ for purposes of relating the input and output signal-to-noise ratios. Since, however, this component is not present in DSSC, we must develop a new equation analogous to (4.10), applicable to DSSC. Note first from (4.14) that the transmitted power is

$$\overline{E_D^2(t)} = \overline{A_D^2 m^2(t) \sin^2 \omega_c t}$$
$$= \frac{1}{2}A_D^2 \overline{m^2(t)}, \tag{4.15}$$

and that this is entirely contained in the sidebands. We thus have

$$P_{SBD} = \overline{E_D^2(t)} = \tfrac{1}{2}A_D^2\overline{m^2(t)}. \tag{4.16}$$

The wave (4.14) must be demodulated synchronously since it lacks a carrier component. Thus,

$$E_D(t)\sin\omega_c t = A_D m(t)\sin^2\omega_c t, \tag{4.17}$$

which after low-pass filtering yields as before [see (4.8)]

$$E_{lpD}(t) = \tfrac{1}{2}A_D m(t). \tag{4.18}$$

Thus the output message power is

$$S_D = \overline{E_{lpD}^2(t)} = \tfrac{1}{4}A_D^2\overline{m^2(t)} = \tfrac{1}{2}P_{SBD}, \tag{4.19}$$

where we have used (4.16) in writing the latter form of (4.19).

Also as before the synchronous demodulator yields noise power

$$N_D = \tfrac{1}{4}\overline{x_s^2(t)} = \tfrac{1}{4}\overline{x^2(t)} = \tfrac{1}{4}(2k^2 B_m), \tag{4.20}$$

where in writing the last form of (4.20) we have introduced the quantities $k^2$, the positive-frequency input (IF) noise power spectral density (watts/cps), and $B_m$, the message bandwidth. Thus the input noise power $N_{in} = \overline{x^2(t)} = 2k^2 B_m$, since we must have the IF bandwidth $B_{IF} = 2B_m$ in order to accommodate both upper and lower sidebands. Thus from (4.19) and (4.20), the output message-to-noise ratio is

$$(S/N)_{out,D} = \frac{A_D^2\overline{m^2(t)}}{2k^2 B_m} = \frac{2P_{SBD}}{N_{in}}. \tag{4.21}$$

Also [see (4.9)] it is evident that

$$(S/N)_{out,\,D} = (S/N)_{out,AM}, \tag{4.22}$$

provided that the sideband power of the AM system equals that of the DSSC system. We noted this result in introducing suppressed-carrier techniques.

### SSSC

In AM and DSSC, both the upper and lower sidebands are transmitted. However, each contains the same information, and it is actually only necessary to transmit one sideband, with a resultant factor-of-two reduction in bandwidth, in order to accomplish satisfactory message transfer. When this is done, and the carrier also is suppressed, we have a single-sideband suppressed-carrier (SSSC) system. We shall now investigate the properties of SSSC; however, the analysis is a bit more involved than is the case for AM and DSSC.

First let us represent the message $m(t)$ in the interval $0 \leq t \leq T$ by the complex Fourier series

$$m(t) = \sum_{n=-\infty}^{\infty}{}' c_n e^{jn\omega_0 t}, \qquad (4.23)$$

where

$$c_n = \frac{2}{T} \int_0^T m(t) e^{-jn\omega_0 t} \, dt, \qquad (4.24)$$

$\omega_0 = 2\pi/T$, and the notation $\sum'$ indicates that $n = 0$ is not to be included in the summation. This is equivalent to specifying that $c_0 = 0$, i. e., that the message $m(t)$ has no average value, or d-c component.

The first step in generating a SSSC wave is to multiply $m(t)$ by a high frequency, which we shall take to be $A_S \cos \omega_c t$. Thus

$$A_S m(t) \cos \omega_c t = \frac{A_S}{2} (e^{j\omega_c t} + e^{-j\omega_c t}) \sum_{n=-\infty}^{\infty}{}' c_n e^{jn\omega_0 t}. \qquad (4.25)$$

Then by filtering (there are other methods, which we shall not discuss in detail), either the upper or lower sideband component of (4.25) is selected, and the other rejected. Let us elect to transmit the upper sideband (USB). Then the transmitted wave is given by

$$E_{USB}(t) = \frac{A_S}{2} \sum_{n=1}^{\infty} [c_n e^{j(\omega_c + n\omega_0)t} + c_{-n} e^{-j(\omega_c + n\omega_0)t}]. \qquad (4.26)$$

Now, the sideband power represented by (4.26) is

$$\overline{E_{USB}^2(t)} = \frac{A_S^2}{4} \sum_{m=1}^{\infty} \sum_{n=1}^{\infty} \overline{[c_m e^{j(\omega_c + m\omega_0)t} + c_{-m} e^{-j(\omega_c + m\omega_0)t}]} \\ \times \overline{[c_n e^{j(\omega_c + n\omega_0)t} + c_{-n} e^{-j(\omega_c + n\omega_0)t}]}. \qquad (4.27)$$

The double summation is a common way of expressing the square of a series. Since, furthermore, orthogonality states that

$$\overline{e^{j(m-n)\omega t}} = \begin{cases} 0, & m \neq n, \\ 1, & m = n, \end{cases} \qquad (4.28)$$

i. e., that both the cross-correlation between different frequencies, and the average value of a sinusoid, are zero, then (4.27) reduces to

$$\overline{E_{USB}^2(t)} = \frac{A_S^2}{2} \sum_{n=1}^{\infty} c_n c_{-n}. \qquad (4.29)$$

Similarly, the message power is

$$\overline{m^2(t)} = \sum_{m=-\infty}^{\infty}{}' \sum_{n=-\infty}^{\infty}{}' c_m c_n e^{j(m+n)\omega_0 t}$$

$$= 2 \sum_{n=1}^{\infty} c_n c_{-n}. \tag{4.30}$$

Thus from (4.29) and (4.30) we have for SSSC

$$P_{SBS} = \overline{E_{USB}^2(t)} = \frac{A_S^2}{4} \overline{m^2(t)}. \tag{4.31}$$

Like DSSC, SSSC lacks an unmodulated carrier component and must be demodulated synchronously. Thus

$$E_{USB}(t) \cos \omega_c t$$

$$= \frac{A_S}{4} \left( e^{j\omega_c t} + e^{-j\omega_c t} \right) \sum_{n=1}^{\infty} [c_n e^{j(\omega_c + n\omega_0)t} + c_{-n} e^{-j(\omega_c + n\omega_0)t}], \tag{4.32}$$

which after low-pass filtering yields

$$E_{lps}(t) = \frac{A_S}{4} \sum_{n=-\infty}^{\infty}{}' c_n e^{jn\omega_0 t} = \frac{A_S}{4} m(t). \tag{4.33}$$

In obtaining (4.32) and (4.33) we have used (4.26) and (4.23). The foregoing mathematical manipulations involving complex Fourier series representation of the message $m(t)$ are performed in order to analyze SSSC for a general message waveform $m(t)$, and are not simply a misguided effort to be rigorous.

In SSSC the noise spectrum is centered $B_m/2$ cps above or below the "carrier" frequency $\omega_c$, depending upon whether the upper or the lower sideband is chosen for transmission. Thus in our case (USB), the appropriate noise representation is

$$x(t) = x_c(t) \cos \left( \omega_c + \frac{B_m}{2} \right)t - x_s(t) \sin \left( \omega_c + \frac{B_m}{2} \right)t. \tag{4.34}$$

Multiplying (4.34) by $\cos \omega_c t$ and retaining only those resultant terms which will be transmitted by a low-pass filter of bandwidth $B_m$ yields (after routine trigonometric manipulation) for the demodulator noise output

$$x_{\text{out}}(t) = \frac{1}{2} x_c(t) \cos \left( \frac{B_m}{2} \right) t - \frac{1}{2} x_s(t) \sin \left( \frac{B_m}{2} \right) t. \tag{4.35}$$

Thus the output noise power is

$$N_S = \overline{x_{\text{out}}^2(t)} = \frac{1}{8} [\overline{x_c^2(t)} + \overline{x_s^2(t)}] = \frac{1}{4} \overline{x^2(t)} = \frac{1}{4} k^2 B_m, \tag{4.36}$$

where in writing the last form of (4.36) we have again introduced the positive-frequency IF noise power spectral density $k^2$, and the

IF bandwidth which for SSSC must only just equal the message bandwidth $B_m$, so that $N_{in} = \overline{x^2(t)} = k^2 B_m$.

From (4.33), the message power output is given by

$$S_S = \overline{E^2_{lps}(t)} = \frac{A_S^2}{16}\overline{m^2(t)} = \frac{1}{4}P_{SBS},\qquad(4.37)$$

where we have also used (4.31). Therefore, using (4.36) and (4.37), the output message-to-noise of an SSSC system is

$$(S/N)_{out,S} = \frac{A_S^2\overline{m^2(t)}}{4k^2B_m} = \frac{P_{SBS}}{N_{in}}.\qquad(4.38)$$

In order to compare SSSC systems equitably with DSSC and AM, we can postulate the same transmitted sideband power. Thus from (4.19) and (4.31) the relation $P_{SBS} = P_{SBD}$ yields

$$\frac{1}{4}A_S^2\overline{m^2(t)} = \frac{1}{2}A_D^2\overline{m^2(t)},$$
$$A_S^2 = 2A_D^2.\qquad(4.39)$$

Therefore from (4.38) we find that

$$(S/N)_{out,S} = \frac{A_D^2\overline{m^2(t)}}{2k^2B_m},\qquad(4.40)$$

and thus from (4.21) and (4.22) that

$$(S/N)_{out,S} = (S/N)_{out,D} = (S/N)_{out,AM}.\qquad(4.41)$$

Hence when the same sideband power is transmitted, and the appropriate minimum IF bandwidths are used ($2B_m$ for AM and DSSC, $B_m$ for SSSC), AM, DSSC, and SSSC systems provide identical performance with respect to the effect of noise. We should also mention that, because of the absence of threshold effects in synchronous AM demodulators, any IF bandwidth wider than $2B_m$ or $B_m$, as the case may demand, may be used and (4.41) will still hold, provided that all systems incorporate a low-pass filter of the same bandwidth ($B_m$) following the synchronous demodulator. We have assumed the minimum permissible IF bandwidth in the foregoing only to simplify the notation, and if wider IF bandwidths are used, the effective input noise power should be calculated on the basis of the post-detection bandwidth, rather than the actual IF bandwidth. Excess IF bandwidth is sometimes provided to accommodate system frequency uncertainties, RF tuning errors, etc.

It may appear somewhat suprising that SSSC does not compare more favorably than is shown by (4.41), when this system transmits the same information with the same sideband power as AM and DSSC, and does so in one-half the bandwidth occupied by the latter. Superficially, one might expect to gain by a factor of two, or 3 db, in output message-to-noise ratio because of the halved noise bandwidth of SSSC. Such a result is not obtained because the upper and lower sidebands of AM and DSSC are completely correlated with respect to the demodulation process. Thus in effect they represent 3 db greater power than would be measured by applying them per se to a wattmeter; this compensates for the greater noise bandwidth of the double-sideband systems. This can readily be illustrated by assuming a sinusoidal message waveform, $m(t) = \sin \omega_m t$. Then, from (4.18),

$$E_{lpD}(t) = \frac{1}{2} A_D \sin \omega_m t. \tag{4.42}$$

Also from (2.34) and (2.40) for equal sideband power,

$$E_{lpS}(t) = \frac{1}{4} A_S \sin \omega_m t = \frac{1}{4} \sqrt{2} A_D \sin \omega_m t. \tag{4.43}$$

Obviously, the voltage expressed by (4.42) for DSSC is 3 db greater than that given by (4.43) for SSSC. However, the output noise powers expressed by (4.20) and (4.36) for respectively DSSC and SSSC also differ by a factor of two, or 3 db. Therefore DSSC and SSSC deliver the same output message-to-noise ratio when the transmitted powers are equal, and the effective noise bandwidth of the former system is twice that of the latter.

### Peak Power Considerations

To this point we have compared AM, DSSC, and SSSC systems on the basis of equal average sideband power. From a theoretical standpoint, unfettered by consideration of equipment capabilities, this clearly is the only legitimate common denominator, and by using it we have gained valuable insight into some of the fundamental characteristics of these modulation schemes. However, we must also be practical, and here the picture changes considerably. It so happens that many ratio transmitters are *peak-power-limited* rather than average-power-limited. Therefore we must investigate the *envelopes* of AM, DSSC, and SSSC waves, and base a more realistic systems appraisal on an equal peak power (or equivalently, equal envelope amplitude) constraint.

We shall first compare AM and DSSC. Here, for equal peak envelope amplitudes we have [see (4.6) and (4.41)]

$$A[1 + \hat{m}(t)] = A_D\hat{m}(t) = A_D, \qquad (4.44)$$

where $\hat{m}(t)$ is the peak message waveform magnitude and is defined equal to unity. Hence $A_D = 2A$, and by comparing (4.21) and (4.9) it is seen that DSSC delivers four times, or 6 db, greater output message-to-noise ratio than does AM, under the equal peak power limitation.

The comparison between the total *average* transmitted power of AM and DSSC systems operating at the same *peak* power level depends on the details of the message waveform $m(t)$. Specifically, for AM,

$$P_{AM} = \overline{E_{AM}^2(t)} = \frac{1}{2} A^2[1 + \overline{m^2(t)}],$$

and for DSSC with $A_D = 2A$, $P_{SBD} = 2A^2\overline{m^2(t)}$, so that

$$\frac{P_{AM}}{P_{SBD}} = \frac{1}{4}\left[1 + \frac{1}{\overline{m^2(t)}}\right]. \qquad (4.45)$$

From (4.45), equality of both average and peak powers corresponds to $\overline{m^2(t)} = \frac{1}{3}$. From $m(t) = \sin \omega_m t$, then $\overline{m^2(t)} = \frac{1}{2}$ and $P_{AM}/P_{SBD} = \frac{3}{4}$. Hence under full-load test-tone conditions, the DSSC system must transmit 1.25 db [$10 \log_{10}(\frac{4}{3}) = 1.25$] higher average power than the AM system, in order to achieve the 6-db superiority of output message-to-noise ratio of which it is capable under a peak power limitation. On the other hand, if we let $m(t)$ be gaussian noise with standard deviation $\sigma_m = \frac{1}{3}$† so that $\overline{m^2(t)} = \sigma_m^2 = \frac{1}{9}$, then (2.46) yields $P_{AM}/P_{SBD} = 2.5$, and the DSSC system provides 6 db *higher* output message-to-noise ratio with 4 db *lower* average transmitted power, compared to AM. This is a substantial gain in performance. For voice and music transmissions, we can infer statistics intermediate between gaussian and those of a sinusoid (neglecting pauses and level changes in program material which favor the DSSC system), so that the foregoing represents a fair estimate of the comparative performance of peak-power-limited AM and DSSC systems. Clearly the balance weighs in favor of DSSC, although the necessity for synchronous detection complicates the receiver design.

A similar analysis can be made to compare SSSC with DSSC under peak-power-limited conditions, although it is somewhat more involved and less explicit in the general case. The primary com-

---

† The probability that a gaussian random variable will exceed $3\sigma$ is about $3 \times 10^{-3}$. The transmitters will thus be overmodulated, i. e., $|m(t)| > 1$, only this tolerable fraction of the time.

plication is that, whereas the envelope of DSSC is related in a clear and simple way to the waveform of the message $m(t)$ [see (4.14)], such is not the case with SSSC. In fact the SSSC envelope is not related in any obvious or easily visualized way to the message waveform, although analytically the relationship is completely deterministic.

We might first inquire qualitatively why such a situation should exist, when actually all that has been done in generating an SSSC wave is to translate the original frequency components of the message by a fixed amount $\omega_c$. The question concerning *why* a simple frequency translation has a great effect on the form of the resulting SSSC envelope can be answered quite explicitly. We first observe that in order for addition of the frequency components of a Fourier series representation of the message waveform to represent it, these components must bear very definite amplitude, phase, and frequency relationships; for example, all the components are *harmonically* related to the fundamental frequency defined by the expansion interval $T$. Now, when these components are frequency translated *en masse* by an amount $\omega_c$, many of the former relationships between them are destroyed; in particular, they are no longer harmonically related. The envelope of the resulting SSSC wave is thus no longer in direct proportion to the message waveform, and a simple translation in frequency has some not-so-simple effects on the form of the transmitted signal. In fact it is possible at times for the translated frequency components of the message to add all in phase, to produce a peak envelope equal in magnitude to the arithmetic sum of the amplitudes of all the original message components.

In order to treat the peak-power-limited SSSC case, we need some more compact expression than (4.26) for the transmitted wave, which promises at least in certain specific instances to simplify the analysis. This we find in a quadrature-carrier representation of SSSC. It is well known that an SSSC signal can be regarded as the resultant of modulating quadrature-carrier phases by a pair of waveforms in phase quadrature.† Thus if $m(t)$ is the message waveform, and $\mu(t)$ is its *harmonic conjugate,* obtained from $m(t)$ by introducing a constant 90-degree phase lag at all frequencies of $m(t)$, then the upper sideband of an SSSC wave can be represented by

$$E_{USB}(t) = m(t) \cos \omega_c t - \mu(t) \sin \omega_c t. \qquad (4.46)$$

† This is the foundation of the *outphasing* method of generating an SSSC wave.

Thus if $m(t) = A_S \cos \omega_m t$, $\mu(t) = A_S \sin \omega_m t$, and from (4.46) we have $E_{USB}(t) = A_s \cos(\omega_c + \omega_m)t$. Thus from (4.44), for equal DSSC and SSSC envelope amplitudes, $A_S = A_D$, and then the average power of the SSSC wave is $\frac{1}{2} A_D^2$. However from (4.16) the average DSSC power with sinusoidal modulation is $\frac{1}{4} A_D^2$. Therefore SSSC can, with sine-wave messages, transmit twice the average power of DSSC at the same peak power, and hence enjoys a 3-db (sinusoidal) message-to-noise ratio advantage under these conditions. If we include the 6-db advantage of DSSC over AM, we obtain a very famous number: 9 db. This is widely quoted as the margin of superiority of SSSC over AM; however, the qualification is often omitted that this is the situation only for sinusoidal modulation and equal peak power.

Equation (4.46) is also well suited to the analysis of SSSC with gaussian noise modulation, and we shall next consider this case in order to complete the comparison with DSSC. First let us express the message $m(t)$ as a Fourier series of the same form as that used in Art. 3.1 to represent gaussian noise (the noise process need not be narrow-band in order to do this). Thus

$$m(t) = \sum_{n=1}^{\infty} (m_{cn} \cos n\omega_0 t + m_{sn} \sin n\omega_0 t), \quad 0 \le t \le T = \frac{2\pi}{\omega_0}. \quad (4.47)$$

Also from the definition of the harmonic conjugate of $m(t)$ we have

$$\mu(t) = \sum_{n=1}^{\infty} (m_{cn} \sin n\omega_0 t - m_{sn} \cos n\omega_0 t). \quad (4.48)$$

The fundamental nature of (4.47) and (4.48) is obviously the same, i. e., the same gaussian random variables $m_{cn}$ and $m_{sn}$ appear in both when $m(t)$ is gaussian, and therefore $\mu(t)$ is also a gaussian variate. Furthermore it is readily verified that

$$\overline{m^2(t)} = \overline{\mu^2(t)} = \sigma_m^2 \quad (4.49)$$

and

$$\overline{m(t)\mu(t)} = 0. \quad (4.50)$$

Therefore $m(t)$ and $\mu(t)$ play the same role in (4.46) as do $x_c(t)$ and $x_s(t)$ in the quardrature-carrier representation of narrow-band gaussian noise; hence $E_{USB}(t)$ as given by (4.46) is itself a sample function of a narrow-band gaussian random process with variance $\sigma_m^2$, when $m(t)$ is gaussian.

We can write this SSSC wave in an envelope-and-phase form

$$E_{USB}(t) = V_S(t) \cos[\omega_c t + \phi_s(t)], \quad (4.51)$$

where in particular the quantity of interest, the envelope $V_S$, is Rayleigh-distributed:

$$p(V_S) = \frac{V_S}{\sigma_m^2} e^{-V_S^2/2\sigma_m^2}, \qquad V_S \geq 0. \qquad (4.52)$$

We see thus that even the statistical nature of the envelope of an SSSC wave can be different from that of the modulating message, here Rayleigh and gaussian respectively, and an obvious correspondence between the two waveforms therefore can scarcely be expected to exist in general.

Remember now that in the gaussian noise-modulated DSSC case, we defined the peak envelope amplitude as that level where the probability of overmodulation is $3 \times 10^{-3}$[†]. Thus for equal defined peak DSSC and SSSC envelopes, we have the condition that: Probability $(V_S > A_D) = 3 \times 10^{-3}$ [see (4.44)]. Then, using (4.52), this condition becomes

$$3 \times 10^{-3} = \int_{A_D}^{\infty} \frac{V_S}{\sigma_m^2} e^{-V_S^2/2\sigma_m^2} \, dV_S. \qquad (4.53)$$

The integration is easily performed by changing variable to $u = V_S^2/2\sigma_m^2$, and the result is

$$\sigma_m^2 = 0.0862 A_D^2 = \overline{E_{USB}^2} = P_{SBS}, \qquad (4.54)$$

where $\sigma_m^2 = P_{SBS}$ is observed from the foregoing analysis of the nature of $E_{USB}(t)$.

Now for DSSC at $3 \times 10^{-3}$ overmodulation probability, we found that $\overline{m^2(t)} = \sigma_m^2 = \frac{1}{9}$, and thus from (4.16) we have

$$P_{SBD} = 0.555 A_D^2. \qquad (4.55)$$

Therefore the ratio of SSSC to DSSC average power with gaussian noise modulation and equal peak powers, defined as the value exceeded 0.3 per cent of the time, is

$$\frac{P_{SBS}}{P_{SBD}} = \frac{0.0862 A_D^2}{0.0555 A_D^2} = 1.55 = 1.9 \text{ db.} \qquad (4.56)$$

Since the output message-to-noise ratio is proportional to average transmitted sideband power, then gaussian-modulated SSSC enjoys an advantage of 1.9 db over DSSC, and of 7.9 db over AM, when all systems are limited to the same peak power.

As previously noted, we can infer statistics intermediate between gaussian and those of a sinusoid for typical program material. Hence SSSC appears to be about 2–3 db superior to DSSC, and

---

† See footnote, p. 78.

8-9 db better than AM, in a peak-power-limited situation. There
are some who would possibly take issue with this conclusion.
Using bandwidth-limited square-wave modulation, they show that
SSSC is upwards of 3-6 db inferior to DSSC in average power
capacity at constant peak power, and that this penalty increases
without limit as the modulating waveform becomes progressively
more perfectly square. There is, of course, no occasion to challenge
the correctness of the square-wave analysis. However, a great many
communication missions exist for which a square wave is by no
means a representative form of modulation, and for which SSSC
is quite likely the best amplitude-modulation technique. Conversely,
in those instances where a square wave is a representative message
waveform, e. g., in time-division multiplexed pulse systems, we
similarly discover that SSSC should be avoided as a method of
carrier modulation. In general, one cannot assert or show that a
single modulation scheme is the best for all applications, or even
best from all standpoints for a given communication mission.

### 4.5   UNSTABLE TRANSMISSION MEDIA

In our discussion thus far we have assumed a stable transmission medium, i. e., fading and multipath effects were not considered. We have also noted that the use of synchronous detection
in DSSC and SSSC receivers, compared to envelope detection as
is commonly used in AM receivers, is of no advantage in itself
if the medium is stable and the carrier-to-noise ratio is fairly high.
Where synchronous detection begins to contribute a significant
operational superiority to DSSC and SSSC over ordinary AM
systems is under marginal or poor carrier-to-noise ratio conditions;
however, a quantitative figure is difficult to assign here since the
envelope detector actually mutilates the message waveform. A
further, and possibly more important, advantage of synchronous
detection appears when the transmission medium is perturbed by
multiplicative factors as well as by additive noise.

Consider selective fading in the transmission circuit, as often
occurs in ionospheric high-frequency links. Selective fading is
qualitatively equivalent to inserting a time-varying filter in the
transmission path, having many sharp attenuation peaks and nulls
which shift in frequency and change in magnitude. In envelope
detection of AM, selective fading can be very serious; for example,
the carrier component may be severely attenuated, and at times

only the sidebands remain. This causes extreme nonlinear distortion of the output waveform, which can render the output "message" virtually unintelligible even though the "message"-to-noise ratio may be excellent. The nature of such nonlinear distortion can be readily described by observing that envelope detection of a DSSC signal delivers an output waveform which is equivalent to full-wave rectification of the original message waveform. We have probably all heard such distortion at night when listening to a distant AM broadcast station.

In contrast, selective fading does not produce nonlinear distortion when synchronous detection is used, as in DSSC and SSSC (synchronous detection is also perfectly applicable to AM but is seldom employed here, largely for economic reasons). In such cases, selective fading results essentially in a linear filtering effect on the output message; some baseband frequencies are attenuated and others not, but no nonlinear distortion products are generated. For many applications, e. g., voice communications, this filtering effect is not serious with regard to loss of intelligibility. Thus DSSC and SSSC may well exhibit a dramatic superiority over AM systems under multiplicatively disturbed path conditions. Again a quantitative measure of this advantage cannot readily be given; it is important to note, however, that it results not from the use of suppressed-carrier modulation, but rather from the use of synchronous demodulation.

It is difficult to judge whether suppressed-carrier techniques will to any large extent eventually supplant AM for narrow-band communication purposes. However, if the recent past is an indication, SSSC would appear to be a sound growth investment. Great pressure exists to accommodate increasingly larger numbers of military and commercial communication services, and since we have traditionally shared the available frequency spectrum on a channelized basis, it is natural to attempt to reduce transmission bandwidths. Thus the bandwidth-conservation properties of SSSC may well decide the balance in its favor over other amplitude-modulation techniques.

REFERENCES

Baghdady, E. J., ed.
   (V) *Lectures on Communication System Theory*. McGraw-Hill, New York, 1961.

Bedrosian, E.
(II) "The Analytic Signal Representation of Modulated Waveforms," *Proc. IRE*, **50** (October 1962).

Bennett, W. R.
(I) "Methods of Solving Noise Problems," *Proc. IRE*, **44** (May 1956).

Blachman, N. M.
(I) "The Output Signal-to-Noise Ratio of a Power-Law Device," *J. Appl. Phys.*, **24** (June 1953).

Black, H. S., *Modulation Theory*. Van Nostrand, Princeton, N. J., 1953.

Bruene, W. B., "Comments on 'Compatible Single Sideband,'" *Proc. IRE*, **50**, (March 1962).

Fubini, E. G., and D. C. Johnson, "Signal-to-Noise Ratios in AM Receivers," *Proc. IRE*, **36** (December 1948).

Goldman, S.
(II) *Frequency Analysis, Modulation, and Noise*. McGraw-Hill, New York, 1948.

Grumet, A., "Demodulation Effect of an Envelope Detector at Low Signal-to-Noise Ratios," *Proc. IRE*, **50** (October 1962).

Kahn, L. R.
(I) "Single-Sideband Transmission by Envelope Elimination and Restoration," *Proc. IRE*, **40** (July 1952).
(II) "Compatible Single Sideband," *Proc. IRE*, **49** (October 1961).

Kallman, H. E., "Transient Response of Single-Sideband Systems," *Proc. IRE*, **28** (December 1940).

Lawson, J. L., and G. E. Uhlenbeck, *Threshold Signals*, MIT Rad. Lab. Series, vol. 24. McGraw-Hill, New York, 1950.

Middleton, D.
(I) *An Introduction to Statistical Communication Theory*. McGraw-Hill, New York, 1960.
(IV) "Rectification of a Sinusoidally Modulated Carrier in the Presence of Noise," *Proc. IRE*, **36** (December 1948).

Powers, K. H., "The Compatibility Problem in Single-Sideband Transmission," *Proc. IRE*, **48** (August 1960).

*Proc. IRE*, **42** (January 1954) (second color television issue; see for special application of AM techniques).

*Proc. IRE*, **44** (December 1956) [single-sideband issue; see also discussion in *Proc. IRE*, **45** (April 1957), pp. 534–543].

Ragazzini, J. R., "The Effect of Fluctuation Voltages on the Linear Detector," *Proc. IRE*, **30** (June 1942).

Schwartz, M., *Information Transmission, Modulation, and Noise.* McGraw-Hill, New York, 1959.

Thaler, S., and S. A. Meltzer, "The Amplitude Distribution and False Alarm Rate of Noise After Post-Detection Filtering," *Proc. IRE,* **49** (February 1961).

Van Kessel, T. J., F. L. H. M. Stumpers, and J. M. A. Uyen, "A Method for Obtaining Compatible Single-Sideband Modulation," *Proc. IRE,* **50** (September 1962).

# Chapter Five

# Angle (Exponential) Modulation

## 5.1 EXPONENTIAL MODULATION

In introducing Part 2, we observed that the general sinusoidal wave $E(t) = A \sin \phi$ could also be modulated so as to convey a message $m(t)$ by varying the angular argument $\phi = (\omega t + \theta)$. This is described as *angle modulation*, and as we shall show in this article, it is a *nonlinear* modulation process of exponential character.

Let us express the general sinusoid in complex form as the phasor

$$
\begin{aligned}
E(t) &= Ae^{j(\omega t + \theta)} \\
&= Ae^{j\theta}e^{j\omega t}.
\end{aligned}
\tag{5.1}
$$

If now we choose to vary $\theta$ in accordance with the message to be conveyed, so that $\theta(t) = \Theta m(t)$, where $\Theta$ is a scale factor, $|\Theta| \leq \pi$, and $\omega = \omega_c$, a constant, then (5.1) becomes

$$
E_{PM}(t) = Ae^{j\Theta m(t)}e^{j\omega_c t}
\tag{5.2}
$$

This represents *phase modulation* (PM), and comparison with (4.1) (in complex form) reveals that in essence we have modulated the carrier $Ae^{j\omega_c t}$ with a *nonlinear*, exponential function of the message: $e^{j\Theta m(t)}$.

If similarly we choose to vary $\omega$ in accordance with the message $m(t)$ (of unity peak magnitude) so that $\omega = \omega_c + 2\pi f_D m(t)$, and for convenience let $\theta = 0$, then (5.1) becomes

$$E_{FM}(t) = Ae^{j[\omega_c + 2\pi f_D m(t)]t}$$
$$= Ae^{j2\pi f_D m(t)t}e^{j\omega_c t}. \tag{5.3}$$

This represents *frequency modulation* (FM), where the constant (for a particular system design) $f_D$ is the *peak frequency deviation*. A close relationship exists between FM and PM (both are angle-modulation techniques), as can be shown by casting (5.3) into the form of (5.2). Thus if we write

$$E_{FM}(t) = Ae^{j\theta_{FM}(t)}e^{j\omega_c t}, \tag{5.4}$$

the instantaneous phase or angular displacement $\theta_{FM}(t)$ of the FM phasor with respect to the unmodulated carrier $Ae^{j\omega_c t}$ is simply given by integrating its instantaneous frequency or angular velocity deviation. This yields, from (5.3),

$$\theta_{FM}(t) = 2\pi f_D \int^t m(\tau)\, d\tau, \tag{5.5}$$

and (5.4) becomes

$$E_{FM}(t) = Ae^{j\omega_c t}e^{j2\pi f_D \int^t m(\tau)\, d\tau}. \tag{5.6}$$

Comparison of (5.2) and (5.6) shows that FM is equivalent to PM wherein the message is operated upon by an integrator; this operation can be realized, if d-c and very low-frequency message components are of no consequence, by a long-time-constant RC low-pass filter. Conversely, PM is equivalent to FM wherein the message is differentiated by, for example, a short-time-constant RC high-pass filter. Of course, both integration and differentiation are linear operations, so that both PM and FM retain the character of non-linear exponential modulation techniques. Correspondingly, the demodulation or message recovery operation involves phase- or frequency-to-amplitude conversion.

Of the two, FM is the far more widely used in communications technology, because in principle no restriction need be placed on the peak frequency deviation $f_D$, and it is not necessary to supply a precise phase reference for demodulation purposes. We shall therefore concentrate here primarily on FM as an analog modulation technique, and observe that the principally digital applications of PM essentially reduce to DSSC.

### Spectrum

Because of the nonlinear exponential transformation of the message which is involved in generating an FM wave, the spectrum of the modulated carrier is related to the message in a much more complex way than is the case in linear (amplitude) modulation. We shall illustrate this situation only for the special case of sinusoidal modulation. Thus let the FM wave be given in the form of (5.6), with $m(t) = \cos \omega_m t$, by

$$E_{FM}(t) = A \operatorname{Im}\left[e^{j(\omega_c + 2\pi f_D \int^t \cos \omega_m \tau \, d\tau)}\right]$$

$$= A \sin\left(\omega_c t + \frac{2\pi f_D}{\omega_m} \sin \omega_m t\right). \qquad (5.7)$$

The quantity $2\pi f_D/\omega_m = D$ in (5.7) is of fundamental importance in FM: $D$ is the ratio of the peak frequency deviation to the (maximum) modulating frequency, and is interchangeably called either the *deviation ratio* or the *modulation index*.

By expanding (5.7) trigonometrically and introducing $D$, we obtain

$$E_{FM}(t) = A[\sin \omega_c t \cos (D \sin \omega_m t) + \cos \omega_c t \sin (D \sin \omega_m t)]. \qquad (5.8)$$

Now, by standard identities in advanced calculus,

$$\cos (D \sin \omega_m t) = J_0(D) + 2 \sum_{n=1}^{\infty} J_{2n}(D) \cos 2n\omega_m t, \qquad (5.9a)$$

$$\sin (D \sin \omega_m t) = 2 \sum_{n=1}^{\infty} J_{2n-1}(D) \sin (2n-1)\omega_m t, \qquad (5.9b)$$

where $J_p(D)$ is the Bessel function of the first kind and order $p$, with argument $D$, the modulation index. Substituting (5.9a) and (5.9b) into (5.8) and trigonometrically expanding the terms involving the forms $\sin \omega_c t \cos 2n\omega_m t$ and $\cos \omega_c t \sin (2n-1)\omega_m t$ yields finally

$$E_{FM}(t) = \underbrace{A J_0(D) \sin \omega_c t}_{\text{Carrier}}$$

$$+ A \sum_{n=1}^{\infty} J_{2n}(D)[\underbrace{\sin (\omega_c + 2n\omega_m)t}_{\text{USB}} + \underbrace{\sin (\omega_c - 2n\omega_m)t}_{\text{LSB}}] \qquad (5.10)$$
$$\underbrace{\qquad\qquad\qquad\qquad\qquad\qquad\qquad\qquad}_{\text{Even Order}}$$

$$+ A \sum_{n=1}^{\infty} J_{2n-1}(D)\{\underbrace{\sin [\omega_c + (2n-1)\omega_m]t}_{\text{USB}} - \underbrace{\sin [\omega_c - (2n-1)\omega_m]t}_{\text{LSB}}\}.$$
$$\underbrace{\qquad\qquad\qquad\qquad\qquad\qquad\qquad\qquad}_{\text{Odd Order}}$$

Equation (5.10) is rather a formidable expression by comparison with (4.5) for sinusoidal amplitude modulation. In particular (5.10) shows that an infinite number of upper and lower sideband components are generated, which are separated in the frequency domain from the carrier component by all integral multiples of the single modulating frequency; the sideband amplitudes are governed by the nonelementary Bessel function $J_p(D)$. In case we were to frequency-modulate simultaneously with two sinusoids, we would also find sideband components separated from the carrier by all orders of intermodulation products between the two modulating frequencies; this is easily understood upon recalling that FM involves a *nonlinear* transformation of the modulating waveform. Thus, to determine the spectrum of a sinusoidal carrier which is angle-modulated by a general random process becomes a quite complex problem, which we shall not pursue in further detail.[†] Such apparently disproportionate complications usually arise whenever a nonlinearity is introduced, but this is not sufficient cause to avoid the use of nonlinear techniques. Conversely, we shall see in this chapter that FM is in many ways far superior to AM.

### Bandwidth Considerations

In view of (5.10), we must inquire how practically to deal with a signal whose spectrum is, in principle, of infinite extent. Rigorously, if any of the sidebands of (5.10) are rejected, or the phase relationships between them are changed, because of finite receiver bandwidth, then the result no longer represents a sinusoidally frequency-modulated carrier. In general, bandwidth restriction leads to distortion of the original message waveform at the FM demodulator output. However, it is true of the Bessel function $J_p(D)$ that it diminishes quite rapidly for $p > D$, i.e., for $p\omega_m > 2\pi f_D$. Thus the sideband amplitudes rapidly vanish outside a bandwidth $\pm f_D$ cps removed from the carrier frequency, and if small but nonzero distortion can be tolerated, then finite-bandwidth FM reception is possible.

There have been many theoretical investigations made of the distortion problem in FM due to predetection (IF) bandwidth restriction.[‡] Except, however, for emphasizing that *linear* receiver phase-vs.-frequency response is of paramount importance in all cases, the result of these studies remains otherwise inconclusive with respect to establishing a usable general engineering criterion for FM bandwidth specification.[§] Failing this, however, two "rules-of-thumb"

---

† See Middleton (I), pp. 604–625, and additional references at end of chapter.
‡ See, for example, Baghdady (II), and additional references at end of chapter.
§ See Rowe.

have been used with some success in FM system design, in conjunction with the requirement for maximally linear phase characteristics.

The first simply gives the required receiver IF bandwidth as

$$B_{IF} = 2(f_D + B_m) = 2f_D\left(1 + \frac{1}{D_{\min}}\right), \tag{5.11}$$

where $B_m$ is the highest-frequency component of interest in the original message, i.e., the message bandwidth. For high-index FM systems where $D_{\min} = f_D/B_m \gg 1$, (5.11) states that a bandwidth approximately equal to the peak-to-peak frequency deviation of the modulated carrier is sufficient; this obviously has antecedents in a quasi-stationary, or "moving delta-function" visualization of the FM signal spectrum. Conversely, for low-index FM systems where $D_{\min} \ll 1$ (these essentially amount to PM, as we shall shortly see), (5.11) states that a receiver bandwidth wide enough to pass at least the first-order sidebands of the highest modulating frequency is required. Now it is evident that this must be true, since if the first (and all higher) order sidebands are rejected, then all information concerning the corresponding portion of the message spectrum is lost and recovery thereof is impossible. However, failure to recognize this point constituted an apparent paradox which puzzled early FM investigators.

The second pragmatic criterion whereby FM-system bandwidth may be specified essentially requires passing unattenuated all sidebands that are greater in amplitude than some chosen fraction $\gamma$ of the unmodulated carrier amplitude, when the carrier is fully modulated—i.e., the peak frequency deviation equals the design value of $f_D$—by the highest message frequency of interest, $B_m$. Qualitatively, one then presumes that the peak resultant distortion is bounded by the chosen small fraction $\gamma$. Mathematically, we solve the equation

$$J_p(D_{\min}) = \gamma \tag{5.12}$$

(with the aid of tables of the Bessel function)[†] for the largest possible value of $p$ (not necessarily an integer); then determine the required bandwidth from

$$B_{IF} = 2pB_m. \tag{5.13}$$

The result of this procedure is shown in Fig. 5.1, where the bandwidth ratio $\beta = B_{IF}/f_D$ is plotted as a function of the modulation index $D_{\min}$ for $\gamma = 0.01$, 0.05, and 0.1.

---

† See Jahnke and Emde.

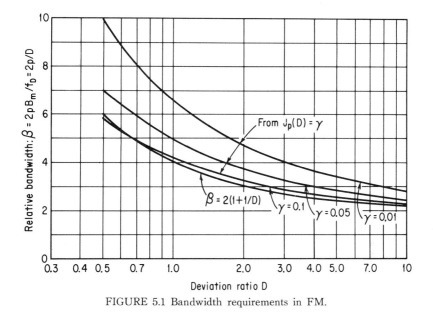

FIGURE 5.1 Bandwidth requirements in FM.

For comparison, Fig. 5.1 also shows results from (5.11), and it is evident that a bandwidth criterion closely comparable to $\gamma = 0.1$ is obtained. From a practical standpoint, $\gamma = 0.01$ is usually regarded as conservative, and $\gamma = 0.05$ to $0.1$ as acceptable.[†] Thus, (5.11) is a particularly simple criterion which serves well in practice, when coupled with the additional moderate excess bandwidth allowances that are commonly made for frequency uncertainty, RF tuning error, etc.

Finally, the time domain structure of an FM wave can be developed by examination of (5.10). First, comparison of the components identified as "even order," with (4.4) for AM, shows that these double-frequency sidebands are so phased with respect to the carrier as to contribute pure amplitude modulation thereof. Second, it is evident that phase reversal (due to the minus sign) of the LSB portion of the "odd-order" FM sideband set causes the resultant of these sidebands always to be in *phase quadrature* with the carrier component. Of course the resultant of the odd-

---

[†] $N$th-harmonic distortion caused by rejecting "significant" sidebands of modulating frequencies $f_1 > (1/N)B_m$ is eliminated by the baseband filter. Thus, specifying the IF bandwidth on the basis $D = D_{\min} = f_D/B_m$ is conservative with respect to the generation of harmonics of lower modulating frequencies [$f_1 < (1/N)B_m$, so that $D = f_D/f_1 > ND_{\min}$], which are passed by the baseband filter.

order sidebands varies (at the fundamental modulation frequency), so that these components cause the over-all resultant to have a time-varying phase, i.e., contribute frequency modulation hereto. The result of vectorially combining the odd-order, or quadrature, sideband set with the carrier component also produces amplitude variations at rates equal to twice the modulating frequency and its harmonics. These double-frequency amplitude variations are *precisely cancelled* by the double-frequency amplitude modulation of the carrier component caused by the even-order sideband set, and the total resultant phasor is one of constant amplitude, but time-varying phase and frequency. The phasor diagram of Fig. 5.2 illustrates this interrelationship of carrier, even-order, and odd-order sidebands, to produce a pure FM wave. It is remarkable that the well-known Bessel function serves to govern this intricate situation.

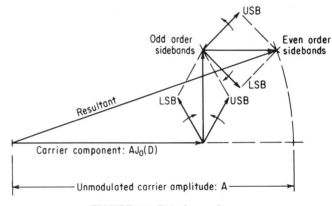

FIGURE 5.2 FM phasor diagram.

From the general infinite series expansion of the Bessel function of the first kind[†]

$$J_p(D) = \sum_{n=0}^{\infty} \frac{(-1)^n (D/2)^{p+2n}}{n! \, \Gamma(p+n+1)} \tag{5.14}$$

we see that for small values of the argument $D$

$$J_p(D) \cong \frac{D^p}{2^p p!}, \qquad D \ll 1, p \text{ integer.} \tag{5.15}$$

Thus in low-index FM systems, where $D \ll 1$, only the lowest-

† The gamma function $\Gamma(k)$ is a generalization of the factorial; for integer arguments $k$, we have $\Gamma(k) = (k-1)!$.

order sidebands, corresponding say to $p = 1, 2$, are of any consequence, and even these are quite small compared to the carrier component $J_0(D \ll 1) \cong 1$. As we have previously noted, therefore, a low-index FM wave has the essential character of a PM wave; Fig. 5.2 also serves to illustrate this observation.

### The Limiter

In FM (and PM), the message information is conveyed by variations of the angular argument of the modulated sinusoidal carrier, and its amplitude is constant. This fact held great intuitive appeal for pioneers in the FM field, since it permits the receiver to clip, or limit, the received wave to a constant amplitude and hence, it was thought, vastly to reduce the influence of noise and "static." Such drastic nonlinear distortion is, of course, out of the question for AM. Actually it is true that "hard" limiting of the FM wave is necessary in order to realize full system performance in the presence of thermal noise, and that substantial reduction of the effect of impulsive noise disturbances and coherent interference is directly attributable to the amplitude limiter.[†] However, the bulk of FM-system performance superiority over AM lies in reduction of the extent to which noise affects the *instantaneous frequency* of the sum of carrier and noise, compared to the impressed modulation, irrespective of amplitude. Although the limiter is a vital adjunct to successful FM reception, the modulation parameters, not the limiter *per se*, are primarily responsible for determining system performance in the presence of noise.

### 5.2   NOISE IN FM

Again, much of the preceding material should be of a review nature for the reader; however, it is well to record these fundamental facts concerning the modulation technique with which we are dealing. Our principal problem, to which we turn in this article, is to determine quantitatively the effect of noise on a limiter-discriminator combination such as that used in FM reception. As in our analysis of AM,

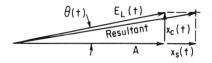

FIGURE 5.3 FM phasor diagram $(S/N)_{in} \gg 1$.

† See Baghdady (I, III), and additional references at end of chapter.

we shall make extensive use of the narrow-band noise representations developed in Chapter 3.

Using the quadrature-carrier noise representation, the phasor diagram applicable to the high carrier-to-noise ratio case is shown in Fig. 5.3. Under these conditions, passing the carrier plus noise through an ideal limiter is substantially equivalent to simply discarding the in-phase noise component $x_s(t)$, which primarily contributes variations in the envelope of the resultant wave $E(t)$. After band-pass filtering, the limiter output is then given by

$$E_L(t) = A \sin \omega_c t + x_c(t) \cos \omega_c t. \qquad (5.16)$$

We may rewrite (5.16) in the envelope-and-phase form

$$E_L(t) = A \sin [\omega_c t + \theta(t)] \qquad (5.17)$$

where the important quantity $\theta(t)$ is given by

$$\theta(t) = \tan^{-1} \frac{x_c(t)}{A} \qquad (5.18a)$$

$$\cong \frac{x_c(t)}{A} \qquad (5.18b)$$

and (5.18) holds with high probability under the assumed high signal-to-noise ratio conditions where $x_c(t) \ll A$. An ideal frequency discriminator responds to the time derivative of the instantaneous phase angle; thus

$$\theta'(t) = \frac{x_c'(t)}{A}. \qquad (5.19)$$

### Total Output Noise

In order to calculate the output noise power $\overline{\theta'^2(t)}$, we must determine the value of $\overline{x_c'^2(t)}$, where $x_c(t)$, as we have found, is a gaussian variate with zero mean, and variance $\sigma_x^2$ equal to the input (IF channel) noise power. We first write

$$x_c'^2(t) = \lim_{\Delta t \to 0} \left[ \frac{x_c(t + \Delta t) - x_c(t)}{\Delta t} \right]^2. \qquad (5.20)$$

Then

$$\overline{x_c'^2(t)} = \lim_{\Delta t \to 0} \frac{1}{(\Delta t)^2} \overline{[x_c^2(t + \Delta t) + x_c^2(t) - 2x_c(t + \Delta t)x_c(t)]} \qquad (5.21a)$$

$$= \lim_{\Delta t \to 0} \frac{1}{(\Delta t)^2} [2\sigma_x^2 - 2R_{x_c}(\Delta t)], \qquad (5.21b)$$

where in writing (5.21a, b) we have, as usually is permissible in engineering problems, interchanged the order of averaging and passing to the limit. The autocovariance function $R_x(\ )$ was introduced in Chapter 2.

If we assume a uniform rectangularly band-limited IF noise power spectrum, then we can write for the power spectrum of the quadrature noise component $x_c(t)$

$$G_{x_c}(f) = \begin{cases} \sigma_x^2/2B, & -B \le f \le B; \\ 0, & |f| > B. \end{cases} \tag{5.22}$$

where $B$ represents one-half the IF bandwidth. Then the autocovariance function is given by

$$R_{x_c}(\Delta t) = \int_{-B}^{B} \frac{\sigma_x^2}{2B} e^{j2\pi f \Delta t} \, df = \sigma_x^2 \frac{\sin 2\pi B \, \Delta t}{2\pi B \, \Delta t}. \tag{5.23}$$

Expansion of (5.23) in a Taylor series yields

$$\sigma_x^2 \frac{\sin 2\pi B \, \Delta t}{2\pi B \, \Delta t} = \sigma_x^2 \sum_{n=0}^{\infty} (-1)^n \frac{(2\pi B \, \Delta t)^{2n}}{(2n+1)!}. \tag{5.24}$$

Substituting from (5.24) into (5.21b) we find

$$\overline{x_c'^2(t)} = 2\sigma_x^2 \lim_{\Delta t \to 0} \frac{1}{(\Delta t)^2} \sum_{n=1}^{\infty} (-1)^{n+1} \frac{(2\pi B \, \Delta t)^{2n}}{(2n+1)!}$$

$$= \frac{4}{3} \pi^2 B^2 \sigma_x^2. \tag{5.25}$$

Then from (5.19) we obtain

$$\overline{\theta'^2(t)} = \frac{4\pi^2 B^2 \sigma_x^2}{3A^2}. \tag{5.26}$$

For a discriminator sensitivity of 1-volt-per-cps deviation, and since $\theta(t)$ is in radian measure, we thus find for the total output noise power

$$N_{\text{out}} = \frac{1}{4\pi^2} \overline{\theta'^2(t)} = \frac{B^2 \sigma_x^2}{3A^2}. \tag{5.27}$$

Again it is convenient to introduce the quantity $k^2$, the positive-frequency input (IF) noise power spectral density (watts per cps), so that $\sigma_x^2 = 2k^2 B$. Thus

$$N_{\text{out}} = \frac{2k^2 B^3}{3A^2}. \tag{5.28}$$

### Output Noise Spectrum

Since in FM the IF channel bandwidth is ordinarily considerably wider than the message bandwidth, we should next, in order to evaluate the effect of post-detection filtering, determine the power spectrum of the discriminator noise output. From (5.28) we note that the total discriminator output noise power varies as the *cube* of the IF bandwidth; thus the noise spectrum cannot be flat, since if this were the case, the total noise power output would be proportional to the first power of $B$. Specifically, if we write

$$N_{\text{out}} = \frac{2k^2 B^3}{3A^2} = \int_0^B G_n(f) \, df, \tag{5.29}$$

it follows by inspection that the positive-frequency discriminator output noise power spectrum $G_n(f)$ is given by

$$G_n(f) = \begin{cases} \dfrac{2k^2 f^2}{A^2}, & 0 \le f \le B; \\ 0, & f > B. \end{cases} \tag{5.30}$$

The resulting parabolic form of the noise spectrum can also be developed by noting from (5.18b) that the phase noise spectrum must have the same form as that of $x_c(t)$, i.e., flat up to $B$ cps, and hence that the power spectrum of the time derivative $\theta'(t)$ of the instantaneous phase, i.e., the frequency noise power spectrum, must have an $f^2$ dependence (see Art. 2.4).

The ultimate FM baseband noise output is obtained by integrating (5.30) over the transfer function of a low-pass filter appropriate to accommodating the spectrum of the desired message $m(t)$. If for the present we assume a zonal, i.e., rectangular-cutoff, baseband filter of bandwidth $B_m$, then

$$N_{\text{out}, \, lp} = \frac{2k^2}{A^2} \int_0^{B_m} f^2 \, df = \frac{2k^2 B_m^3}{3A^2}. \tag{5.31}$$

We shall return later to a consideration of the noise output which results with other forms of baseband filtering.

### Effect of Modulation

An unmodulated carrier has been used in the foregoing analysis. We must next inquire what happens, if anything, when the carrier is modulated, i.e., shifted away from the center of the IF noise spectrum. This is necessary in order to be certain that (5.31) properly applies to calculating the actual output message-to-noise ratio.

Thus, consider the situation shown in Fig. 5.4(b); we already know what results from the symmetrical part of the IF noise spectrum shown shaded in Fig. 5.4(a). From Fig. 5.4(b) we have for the resultant of carrier plus antisymmetrical noise

$E_b(t) = A \sin 2\pi(f_c - f_D)t$

$\qquad + x_c(t) \cos 2\pi(f_c + B - f_D)t$

$\qquad - x_s(t) \sin 2\pi(f_c + B - f_D)t,$

$$(5.32)$$

where $f_D$ is the frequency deviation of the carrier from the center frequency $f_c$. Expanding the terms involving $(f_c + B - f_D)$ and discarding those which are in phase with the carrier $A \sin 2\pi$ $(f_c - f_D)t$ because of limiter action, we find for the discriminator input corresponding to Fig. 5.4(b)

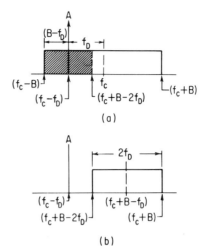

FIGURE 5.4 Input noise spectra for modulated FM.

$E_{LB}(t) = A \sin 2\pi(f_c - f_D)t$

$\qquad + [x_c(t) \cos 2\pi Bt$

$\qquad - x_s(t) \sin 2\pi Bt] \cos 2\pi(f_c - f_D)t.$ $\qquad\qquad (5.33)$

Note that both the in-phase and quadrature components $x_s(t)$ and $x_c(t)$ of the antisymmetrical noise spectrum must be considered.

For high carrier-to-noise ratio, the phase $\theta_b(t)$, with respect to the carrier, of the wave of (5.33) is

$$\theta_b(t) \cong \frac{1}{A} [x_c(t) \cos 2\pi Bt - x_s(t) \sin 2\pi Bt] \qquad (5.34)$$

and its instantaneous frequency deviation $\theta'_b(t)$ is

$$\theta'_b(t) = \frac{1}{A} \{-2\pi B[x_s(t) \cos 2\pi Bt - x_c(t) \sin 2\pi Bt]$$
$$- x'_s(t) \sin 2\pi Bt + x'_c(t) \cos 2\pi Bt\}. \qquad (5.35)$$

The mean-square value of $\theta'_b(t)$, i.e., the output noise power, is found to be

$$\overline{\theta'^2_b(t)} = \frac{1}{2A^2} \overline{\{4\pi^2 B^2 [x^2_s(t) + x^2_c(t)] + x'^2_s(t) + x'^2_c(t)\}}. \qquad (5.36)$$

Proceeding in the same manner as previously, using the relationships

$$\overline{x^2_s(t)} = \overline{x^2_c(t)} = 2k^2 f_D, \quad \text{and} \quad R_{x_s}(\Delta t) = R_{x_c}(\Delta t) = 2k^2 f_D \frac{\sin 2\pi f_D \Delta t}{2\pi f_D \Delta t},$$

where the covariance functions are needed to evaluate $\overline{x'^2_s(t)}$ and $\overline{x'^2_c(t)}$, we have

$$\overline{\theta_b'^2(t)} = \frac{8\pi^2 k^2}{A^2}\left(B^2 f_D + \frac{f_D^3}{3}\right) \tag{5.37}$$

and hence that

$$
\begin{aligned}
N_{\text{out},b} &= \frac{1}{4\pi^2}\overline{\theta_b'^2(t)} \\
&= \frac{2k^2}{A^2}\left(B^2 f_D + \frac{f_D^3}{3}\right).
\end{aligned} \tag{5.38}
$$

If we take the form of the discriminator noise output power spectrum as $G_{nb}(f) = K_b f^2$ and note that

$$
\begin{aligned}
N_{\text{out},b} &= K_b \int_{B-f_D}^{B+f_D} f^2 \, df = \frac{K_b}{3}[(B+f_D)^3 - (B-f_D)^3] \\
&= 2K_b\left(B^2 f_D + \frac{f_D^3}{3}\right)
\end{aligned} \tag{5.39}
$$

then the constant $K_b$ is found, by comparing (5.38) and (5.39), to be $K_b = k^2/A^2$, and the discriminator output noise power spectrum corresponding to Fig. 5.4(b) is thus given by

$$G_{nb}(f) = \frac{k^2 f^2}{A^2}, \qquad (B-f_D) \leq f \leq (B+f_D). \tag{5.40}$$

The part of the output noise power spectrum corresponding to the symmetrical shaded area in Fig. 5.4(a) is, from (5.30),

$$G_{na}(f) = \frac{2k^2 f^2}{A^2}, \qquad 0 \leq f \leq (B-f_D). \tag{5.41}$$

The total output noise power spectrum is $G_n(f) = G_{na}(f) + G_{nb}(f)$ from (5.40) and (5.41), and is seen to be discontinuous by a factor of two at the baseband frequency $(B - f_D)$ as depicted in Fig. 5.5. However, if the message filter bandwidth $B_m$ satisfies $B_m \leq (B - f_D)$, or alternately

$$B \geq (f_D + B_m), \tag{5.42}$$

a frequently used rule-of-thumb (see Art. 5.1), then the discontinuity does not matter and (5.31) does yield the correct result for baseband output noise power.

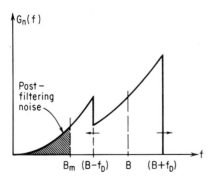

FIGURE 5.5 Baseband noise spectrum: modulated FM.

### Wideband Improvement

We are now prepared to calculate the FM output message-to-noise ratio, assuming that (5.42) is satisfied. Let the instantaneous frequency deviation caused by the message be given by

$$\theta'_m = 2\pi f_D m(t), \tag{5.43}$$

where we assume that $|m(t)|$ never exceeds unity so that $f_D$ is the peak frequency deviation in cps. Using 1-volt-per-cps discriminator sensitivity as before, the message output power is

$$S_{\text{out}} = \frac{1}{4\pi^2} \overline{\theta'^2_m(t)} = f_D^2 \overline{m^2(t)}, \tag{5.44}$$

and using (5.31), the output message-to-noise ratio is thus

$$(S/N)_{\text{out}, FM} = \frac{3A^2 f_D^2 \overline{m^2(t)}}{2k^2 B_m^3}; \tag{5.45}$$

multiplying (5.45) by $B_{IF}/B_{IF}$ and noting $N_{\text{in}} = k^2 B_{IF}$ and $S_{\text{in}} = A^2/2$ yields

$$(S/N)_{\text{out}, FM} = \frac{3 f_D^2 B_{IF} \overline{m^2(t)}}{B_m^3} (S/N)_{\text{in}, FM}, \tag{5.46}$$

where $B_{IF} = 2B$. With a full-load test tone $m(t) = \sin \omega_1 t$ for the message,

$$S_{\text{out}} = \frac{1}{2} f_D^2, \tag{5.47}$$

and (5.46) becomes the familiar form

$$(S/N)_{\text{out}, FM} = 3D^2 \left( \frac{B_{IF}}{2B_m} \right) (S/N)_{\text{in}, FM}, \tag{5.48}$$

where the deviation ratio $D = f_D/B_m$. It is important to note that the deviation ratio $D$ is determined by the bandwidth $B_m$ of a zonal post-detection (baseband) filter, and is *not* related to the sinusoidal message frequency $f_1 = \omega_1/2\pi$, except insofar as the low-pass post-detection filter is usually chosen so as to pass the spectrum of the desired message; this is merely a matter of consistent design. The sinusoidal message frequency $f_1$ could be chosen anywhere from 0 to $B_m$, and (5.48) would still yield the same result, as long as the baseband filter bandwidth $B_m$ remains unchanged.

Another common form of (5.48) makes use of a comparison double-sideband AM system with $B_{IF, AM} = 2B_m$ so as to accommodate the same message bandwidth as the FM system. Thus

$$N_{\text{in}, AM} = \frac{2B_m}{B_{IF, FM}} N_{\text{in}, FM} \tag{5.49}$$

so that

$$(S/N)_{\text{out},FM} = 3D^2(S/N)_{\text{in,out},AM}. \qquad (5.50)$$

The term "FM improvement" is commonly applied to the factor $3D^2$ in (5.50).

### Baseband Filter

Since zonal filters are physically unrealizable, a further interpretation of the quantity $B_m$ is desirable. Specifically, if the actual baseband filter or other data-processing device, such as a keyed integrator, has a voltage transfer function $Y(f)$, then an effective post-detection noise bandwidth $B'_m$ can be defined by

$$\int_0^{B'_m} G_n(f)\, df = \int_0^\infty |Y(f)|^2 G_n(f)\, df. \qquad (5.51)$$

In effect, (5.51) defines the bandwidth of a fictitious zonal baseband filter for use in (5.31) and (5.46), on the basis of output noise power equal to that delivered by the actual baseband filter $Y(f)$, operating on the actual system post-detection noise spectrum. It is important to note that the demodulator output noise power spectrum $G_n(f)$ is a factor affecting the definition of $B'_m$, and since the shape of this noise spectrum generally is different for various modulation methods, a universal definition of the equivalent noise bandwidth $B'_m$ cannot be given solely in terms of the filter transfer function $Y(f)$.

Actually the upper limit of the right-hand integral in (5.51) should be $B$, one-half the IF bandwidth. However in FM systems, $B$ is ordinarily much greater than the message bandwidth or the pass band of the baseband filter, and an extension of the range of integration to infinity usually introduces little error; furthermore, this makes the integral much easier to evaluate.

In case we assume a Butterworth (maximally-flat amplitude) form for the baseband filter function $Y(f)$,

$$Y(f) = \left[1 + \left(\frac{f}{f_0}\right)^{2k}\right]^{-1/2}, \qquad (5.52)$$

where $f_0$ is the 3-db filter bandwidth and $k$ is the number of poles of $Y(f)$ (cutoff rate $= 6k$ db/octave), then from an evaluation of (5.51), (5.48) becomes

$$(S/N)_{\text{out},FM} = \frac{2k}{\pi} \sin\left(\frac{3\pi}{2k}\right) D_0^2 \left(\frac{B_{IF}}{2f_0}\right) (S/N)_{\text{in},FM}, \qquad (5.53)$$

where we define $D_0 = f_D/f_0$. The ratio (in db) of $(S/N)_{\text{out},FM}$ from (5.48) and (5.53) is plotted in Fig. 5.6. It is evident that if $n$ is

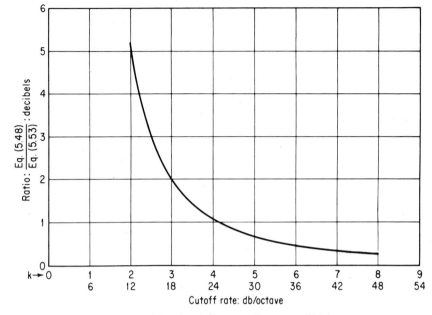

FIGURE 5.6 Effect of baseband filter cutoff rate on FM improvement.

small, i.e., the baseband filter rolls off gradually, then the performance of an FM system is substantially inferior to that indicated by use of (5.48) with $B_m = f_0$. For example, with $k = 2$, corresponding to 12 db per octave cutoff, the difference is 5.2 db, or a factor of 3.3 in power.

In commercial FM broadcasting we find a special case where the characteristics of the baseband filter must be taken into account. Here a 75 microsecond preemphasis-deemphasis characteristic is used, corresponding to the addition of a single-pole (RC) low-pass filter, which is down 3 db at $f_0 = 2120$ cps, to whatever other sharp-cutoff baseband filter as may be used. Accordingly, let the total baseband filter transfer function be

$$|Y(f)| = \begin{cases} \left[1 + \left(\dfrac{f}{f_0}\right)^2\right]^{-1/2}, & 0 \le f \le B_a; \\ 0, & f > B_a; \end{cases} \tag{5.54}$$

i.e., an RC de-emphasis filter cascaded with an essentially zonal low-pass filter of bandwidth $B_a$ equal to the highest audio frequency of interest (about 15 Kc). Then from (5.51) we find for the effective noise bandwidth $B_m'$ to be used in place of $B_m$ in (5.46) or (5.48)

$$\frac{2k^2 B_m'^3}{3A^2} = \frac{2k^2}{A^2} \int_0^{B_a} \frac{f^2\, df}{1 + (f/f_0)^2},$$

$$B_m' = f_0 \left[ \frac{3B_a}{f_0} - 3 \tan^{-1}\left(\frac{B_a}{f_0}\right) \right]^{1/3}$$

(5.55)

In (5.55) we use $B_a$ instead of $B$ or infinity for the upper limit of integration because of the assumed presence of a nearly zonal baseband filter of this bandwidth. Substituting $B_a = 15$ Kc and $f_0 = 2.12$ Kc in (5.55) yields $B_m' = 5.45$ Kc. Then from (5.46) it is seen that an additional increase in message-to-noise ratio equal to $30 \log_{10}(15/5.45) = 13.2$ db is obtained by the use of the 75-microsecond pre-emphasis-de-emphasis characteristic.

## 5.3    THRESHOLD EFFECTS IN FM

It is apparent from (5.47) and (5.48) that the output message-to-noise ratio of an FM system can be much greater than the input carrier-to-noise ratio. Since the peak frequency deviation $f_D$ can be comparable to $B$, one half the IF bandwidth, this improvement in signal-to-noise ratio is of the order of magnitude of $(B/B_m)^3$. However, the equations upon which this observation is based, were derived using approximations which are valid only under high carrier-to-noise ratio conditions. Actually, below a certain critical or *threshold* value of input carrier-to-noise ratio, the performance of an FM system deteriorates very rapidly. Furthermore, because of the large improvement in signal-to-noise ratio which can be realized in FM systems, satisfactory reception quality is obtainable at carrier-to-noise ratios in the neighborhood of the threshold region. Therefore, the threshold characteristics of FM systems assume far greater significance than is the case in AM, which does not exhibit a wideband improvement. In fact, in a great many instances threshold considerations largely govern FM system design.

The detailed mathematical analysis of the threshold and below-threshold performance of FM systems is extremely complicated, and beyond the scope of this book. However, we can use the results of published analyses,[†] supplemented by some qualitative notions, to develop the essential information concerning the threshold characteristics of FM systems.[‡]

[†] See Rice (II, III), Stumpers (I).

[‡] Neither shall we consider the moderate threshold suppression offered by phase-lock and FM-feedback techniques. See, for example, Develet, Enloe, and other references at end of chapter.

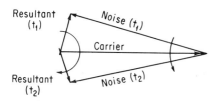

FIGURE 5.7 FM phasor diagram: threshold.

Fundamentally, FM threshold effects begin to appear when, with significant probability, the Rayleigh-distributed envelope of the IF noise alone can exceed the carrier amplitude. Under these circumstances, the situation depicted by Fig. 5.7 occasionally arises, where the noise (visualized in envelope-and-phase form) almost cancels the carrier. Then only a small change in the relative phase of noise and carrier, which can occur in a short time, causes the resultant almost to reverse instantaneous phase in the same short period. Thus during this event, the instantaneous frequency deviation (identified with phasor angular velocity) of the resultant is quite large, and the discriminator output correspondingly exhibits a "spike." The fact that the output noise of an FM receiver assumes a rather impulsive character in the threshold region is descriptively termed the "splutter effect"; this is very distinctive aurally, and has probably been heard by all who experience fringe-area FM reception.

The tendency of FM baseband noise toward an impulsive nature under threshold conditions correspondingly reflects changes in the output noise power spectrum. Recognizing that the spectrum of an impulsive waveform is broad and relatively uniform with respect to zero frequency, we can correctly anticipate that a more-or-less flat component arises in the output FM noise power spectrum, modifying the purely parabolic form exhibited at high carrier-to-noise ratios. Quantitatively, it is found that such changes in the post-detection FM noise spectrum begin to appear in the neighborhood of 10 db IF carrier-to-noise ratio, and become progressively more dominant below this point, as illustrated by Fig. 5.8.

In order to find the effective output noise power, it is necessary to integrate the spectra shown by Fig. 5.8 up to the maximum baseband frequency of interest; we assume a zonal post-detection filter for this purpose, and can perform the integration graphically. The result of this procedure is shown in Fig. 5.9. We assume that the spectrum of the modulating waveform in all instances falls entirely within the bandwidth of the baseband filter $B_m$, and vary the bandwidth ratio $B/B_m$ by changing $B_m$. The abscissa scale presumes a constant IF bandwidth $2B$, and since we are interested only in threshold effects, the ordinate scale of Fig. 5.9 uses an

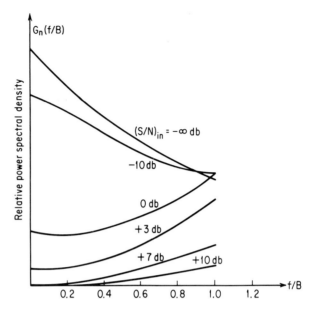

FIGURE 5.8 FM baseband noise power spectra.

arbitrary reference; however, a modulation-suppression effect which occurs at low carrier-to-noise ratios is taken into account.[†] The threshold carrier-to-noise ratio is defined as that at which the output message-to-noise ratio falls 0.5 db below the value which would be obtained on the basis of high carrier-to-noise ratio assumptions.

It is seen that the threshold carrier-to-noise ratio depends on the ratio of IF-to-baseband bandwidth $2B/B_m$. As shown by the heavy dashed line in Fig. 5.9, we can write that the threshold carrier-to-noise ratio is given, in decibels, by

$$(S/N)_{in,th} = 5 + 5 \log_{10} (B/B_m): \text{decibels},\qquad(5.56a)$$

or in numeric terms by

$$(S/N)_{in,th} = \sqrt{10B/B_m}: \text{numeric}.\qquad(5.56b)$$

Equations (5.56a, b) hold within 1 db for bandwidth ratios in the range $1 \le B/B_m \le 100$, which represents the vast majority of all FM applications.

Qualitatively, the dependence of the threshold carrier-to-noise ratio on the IF-to-baseband bandwidth ratio is the result of the approximately flat nature of the component of the post-detection

† See Stumpers (I).

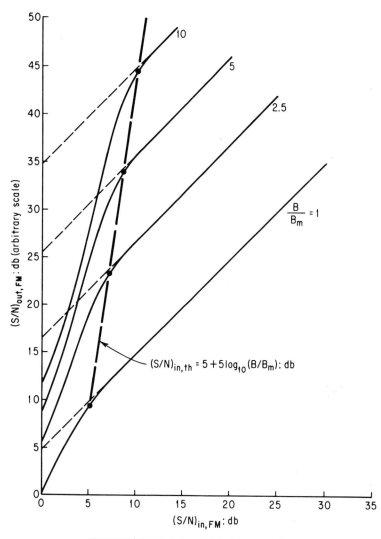

FIGURE 5.9 FM threshold characteristics.

noise spectrum which arises at low carrier-to-noise ratios. Obviously this component will have an earlier significance, i.e., at higher carrier-to-noise ratios, compared to the parabolic component, for higher bandwidth-ratio FM systems wherein the parabolic component of the noise spectrum is relatively weaker within the narrow post-detection bandwidth. Hence FM systems with a high deviation ratio, which implies a large ratio $B/B_m$, require a higher value of input carrier-to-noise ratio to realize the full wideband improvement than do lower deviation-ratio systems.

The threshold effect is why one cannot increase the output message-to-noise ratio of an FM system indefinitely simply by increasing the frequency deviation, for a corresponding increase in IF bandwidth and hence in input noise is also necessary. Ultimately the point of threshold carrier-to-noise ratio is reached below which, because of the rapid deterioration in performance with decreasing carrier-to-noise ratio, little further improvement can be obtained. Conversely, if an FM system is below threshold, a relatively modest increase in transmitted power will yield a more-than-proportionate improvement in system performance. Because of the threshold effect, it actually turns out that the minimum-power FM system is one for which the modulation parameters are chosen so that the specified level of reception quality is achieved in the close neighborhood of the threshold carrier-to-noise ratio. Missile and space-probe telemetry is an obvious example where minimum-power system optimization is desirable.

## 5.4  INTERFERENCE IN FM SYSTEMS

We have seen that FM systems are capable of effecting a substantial suppression of input noise, in the sense that the output message-to-noise ratio generally is considerably higher than the input (IF) carrier-to-noise ratio. A similar kind of suppression also takes place with respect to co-channel interference, as can be appreciated by visualizing noise, expressed in a narrow-band envelope-and-phase form, simply as co-channel interference. We shall now discuss co-channel interference effects in FM, the primary difference from the noise problem being that now the amplitude of the disturbance is constant rather than Rayleigh-distributed.

Consider the situation in which interference is caused by another sinusoidal signal which lies within or not very far outside the IF passband. Thus we have the desired and interfering carriers with amplitudes $A$ and $aA$ $(a < 1)$, at frequencies $\omega_c$ and $\omega_c + r$ respectively. We assume that these signals are unmodulated in amplitude, and that their frequency modulations are sufficiently slow relative to the difference frequency $r$, so that the signal frequencies and amplitudes (where the interference falls on the sloping side of the IF selectivity characteristic) do not change appreciably during several cycles of the phenomena which occur at the beat frequency.

The resultant signal can thus be expressed as

$$E(t) = A \sin \omega_c t + aA \sin (\omega_c + r)t$$
$$= V(t) \sin [\omega_c t + \theta(t)], \qquad (5.57)$$

where the phase angle $\theta(t)$, in which we are interested after limiting, is given by

$$\theta(t) = \sin^{-1}\left[\frac{a \sin rt}{\sqrt{1 + a^2 + 2a \cos rt}}\right]. \qquad (5.58)$$

This relationship is evident on inspection of the phasor diagram shown in Fig. 5.10. The discriminator output (assuming sufficient bandwidth) is given by the time derivative of $\theta(t)$ as expressed by (5.58); thus

$$\theta'(t) = ar\left(\frac{a + \cos rt}{1 + a^2 + 2a \cos rt}\right). \qquad (5.59)$$

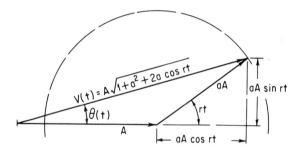

FIGURE 5.10 Phasor diagram: FM co-channel interference.

Equation (5.59) is plotted in Fig. 5.11 for $a = 0.8$. Clearly the net change in phase of the resultant signal over any complete cycle of the difference frequency is equal to the phase change acquired by the stronger signal. Therefore the *average frequency* of the resultant signal is exactly equal to that of the stronger component. The "spikes" occur when the two interfering signals are nearly out of phase, i.e., $rt \cong \pi$, and the resultant signal experiences a rapid change of phase.

It is important to note that both the magnitude and the period of the disturbance created by co-channel interference depend on the difference frequency $r$. This quantity is thus a very important parameter with respect to the severity of co-channel interference. For example, if the difference frequency lies outside the bandwidth

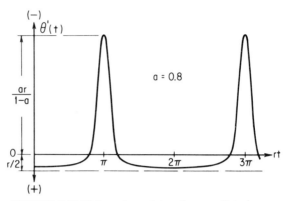

FIGURE 5.11 FM co-channel interference disturbance.

occupied by the desired message (assumed to be conveyed by the stronger carrier) then the effects of interference can be completely eliminated by a sharp-cutoff baseband filter (assuming perfect limiting and low noise conditions).

If $r$ falls within the expected message bandwidth, then two factors can combine to reduce the intensity of the disturbance. First, as in commercial FM broadcasting, the use of pre-emphasis-de-emphasis techniques permits some discrimination to be made against the fundamental difference frequency and its harmonics. Second, the magnitude of the disturbance, and hence that of each of its harmonics, varies proportionately to the difference frequency $r$. Thus even with $r$ well within the message bandwidth, the increased number of disturbance harmonics which cannot be completely rejected by baseband filtering does not imply a proportionate increase in the net effect of the interference.

The total result of the co-channel interference characteristics discussed above—first that the average resultant frequency is identical to that of the stronger signal, and second that the disturbance created by interference can often be greatly reduced by appropriate post-detection filtering—leads to the "capture" effect in FM. Specifically, if we were to apply two carriers to an FM receiver, within its bandwidth, each sinusoidally modulated in order to identify its contribution to the detected output, and plot the strengths of each of the output tones as a function of the carrier amplitude ratio, we would typically find a characteristic such as shown in Fig. 5.12. Note that at relative carrier levels of the order of 3 db, the output contribution due to the weaker carrier is almost

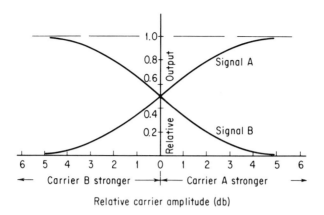

FIGURE 5.12 FM capture characteristics.

completely suppressed, and that of the stronger virtually unaffected. This narrow range of relative strengths over which one or the other carrier becomes predominant results in the descriptive term "capture effect."


## 5.5   CONCLUDING REMARKS

In this chapter we have developed the essential characteristics of frequency modulation, finding that FM is capable of providing a large measure of immunity to the effects of noise and interference. Although we treated only the gaussian noise case, the same observation also holds for impulsive noise such as is generated by automotive ignition systems. However, the wide variety of impulsive noise disturbances, and the lack of a convenient general statistical description for them, largely precludes undertaking an exact analysis of this problem. In a sense, though, one can regard impulsive noise as pulsed interference, which becomes suppressed in FM by the stronger-signal capture effect.

With all the advantages that FM has to offer, one might inquire why this technique is not used exclusively. The answer is that in order to obtain the performance benefits of FM, one must pay a significant price in bandwidth. Commonly the RF bandwidth occupied by an FM system is many times that of the message to be conveyed; for example, in commercial FM broadcasting, a channel 200 Kc wide is assigned for the transmission of audio messages of about 15 Kc bandwidth (disregarding stereo). A bandwidth expansion factor of at least 10 is thus customary, and in transcontinental FM microwave relay networks a bandwidth ratio as large as 100 might be found. This represents a fairly extravagant expenditure of a strictly limited natural resource: spectrum space. There are many applications for which the superior performance characteristics of wideband FM are not required, e.g., military communications, but wherein a critical demand exists to accommodate the maximum possible number of users. In such cases, narrow-band transmission techniques such as SSSC are more appropriately used. Moreover, there are other instances, e.g., ionospheric high-frequency circuits, where natural factors such as path dispersion preclude the successful use of a wideband FM signal.† We thus find that whereas FM is an extremely attractive technique from many standpoints, it has drawbacks as well; again neither FM nor any other modulation scheme represents the panacea for all of man's communication problems.

REFERENCES

Assadourian, F., "Distortion of a Frequency-Modulated Signal by Small Loss and Phase Variations," *Proc. IRE*, **40** (February 1952).

Baghdady, E. J.
(I) "Frequency-Modulation Interference Rejection with Narrow-Band Limiters," *Proc. IRE*, **43** (January 1955).
(II) "Theory of Low-Distortion Reproduction of FM Signals in Linear Systems," *IRE Trans. on Circuit Theory*, **CT-5** (September 1958).
(III) "FM Demodulator Time-Constant Requirements for Interference Rejection," *Proc. IRE*, **46** (February 1958).
(IV) "Theory of Stronger-Signal Capture in FM Reception," *Proc. IRE*, **46** (April 1958).
(V) *Lectures on Communication System Theory*. McGraw-Hill, New York, 1961.

Bedrosian, E.
(II) "The Analytic Signal Representation of Modulated Waveforms," *Proc. IRE*, **50** (October 1962).

Bennett, W.R.
(I) "Methods of Solving Noise Problems," *Proc. IRE*, **44** (May 1956).

Blachman, N. M.
(I) "The Output Signal-to-Noise Ratio of a Power-Law Device," *J. Appl. Phys.*, **24** (June 1953).

† See, for example, Corrington (II), Meyers.

(II) "The Demodulation of an FM Carrier and Random Noise by a Limiter and Discriminator," *J. Appl. Phys.*, **20** (January 1949).

Black, H. S., *Modulation Theory*. Van Nostrand, Princeton, N.J., 1953.

Cahn, C. R., "A Note on Signal-to-Noise Ratio in Band-Pass Limiters," *IRE Trans. on Information Theory*, **IT-7** (January 1961).

Carson, J. R., and T. C. Fry, "Variable-Frequency Electric Circuit Theory," *Bell Sys. Tech. J.*, **16** (October 1937).

Corrington, M. S.
(I) "Variation of Bandwidth with Modulation Index in Frequency Modulation" *Proc. IRE*, **35** (October 1947).
(II) "Frequency-Modulation Distortion Caused by Multipath Transmission," *Proc. IRE*, **33** (December 1945).

Crosby, M. G., "Frequency Modulation Noise Characteristics," *Proc. IRE*, **25** (April 1937).

Davenport, W. B., Jr., "Signal-to-Noise Ratios in Band-Pass Limiters," *J. Appl. Phys.*, **24** (June 1953) [see also Blachman (I)].

Develet, J. A., Jr.
(II) "Threshold Criterion for Phase-Lock Demodulation," *Proc. IEEE*, **51** (February 1963).

Enloe, L. H., "Decreasing the Threshold in FM by Frequency Feedback," *Proc. IRE*, **50** (January 1962).

Gerlach, A. A., "Distortion-Band-Pass Considerations in Angular Modulation," *Proc. IRE*, **38** (October 1950).

Goldman, S.
(II) *Frequency Analysis, Modulation, and Noise.* McGraw-Hill, New York, 1948.

Heitzman, R. E., "A Study of the Threshold Power Requirements of FMFB Receivers," *IRE Trans. on Space Electronics and Telemetry*, **SET-8** (December 1962).

Hupert, J. J., "Normalized Phase and Gain Derivatives as an Aid in Evaluation of FM Distortion," *Proc. IRE*, **42** (February 1954).

Jaffee, R., and R. Rechtin, "Design and Performance of Phase-Lock Circuits Capable of Near-Optimum Performance Over a Wide Range of Input Signal and Noise Levels," *IRE Trans. on Information Theory*, **IT-1** (March 1955).

Jahnke, E., and F. Emde, *Tables of Functions*, 4th ed. Dover, New York, 1945.

Landon, V. D.
(I) "Impulse Noise in FM Reception," *Electronics*, **14** (February 1941).

Lawson, J. L., and G. E. Uhlenbeck, *Threshold Signals*, MIT Rad. Lab. Series, Vol. 24. McGraw-Hill, New York, 1950.

Loughlin, B. D., "The Theory of Amplitude-Modulation Rejection in the Ratio Detector," *Proc. IRE*, **40** (March 1952).

Margolis, S. G., "The Response of a Phase-Locked Loop to a Sinusoid Plus Noise," *IRE Trans. on Information Theory*, **IT-3** (June 1957).

Meyers, S. T., "Nonlinearity of Frequency Modulation Radio Systems Due to Multipath Propagation," *Proc. IRE*, **34** (May 1946).

Middleton, D.
(I) *An Introduction to Statistical Communication Theory*. McGraw-Hill, New York, 1960.

Mullen, J. A., and D. Middleton, "Limiting forms of FM Noise Spectra," *Proc. IRE*, **45** (December 1957).

Rice, S. O.
(II) "Statistical Properties of a Sine-Wave Plus Random Noise," *Bell Sys. Tech. J.*, **27** (January 1948).

(III) "Noise in FM Receivers," *Proc. Symposium on Time Series Analysis*, M. Rosenblatt, ed., Wiley, 1963.

Rowe, H. E., "Distortion of Angle-Modulated Waves by Linear Networks," *IRE Trans. on Circuit Theory*, **CT-9** (September 1962).

Ruthroff C. L., and W. F. Bodtman, "Design and Performance of a Broad-Band FM Demodulator with Frequency Compression," *Proc. IRE*, **50** (December, 1962).

Schwartz, M., *Information Transmission, Modulation, and Noise*. McGraw-Hill, New York, 1959.

Stewart, J. L., "The Power Spectrum of a Carrier Frequency Modulated by Gaussian Noise," *Proc. IRE*, **42** (October 1954).

Stumpers, F. L. H. M.
(I) "Theory of Frequency-Modulation Noise," *Proc. IRE*, **36** (September 1948).
(II) "Distortion of Frequency-Modulated Signals in Electrical Networks," *Communication News*, **9** (April 1948).

Van der Pol, B., "The Fundamental Principles of Frequency Modulation," *J. IRE* (London), **93**, pt. 3 (May 1946).

Ward, R. C., "FM Noise Spectra," *Proc. IRE*, **45** (December 1957).

Wilmotte, R. M., "Reduction of FM Interference in FM Receivers by Feedback Across the Limiter," *Proc. IRE*, **40** (January 1952).

Zweig, F., P. M. Schultheiss, and C. A. Wogrin, "On the Response of Linear Systems to Signals Modulated in Both Amplitude and Frequency," *IRE Trans. on Circuit Theory*, **CT-2** (December 1955).

# PART 3  Multiplex and Discrete Systems

To this point we have considered linear and exponential modulation processes, and the effect of noise thereon, as though only a single message were to be conveyed. Also we have implicitly visualized modulation by and recovery of the entire message waveform in a literal sense. Fundamental insight has thus been gained into the characteristics of common modulation techniques, and the methods of applying mathematical models to the calculation of their performance in the presence of noise.

However, many communication missions are not so elementary; for example, in long-distance telephone transmission and in radio-telemetry practice, it is common to *multiplex* several hundred distinct voice messages or channels of data onto a single radio-frequency carrier. *Multiplexing* is the generic term which is used to refer to obtaining such a multichannel capability upon a single RF resource.† As we shall shortly see, multiplexing can be carried out either in the fre-

† See Zadeh and Miller.

quency domain, as *frequency-division multiplexing* (FDM), or in the time domain, as *time-division multiplexing* (TDM).

In essence, all multiplexing schemes involve modulating some property of a *subcarrier* with a message; multichannel capability is then achieved by combining the requisite number of subcarriers into a single waveform, which in turn modulates the RF carrier. The subcarriers must, of course, be combined in such a way that they can be separated without mutual interference after being recovered by demodulation of the RF carrier. The subcarriers are thus said to be *orthogonal*; orthogonality can be achieved either in the frequency domain or in the time domain.

In FDM, the modulation methods that have already become familiar are largely used at the subcarrier level. In TDM, however, advantage is taken of the fact that it is not necessary to transmit an entire literal message waveform; a sequence of *discrete time samples* thereof suffices under well-known restrictions which we shall thoroughly explore. Further, in TDM, one may choose to represent uniquely only a set of *discrete levels* of the instantaneous message waveform; this process is known as *quantizing*, and is the basis for coded, or *pulse code modulation* (PCM). Such discrete-level representations of a message are also commonly grouped under the term *digital*, in contrast to *analog* representations where a continuous input-output relationship is used. Digital message coding permits some special modulation techniques to be used to substantial advantage.

A great variety of multiple subcarrier-carrier modulation combinations can be applied to the synthesis of a multiplex communication system. It would be scarcely profitable to analyze all of them in detail.† However, in this part we shall thoroughly consider several multiplexing formats that embody the principles involved; from an understanding of these, the reader will be prepared to calculate the performance of practically any other system with which he may be confronted. We shall draw extensively upon the material already presented.

A word now about nomenclature convention. First, we shall extensively abbreviate reference to various modulation processes, e.g., AM, FM, SSSC, etc. Second, in multiplexing at least two modulation processes are involved, first of a subcarrier by message information, and then of an RF carrier by the modulated subcarriers. We shall designate multiple modulation processes in this order, from messages to subcarrier(s) to carrier. Thus, for example, SSSC-FM means that first the subcarriers are single-sideband suppressed-carrier amplitude-modulated, then the subcarriers frequency-modulate the RF carrier.

† See, for example, Landon (II), Nichols and Rauch, Sanders, Stiltz, Watt.

# Chapter Six

# Frequency-Division Multiplexing

In frequency-division multiplexing (FDM), a multichannel capability is obtained by modulating a different subcarrier frequency by each message which is to be conveyed. The term frequency-division is descriptive of the partitioning of the RF baseband into a number of channels, one per subcarrier. Orthogonality of the subcarriers is obtained through their distribution in frequency, and linear filtering is used to separate the individual subcarriers after their group recovery by demodulation of the RF carrier. Figure 6.1 illustrates the essential elements of an FDM multichannel communication system.

In this chapter we shall consider two FDM techniques: SSSC-FM and FM-FM. The first is extensively used in long-haul telephone communications and the second has for many years represented standard radio-telemetry practice.

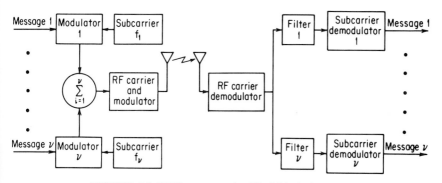

FIGURE 6.1 FDM system—simplified block diagram.

## 6.1   SSSC-FM

In SSSC-FM, each of a sequence of sinusoidal subcarriers is single-sideband suppressed-carrier amplitude-modulated, one by each message to be transmitted. The subcarriers are then linearly combined into a single composite waveform which frequency-modulates the RF carrier. Typically, all of the messages are limited to the same bandwidth, e. g., about 4 Kc (including guard bands) in voice telephony applications, and the SSSC modulation process may be viewed simply as frequency translation of the messages, each to an otherwise unoccupied channel in the RF baseband spectrum. As shown in Fig. 6.1, band-pass filters are used at the receiving terminal to separate the message channels, and synchronous demodulators serve to effect final message recovery. The process of synchronously demodulating a number of SSSC subcarriers is usually controlled by transmitting an unmodulated pilot subcarrier, by direct FM of the RF carrier, from which all of the needed demodulator reference frequencies can be derived by frequency division and multiplication techniques. We shall not further elaborate the detailed technology of implementing SSSC-FM systems, but simply note that it is common practice to transmit 600 or more voice messages on a single RF carrier by this technique. Our principal concern is to analyze theoretically the role of noise in SSSC-FM, and to show how this consideration governs the proportioning of the modulation parameters of an SSSC-FM system.

It is first necessary to recall some results from Chapters Four and Five. First, the input and output signal-to-noise ratios are equal for synchronously demodulated SSSC; from (4.38)

$$(S/N)_{\text{out},S} = \frac{P_{SBS}}{N_{\text{in}}}. \tag{6.1}$$

Second, in FM the above-threshold baseband noise power spectrum is parabolic in form; from (5.30), for 1-volt-per-cps deviation discriminator sensitivity

$$G_{n,\,FM}(f) = \frac{2k^2 f^2}{A^2}, \qquad 0 \le f \le B. \tag{6.2}$$

Third, the message output power in FM is proportional to the square of the carrier frequency deviation; from (5.44)

$$S_{\text{out}} = f_D^2 \overline{m^2(t)}. \tag{6.3}$$

In SSSC-FM, the quantity $m(t)$ appearing in (6.3) is actually the sum of a number $\nu$ of individual SSSC subcarrier channels. We thus index each of these by using the notation $m_i(t)$, $i = 1$, $2, \ldots, \nu$, where each of the $m_i(t)$ is now assumed scaled so that $\overline{m_i^2(t)} = 1$. For purposes of modulating the RF carrier, we associate with each message channel a proportionality factor $K_i$, so that

$$m(t) = \sum_{i=1}^{\nu} K_i m_i(t). \qquad (6.4)$$

Of course, the overmodulation constraint $|m(t)| \leq 1$ (with high probability) applies, and thus a relationship between the peak carrier frequency deviation $f_D$ and the proportionality factors $K_i$ must next be determined.

Since the composite modulating waveform $m(t)$ is a linear sum of $\nu$ SSSC subcarrier channels, where further we assume $\nu \gg 1$ and that the $m_i(t)$ are independent but identically distributed statistically, then from the central limit theorem it is reasonable to postulate that $m(t)$ can be taken as a gaussian variate. The variance $\sigma_m^2$ of this quantity is given from (6.4) by

$$\sigma_m^2 = \sum_{i=1}^{\nu} K_i^2, \qquad (6.5)$$

where we recall (1.39) and that $\overline{m_i^2(t)} = 1$. Further, it is common to regard $3\sigma$ as the "peak" value of a normally distributed (gaussian) variate.[†] Thus we have for the desired relationship between $f_D$ and the $K_i$, with $P[|m(t)| \leq 1] = 0.997$,

$$f_D^2 = 9\sigma_m^2 = 9 \sum_{i=1}^{\nu} K_i^2. \qquad (6.6)$$

The postulate that $m(t)$ is a gaussian variate, used in obtaining the modulation-parameter relationship (6.6), is quite good in FDM voice telephony, where each of the frequency-translated voice messages $m_i(t)$ is itself a relatively gaussian variate.

It is considered good practice in most multiplexing applications to proportion the subcarrier-carrier modulation parameters so that the same quality of service, i. e., ultimate message-to-noise ratio, is provided by all channels. From the facts expressed by (6.1) and (6.2) then, we must evidently calculate the RF baseband noise power which is passed by the $i$th SSSC message channel band-pass filter. This problem is depicted by Fig. 6.2, which shows the parabolic FM baseband noise power spectrum, and the $i$th channel

---

† The probability of exceeding $3\sigma$ is about $3 \times 10^{-3}$. We also used this criterion in Art. 4.4 when considering peak power limitations in SSSC and DSSC.

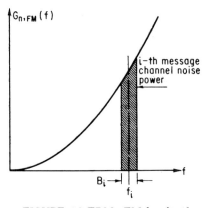

FIGURE 6.2 FDM—FM baseband
noise.

noise as a shaded segment of width $B_i$. Obviously, the higher the baseband frequency at which a message channel is placed, the greater is the associated noise power. Qualitatively, then, equal per-channel message-to-noise ratio requires that the higher-frequency channels more strongly modulate the RF carrier than do the lower-frequency ones. Thus some form of pre-emphasis is necessary in our selection of the set of weighting factors $K_i$.

In SSSC-FM multiplexing, each of the message-channel bandwidths $B_i$ is ordinarily the same, equal to the message bandwidth $B_m$ (including guard bands), and is much smaller than the total baseband bandwidth. Thus the $i$th channel noise power $N_i$ is given with entirely sufficient accuracy by the approximate relationship

$$N_i \cong \frac{2k^2 f_i^2}{A^2} B_m, \qquad (6.7)$$

where in (6.2) we consider $G_{n,FM}(f)$ to be essentially constant, equal to $G_{n,FM}(f_i)$, over the frequency range $\pm B_m/2$ about the message-channel center frequency $f_i$. The error involved by the approximation (6.7) is relatively more significant at the lower baseband frequencies; however, we shall see that other considerations govern the selection of modulation parameters in this region, but do not materially affect the net result which we shall obtain by using (6.7).

The $i$th-channel message power at the output of a 1-volt-per-cps deviation FM carrier discriminator is evidently just $S_i = K_i^2$, remembering $\overline{m_i^2(t)} = 1$, and hence the $i$th channel message-to-noise ratio is

$$\frac{S_i}{N_i} = \frac{A^2 K_i^2}{2k^2 f_i^2 B_m}. \qquad (6.8)$$

Thus for constant message quality over all channels, the weighting factors $K_i$ must be proportional to the channel center frequencies $f_i$; the proportionality depends on the numer $\nu$ and bandwidth $B_m$ of the channels, and the carrier modulation constraint expressed by (6.6).

Therefore let $f_i = iB_m$,† and then we have

$$K_i = Kf_i = KiB_m, \tag{6.9}$$

where the fundamental modulation-parameter constant $K$ is to be determined, given $f_D$, $\nu$, and $B_m$. Thus, substituting from (6.9) into (6.6) yields

$$f_D^2 = 9K^2 B_m^2 \sum_{i=1}^{\nu} i^2. \tag{6.10}$$

From standard arithmetic identities we have

$$\sum_{i=1}^{\nu} i^2 = \frac{\nu(\nu + 1)(2\nu + 1)}{6}, \tag{6.11}$$

and obtain finally from (6.10) and (6.11)

$$K^2 = \frac{2f_D^2}{3B_m^2 \nu(\nu + 1)(2\nu + 1)}. \tag{6.12}$$

From the derived quantity $K$, and the given system constraints $f_D$, $\nu$, and $B_m$, we now can suitably proportion the rms per-channel RF carrier frequency deviations in SSSC-FM FDM, and calculate the service quality, or ultimate message-to-noise ratio, for all channels. An example will best serve to summarize and illustrate this. Let the following system constraints be given:

Peak RF carrier-frequency deviation $= f_D = 4$ Mc
(rms RF carrier-frequency deviation $= f_D/3 = 1.33$ Mc),
Number of message channels $= \nu = 600$,
Message-channel bandwidth (including guard bands) $= B_m = 4$ Kc.

Thus (6.12) yields $K = 0.0392$. From (6.9), for example, the rms RF carrier-frequency deviation due to the highest baseband-frequency message channel is $K_{600} = 94.2$ Kc. By substituting from (6.9) into (6.8), multiplying the *RHS* by $B_{IF}/B_{IF}$, and recognizing $A^2/2k^2 B_{IF} = (S/N)_{\text{in, FM}}$, we obtain for the output message-to-noise ratio of all channels

$$\frac{S_i}{N_i} = K^2 \frac{B_{IF}}{B_m} (S/N)_{\text{in, FM}}. \tag{6.13}$$

Assuming that 10 Mc IF bandwidth will satisfactorily accommodate $\pm 4$ Mc peak carrier-frequency deviation, then (6.13) yields for our example system

$$\frac{S_i}{N_i} = 3.86(S/N)_{\text{in, FM}}. \tag{6.14}$$

† This leaves a baseband space $0 \leq f \leq B_m/2$ vacant below the first message channel. This is commonly used for "order-wire" purposes, i. e., for administrative control of the communication system.

Thus 5.86 db improvement in message-to-noise ratio is obtained in each channel of this particular SSSC-FM FDM system.

We previously mentioned that considerations other than thermal noise actually govern the selection of modulation parameters for the lowest-frequency message channels in SSSC-FM FDM; note that (6.9) would yield only $K_1 = 157$ cps rms carrier-frequency deviation for the first channel of our example system. However, short-term transmitter-frequency instabilities of microphonic and similar origin render it impractical to use such small frequency deviations, and in practice values less than a few kilocycles rms are not attempted. Thus the linear pre-emphasis characteristic specified by (6.9) on the basis of receiver thermal noise considerations alone is modified to become constant at the low baseband frequencies, as shown schematically by Fig. 6.3. It is also noted that this type of pre-emphasis characteristic yields essentially an FM system for low modulating frequencies and (see Art. 5.1) a PM system for high modulating frequencies. The increased carrier-frequency deviation permitted due to the lower-frequency message channels does not significantly affect the modulation parameters that would be calculated for the higher-frequency channels according to the foregoing analysis; two factors account for this. First, relatively few channels fall in the constant-deviation category; if, in our example system of 600 channels, we select 2 Kc as the minimum permissible rms per-channel carrier-frequency deviation, then only the 13 lowest-frequency channels are affected. Thus, second, the total rms carrier-frequency deviation involved is only a very small fraction of the total; again in our example, this is (since the message channels are independent) equal to $2\sqrt{13} = 7.2$ Kc rms, out of $4/3 = 1.33$ Mc rms total.

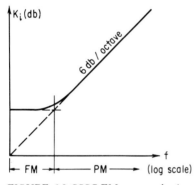

FIGURE 6.3 SSSC-FM pre-emphasis characteristic.

We should finally treat one factor of practical significance to the design and performance of some SSSC-FM FDM systems: this is the channel-activity probability. In FDM voice telephony, for example, a value of 0.25 is considered conservative for this quantity; in essence, if one were to observe a randomly selected SSSC channel at some instant, then the probability of finding it active would be less than 0.25. It is important to realize that this factor does *not* reduce the effective number of channels $v$ by a factor of four,[†] since in general the active channels are uniformly distributed throughout the same wide baseband bandwidth as is required to accommodate *all* of the channels. However, the rms value of the composite modulating waveform $m(t)$ *is* reduced by a factor of $\sqrt{4} = 2$. Thus the modulation parameter $K$ can be increased by a factor of about two, relative to that calculated for the all-channels-active condition, without incurring significant risk of overdeviating the RF carrier frequency. In a 600-channel system with a channel-activity probability of 0.25, for example, the binomial probability distribution (1.10) yields (using tables)

$$P(n \leq 183;\ 600) = \sum_{n=0}^{183} \binom{600}{n}(0.25)^n(0.75)^{600-n} = 0.99902. \qquad (6.15)$$

Thus with 99.9 per cent confidence the number of active channels will not exceed 183, and the modulation parameter $K$ can correspondingly be increased by the factor $\sqrt{600/183} = 1.81$ without overmodulating the transmitter more than 0.1 per cent of the time. This yields, in (6.13), an additional message-to-noise ratio improvement of 5.16 db.

In the foregoing we have presented the essential theoretical description of the role played by noise in SSSC-FM FDM systems. We have avoided recourse to the details of a wide variety of implementation methods, and consideration of operational factors such as interference, or the probability of finding all channels busy. The reader is, however, now equipped to cope with the extensive literature on SSSC-FM which has been authored by the telephone and other industries.

## 6.2  FM-FM

In FM-FM, each of a number of sinusoidal subcarriers is frequency-modulated, one by each message to be transmitted. As in SSSC-FM, the several subcarriers are then linearly combined into a single composite waveform which frequency-modulates the RF carrier. Ordinarily, considerably fewer subcarrier channels, about 20, comprise an FM-FM system than is the case in SSSC-FM. Moreover, the message bandwidth capacity of each of the FM

[†] Unless adaptive techniques, which would be quite complicated and will not be considered, were to be used.

subcarrier channels may not be the same as the others, although the frequency-modulation parameters at the subcarrier level are usually chosen on some common basis. Thus we shall consider two FM-FM system configurations; *proportional-bandwidth* and *constant-bandwidth* subcarriers. As before, our principal concern is with the performance of these systems in the presence of noise, and with the proportioning of their modulation parameters so as to provide uniform recovered message quality in all channels.

We shall begin by developing the general equation which describes the performance of any FM-FM system in the presence of noise. We recall again the form of the above-threshold FM baseband noise power spectrum, which is

$$G_{n,FM}(f) = \frac{2k^2 f^2}{A^2}, \qquad 0 \le f \le B. \tag{6.16}$$

Thus, subject to the same qualifications as stated in connection with (6.7), we have for the $i$th subcarrier channel noise power approximately

$$N_i = \frac{2k^2 f_i^2 B_i}{A^2}, \tag{6.17}$$

where $B_i$ is the full bandwidth of the $i$th FM subcarrier channel. The power of the $i$th subcarrier, after recovery by demodulation of the RF carrier, is

$$S_i = \frac{1}{2} f_{Di}^2, \tag{6.18}$$

where $f_{Di}$ is the *peak* frequency deviation of the RF carrier caused by the $i$th sinusoidal subcarrier alone. Thus the $i$th subcarrier-to-noise ratio is

$$\frac{S_i}{N_i} = \frac{A^2 f_{Di}^2}{4k^2 f_i^2 B_i} \tag{6.19}$$

At this point we can directly apply (5.46) to determine the $i$th channel message-to-noise ratio, using $S_i/N_i$ to replace $(S/N)_{in,FM}$, and retaining the general message power notation $\overline{m_i^2(t)}$; thus the $i$th channel message-to-noise ratio $S_{0i}/N_{0i}$ is given by

$$\frac{S_{0i}}{N_{0i}} = \frac{3(\Delta f)_i^2 B_i}{B_m^3} \overline{m_i^2(t)} (S_i/N_i)$$

$$= 3\overline{m_i^2(t)} \frac{(\Delta f)_i^2}{B_m^2} \frac{f_{Di}^2}{f_i^2} \frac{B_{IF}}{2B_m} \frac{A^2}{2k^2 B_{IF}}, \tag{6.20a}$$

where we have introduced $(\Delta f)_i$, the *peak* frequency deviation of the $i$th subcarrier caused by its message (of unity peak magnitude), and multiplied above and below by $B_{IF}$, the full bandwidth of the RF carrier channel. The grouping of terms used in (6.20a) permits its being written in the abbreviated form

$$\frac{S_{0i}}{N_{0i}} = 3\overline{m_i^2(t)}D_m^2 D_i^2 \frac{B_{IF}}{2B_m}(S/N)_{\text{in, }FM},\qquad(6.20b)$$

where $(\Delta f)_i/B_m = D_m$ is the deviation ratio of the $i$th subcarrier due to its message, and $f_{Di}/f_i = D_i$ is the deviation ratio of the RF carrier due to the $i$th subcarrier. Thus we see that the net wideband improvement in FM-FM is determined jointly by the subcarrier and the RF carrier modulation parameters. The form (6.20b) is convenient for the continued analysis of FM-FM systems, since ordinarily the subcarrier deviation ratio $D_m$ is chosen to be some constant value for all subcarriers, and the RF carrier modulation parameter $D_i$ is manipulated so as to provide uniform message quality in all channels, and to satisfy the modulation constraints of the RF link. We must now separately consider proportional-bandwidth and constant-bandwidth FM-FM systems.

### Proportional-Bandwidth Subcarriers

The use of proportional-bandwidth subcarriers has been standard practice in FM-FM radio telemetry since 1948, and a detailed consideration of this system configuration is therefore appropriate. Here, the peak subcarrier frequency deviation $(\Delta f)_i$ is chosen as a constant percentage of the subcarrier frequency $f_i$, and the subcarrier deviation ratio $D_m$ is also chosen to be constant for all subcarriers. Thus the message bandwidth capacity of a subcarrier is proportional to the subcarrier frequency, and it is evident from (6.20a) that we must then have for the carrier modulation parameter $f_{Di}$ the relationship

$$f_{Di}^2 = C_0 f_i^3 \qquad (6.21)$$

in order to secure constant message-to-noise ratio for all subcarrier channels. The quantity $C_0$ is a constant of proportionality which is determined by constraints on the modulation properties of the RF link: a specified peak carrier-frequency deviation $f_D$ (due to all subcarriers combined) must not be exceeded with significant probability. In essence, (6.21) stipulates that we must, in a proportional-bandwidth FM-FM system, pre-emphasize modulation of the RF carrier at the rate of 9 db per octave.

A quantitative exposition of these constraints is readily achieved. Thus at the subcarrier level we have

$$(\Delta f)_i = K_D f_i = D_m B_m \tag{6.22a}$$

and therefore that

$$B_m = \frac{K_D}{D_m} f_i, \tag{6.22b}$$

where $K_D$ is the constant-percentage-of-subcarrier-frequency deviation permitted due to the message. Next, in accordance with (5.11), let

$$B_i = 2(\Delta f)_i \left(1 + \frac{1}{D_m}\right) \tag{6.23a}$$

$$= 2K_D \left(1 + \frac{1}{D_m}\right) f_i \tag{6.23b}$$

$$= \gamma f_i, \tag{6.23c}$$

where in (6.23) we use (6.22a), and for convenience define the constant $\gamma = 2K_D(1 + 1/D_m)$. Now, for noninterfering subcarrier bands we must have

$$f_i - \frac{B_i}{2} = f_{i-1} + \frac{B_{i-1}}{2} \tag{6.24a}$$

or, using (6.23c),

$$f_i = f_{i-1} \frac{(1 + \gamma/2)}{(1 - \gamma/2)} = f_{i-1} r, \tag{6.24b}$$

where, again for notational convenience, we introduce the constant $r = (1 + \gamma/2)/(1 - \gamma/2)$. Iteration of (6.24b) yields utimately

$$f_i = f_1 r^{i-1}. \tag{6.24c}$$

Thus we obtain an ordering relationship for the subcarrier frequencies $f_i$ in terms of the constant modulation parameters of the system $K_D$ and $D_m$, as involved in the constant $r$; for convenience of reference, we write this quantity out as

$$r = \frac{1 + \gamma/2}{1 - \gamma/2} = \frac{1 + K_D(1 + 1/D_m)}{1 - K_D(1 + 1/D_m)}. \tag{6.25}$$

We are now in a position to specify modulation parameters so as to satisfy uniform message-to-noise ratio requirements, and RF carrier modulation constraints. Since we are dealing with a set of $\nu$ *different* subcarrier frequencies, we can write for the mean-square carrier-frequency deviation $\overline{f_D^2}$ that

$$\overline{f_D^2} = \sum_{i=1}^{\nu} \overline{f_{Di}^2} = \frac{1}{2} \sum_{i=1}^{\nu} f_{Di}^2 \tag{6.26a}$$

$$= \frac{C_0}{2} \sum_{i=1}^{\nu} f_i^3 \tag{6.26b}$$

$$= \frac{C_0}{2} f_1^3 \sum_{i=1}^{\nu} r^{3(i-1)}. \tag{6.26c}$$

In (6.26a) we note that the mean-square value of a sinusoid of amplitude $A$ is $A^2/2$; in (6.26b) we invoke the constant message-to-noise ratio condition (6.21); and finally we use (6.24c) to obtain (6.26c). The summation in (6.26c) is a geometric series, and yields

$$\overline{f_D^2} = \frac{C_0}{2} f_1^3 \frac{r^{3v} - 1}{r^3 - 1} \tag{6.27}$$

for the mean-square RF carrier-frequency deviation, in terms of constant (chosen and to-be-determined) system modulation parameters.

The ultimate objective is to specify appropriate subcarrier-carrier modulation proportions, i. e., the $f_{Di}$; thus we solve (6.27) for the constant $C_0$ and then substitute this result in (6.21), which, using (6.24c), becomes

$$f_{Di}^2 = C_0 f_1^3 r^{3(i-1)}. \tag{6.28}$$

From (6.27) we obtain

$$C_0 = \frac{2\overline{f_D^2}}{f_1^3} \frac{r^3 - 1}{r^{3v} - 1}, \tag{6.29}$$

and substituting (6.29) into (6.28) yields finally

$$f_{Di}^2 = 2\overline{f_D^2} r^{3(i-1)} \frac{r^3 - 1}{r^{3v} - 1}. \tag{6.30}$$

The final result (6.30) yields the *peak* subcarrier-carrier modulation proportions in terms of the mean-square RF carrier-frequency deviation $\overline{f_D^2}$, and (through the constant $r$) the chosen system modulation parameters at the subcarrier level. It remains only now to relate $\overline{f_D^2}$ to the *peak* permissible carrier-frequency deviation, which ordinarily is specified on the basis of adjacent-channel interference considerations. However, we shall defer this topic momentarily, in order to develop the analysis of constant-bandwidth subcarrier FM-FM systems to a point equivalent to (6.30). The final step, concerning RF carrier modulation constraints, is sufficiently similar for both FM-FM system configurations to recommend such independent treatment.

### Constant-Bandwidth Subcarriers

In constant-bandwidth subcarrier FM-FM, a constant peak frequency deviation $(\Delta f)_i$ is used for all subcarriers, and the subcarrier deviation ratio $D_m$ is also constant. Thus the subcarrier message bandwidth capacities are independent of the subcarrier frequency, and we see from (6.20a) that we must have

$$\frac{f_{Di}}{f_i} = D_i = \text{constant} \tag{6.31}$$

in order to secure constant message-to-noise ratio for all subcarrier channels. The situation here is entirely analogous to SSSC-FM, except for considerations of the subcarrier channel bandwidth.

Paralleling our previous FM-FM development, we have

$$(\Delta f)_i = D_m B_m \tag{6.32}$$

and taking

$$B_i = 2(\Delta f)_i \left( 1 + \frac{1}{D_m} \right) \tag{6.33a}$$

thus yields

$$B_i = 2B_m(D_m + 1). \tag{6.33b}$$

For noninterference among the subcarriers we must have

$$f_i = f_{i-1} + B_i, \tag{6.34a}$$

from which we obtain by iteration

$$f_i = iB_i, \tag{6.34b}$$

and thus (6.31) becomes

$$f_{Di} = iD_iB_i. \tag{6.35}$$

At the RF carrier level, we have from (6.26a)

$$\overline{f_D^2} = \sum_{i=1}^{\nu} \overline{f_{Di}^2} = \frac{1}{2} \sum_{i=1}^{\nu} f_{Di}^2 \tag{6.36a}$$

which, using (6.35), becomes

$$\overline{f_D^2} = \frac{D_i^2 B_i^2}{2} \sum_{i=1}^{\nu} i^2. \tag{6.36b}$$

From the arithmetic identity (6.11), (6.36b) yields

$$\overline{f_D^2} = \frac{D_i^2 B_i^2}{12} \nu(\nu + 1)(2\nu + 1) \tag{6.37a}$$

and using (6.33b)

$$\overline{f_D^2} = \frac{D_i^2 B_m^2 (D_m + 1)^2}{3} \nu(\nu + 1)(2\nu + 1). \tag{6.37b}$$

Solution of (6.37) for $D_i^2$ yields

$$D_i^2 = \frac{12\overline{f_D^2}}{B_i^2 \nu(\nu + 1)(2\nu + 1)} \tag{6.38a}$$

$$= \frac{3\overline{f_D^2}}{B_m^2 (D_m + 1)^2 \nu(\nu + 1)(2\nu + 1)}. \tag{6.38b}$$

Finally, substitution of (6.38a) into (6.35) yields

$$f_{Di}^2 = \frac{12i^2 \overline{f_D^2}}{\nu(\nu + 1)(2\nu + 1)}. \qquad (6.39)$$

Equation (6.39), for constant-bandwidth subcarriers, is analogous to (6.30), for proportional-bandwidth subcarriers; it relates the peak subcarrier-carrier modulation proportions to the mean-square RF carrier-frequency deviation, and other system parameters.

### RF Carrier Modulation

In equations (6.30) and (6.39), governing the subcarrier-carrier modulation proportions, the mean-square RF carrier-frequency deviation $\overline{f_D^2}$ appears. However, the *peak* RF carrier-frequency deviation $f_D$ is more usually specified, in consequence of fixed frequency allocations and adjacent-channel interference considerations. In this section, therefore, we shall explore the possible relationships which can be obtained between the peak and the rms carrier-frequency deviation.

Basically, two approaches are possible. First, we can state with absolute certainty that the peak RF carrier-frequency deviation will never exceed the arithmetic sum of the peak subcarrier-carrier modulation parameters $f_{Di}$; symbolically

$$f_D \le \sum_{i=1}^{\nu} f_{Di}. \qquad (6.40)$$

Equality obtains in (6.40) at those instants when all the sinusoidal subcarriers add up in phase, an event which may occur only very rarely if a substantial number of subcarriers is involved. One can, however, design an FM-FM system on this conservative basis, and in some cases it is preferable to do so. Thus, for proportional-bandwidth subcarriers, using (6.28), we have from (6.40)

$$f_D = \sqrt{C_0} f_1^{3/2} \sum_{i=1}^{\nu} r^{3(i-1)/2} \qquad (6.41a)$$

$$= \sqrt{C_0} f_1^{3/2} \frac{r^{3\nu/2} - 1}{r^{3/2} - 1}, \qquad (6.41b)$$

where in (6.41b) we have summed the geometric series in (6.41a). Solving (6.41b) for $\sqrt{C_0}$ we get

$$\sqrt{C_0} = \frac{f_D}{f_1^{3/2}} \frac{r^{3/2} - 1}{r^{3\nu/2} - 1}, \qquad (6.42)$$

and substituting (6.42) back into the square-root of (6.28) yields

$$f_{Di} = f_D r^{3(i-1)/2} \frac{r^{3/2} - 1}{r^{3\nu/2} - 1}. \qquad (6.43)$$

For constant-bandwidth subcarriers we have, from (6.40), using (6.35),

$$f_D = D_i B_i \sum_{i=1}^{v} i \qquad (6.44a)$$

$$= \frac{1}{2} D_i B_i v(v + 1), \qquad (6.44b)$$

where in (6.44b) we have summed the arithmetic series in (6.44a). Solving (6.44b) for $D_i$ we get

$$D_i = \frac{2f_D}{B_i v(v + 1)}, \qquad (6.45)$$

and substituting (6.45) back into (6.35) yields

$$f_{Di} = \frac{2if_D}{v(v + 1)}. \qquad (6.46)$$

Equations (6.43) and (6.46) give the subcarrier-carrier modulation parameters $f_{Di}$ in terms of the *peak* permissible RF carrier-frequency deviation $f_D$ and other system constants, under the conservative criterion of equality in (6.40); we refer to use of this equality criterion as *arithmetic weighting* of the $f_{Di}$.

At the outset we noted in connection with (6.40) that equality may obtain only very seldom if a substantial number of subcarriers is involved. This naturally suggests that we might increase the $f_{Di}$ to larger values than specified by (6.43) or (6.46) with little consequent risk of exceeding the maximum permissible RF carrier-frequency deviation $f_D$, and thereby obtain higher subcarrier-to-noise ratios [see (6.18)–(6.20)]. In essence we would assume that

$$f_D^2 \leq p^2 \overline{f_D^2} \qquad (6.47)$$

with appropriately high probability, where the quantity $p$ is called the *peaking factor*. The choice of an "appropriately high proba-bility" is arbitrary, and the corresponding value of $p$ depends on the probability distribution of the composite waveform which modulates the transmitter. The use of (6.47) in (6.30) or (6.39) to obtain equations analogous to (6.43) or (6.46), respectively, is obvious.

It is tempting to invoke the central limit theorem, and assert that the sum of a reasonably large number (say more than 10) of frequency-modulated subcarriers yields a waveform which can be described with sufficient accuracy by the normal, or gaussian, distribution. Thus with $p = 3$, we would assert that the overmodulation probability $P(f_D^2 > 9\overline{f_D^2}) = 0.003$ approximately, which we have previously considered to be "appropriately small."

Nevertheless, we are dealing with a relatively small ensemble of nongaussian waveforms (specifically, sinusoids), and the validity of the central limit theorem approach is open to serious challenge. Unfortunately, disproportionate computational labor would be required to resolve this question quantitatively; although the statistics of small ensembles of equal-amplitude sinusoids are known,[†] here we deal with unequal amplitudes. However, the Chebyshev inequality (see Art. 1.11) provides a reasonably satisfactory upper bound on the situation. Specifically, from (1.55) we can state with certainty for the overmodulation probability: $P(f_D^2 > 9\overline{f_D^2}) \leq \frac{1}{9} = 0.111$. We cannot readily infer unimodal properties for the probability density function of the sum of a set of amplitude-weighted sinusoids, however, so we do not assert the improved bound of (1.56). Thus, in summary, we can state for the overmodulation probability, with the peaking factor $p = 3$:

$$P(f_D^2 > 9\overline{f_D^2}) \leq \tfrac{1}{9}, \qquad \text{always;}$$
$$P(f_D^2 > 9\overline{f_D^2}) = 0.003, \qquad \text{assumed gaussian statistics.} \tag{6.48}$$

Subject to the qualifications just set forth, then, we can consider *statistical weighting* of the FM-FM subcarrier-carrier modulation parameters $f_{Di}$. For numerical purposes we shall continue to assume the specific value $p = 3$ for the peaking factor, and evaluate the preferability of arithmetic weighting, or statistical weighting, as a function of the number $\nu$ of subcarriers comprising an FM-FM system.

Our objective is to obtain the largest possible values for the parameters $f_{Di}$, or equivalently for the constants $C_0$ or $D_i$. Thus we seek to determine the number of subcarriers $\nu'$ for which

$$\left[ \sum_{i=1}^{\nu'} f_{Di} \right]^2 = p^2 \overline{f_D^2} = 9\overline{f_D^2}; \tag{6.49}$$

then, in a system involving fewer than $\nu'$ subcarriers, arithmetic weighting is preferable, and conversely, for more than $\nu'$ subcarriers statistical weighting is better.[‡]

By applying (6.49) to the proportional-bandwidth subcarrier case, we obtain, using (6.28) and (6.27),

---

† See Fox and Starr, Slack.

‡ Note that the peaking factor for a single sinusoid is, with 100 per cent confidence, $p = \sqrt{2} = 1.414$.

$$C_0 f_1^3 \left[ \sum_{i=1}^{\nu'} r^{3(i-1)/2} \right]^2 = \frac{9 C_0}{2} f_1^3 \frac{r^{3\nu'} - 1}{r^3 - 1} \tag{6.50a}$$

which yields, upon summing the geometric series and cancelling constants,

$$\left( \frac{r^{3\nu'/2} - 1}{r^{3/2} - 1} \right)^2 = \frac{9}{2} \left( \frac{r^{3\nu'} - 1}{r^3 - 1} \right). \tag{6.50b}$$

The solution of (6.50b) for $\nu'$ is best accomplished by numerical methods, for the particular system under consideration. To give an example, we have in IRIG (*Inter-Range Instrumentation Group*) standard telemetry practice, that the subcarrier deviation percentage $K_D = 0.075$ [see (6.22a)], and the subcarrier deviation ratio $D_m = 5$ for all subcarriers. Thus from (6.25) we obtain $r = 1.197802$, and using this value in (6.50b) yields equality for $\nu'$ between 5 and 6. Thus (with $p = 3$), arithmetic weighting is preferable for 5 or fewer IRIG-standard proportional-bandwidth subcarriers, and statistical weighting is better when 6 or more subcarriers must comprise the FM-FM system. This criterion will, of course, change, when different subcarrier modulation parameters are used, or if a peaking factor other than $p = 3$ is assumed.[†]

In the constant-bandwidth subcarrier case, we can obtain a less system-dependent solution for the critical number of subcarriers $\nu'$. Applying (6.49), using (6.35a), we obtain

$$D_i^2 B_i^2 \left[ \sum_{i=1}^{\nu'} i \right]^2 = \frac{3}{4} D_i^2 B_i^2 \nu'(\nu' + 1)(2\nu' + 1), \tag{6.51a}$$

which, upon summing the arithmetic series, cancelling constants, and reducing algebraically, yields the quadratic equation

$$\nu'^2 - 5\nu' - 3 = 0. \tag{6.51b}$$

Solution of (6.51b) yields $\nu' = 5.54$, and again 5 or less, or 6 or more, subcarriers is (for $p = 3$) the point at which arithmetic or statistical weighting, respectively, becomes preferable. The subcarrier modulation parameters do not influence this conclusion for constant-bandwidth subcarrier FM-FM systems, although choice of the peaking factor $p$ does.

In general, the larger the peaking factor chosen, the larger is the critical number of subcarriers $\nu'$ in either the proportional- or the constant-bandwidth FM-FM system configuration. However, the wisdom of choosing a peaking factor much larger than $p = 3$ is

---

[†] For example, when allowance for guard bands is included, the IRIG system has $r \cong 1.3$, and $\nu'$ falls between 6 and 7.

questionable, since then the correspondingly larger critical number of subcarriers lends definite plausibility to use of the central-limit-theorem approach—i. e., statistical weighting—for fewer than this number of subcarriers. In essence, it is necessary to temper the results of a mathematical analysis with intuition and experience concerning the postulates upon which it is based.

## REFERENCES

Bennet, W. R., H. E. Curtis, and S. O. Rice
(III) "Interchannel Interference in FM and PM Systems," *Bell Sys. Tech. J.*, **34** (May 1955).

Black, H. S., *Modulation Theory*. Van Nostrand, Princeton, N. J., 1953.

Brock, R. L., and R. C. McCarty, "On the Modulation Levels in a Frequency-Multiplexed Communication System by Statistical Methods," *IRE Trans. on Information Theory*, **IT-1** (March 1955).

Combellick, T., "Synchronization of Single-Sideband Carrier Systems for High-Speed Data Transmission," *IRE Trans. on Communication Systems*, **CS-7** (June 1959).

Develet, J. A., Jr.
(I) "Coherent FDM/FM Telephone Communication," *Proc. IEEE*, **51** (February 1963).

Fox, H. L., and E. A. Starr, "Measurements of Probability Densities of Small Ensembles of Periodic Waveforms," *Proc. IRE*, **50** (October 1962).

Holbrook, B. D., and J. T. Dixon, "Load Rating Theory for Multi-Channel Amplifiers," *Bell Sys. Tech. J.*, **18** (October 1939).

Landon, V. D.
(II) "Theoretical Analysis of Various Systems of Multiplex Transmission," *RCA Review*, **9** (June-September 1948).

Medhurst, R. G.
(I) "RF Spectra and Interfering Carrier Distortion in FM Trunk Radio Systems with Low Modulation Ratios," *IRE Trans. on Communication Systems*, **CS-9** (June 1961).
(II) "RF Bandwidth of Frequency-Division Multiplex Systems Using Frequency Modulation," *Proc. IRE*, **44** (February 1956).

Nichols, M. H., and L. L. Rauch, *Radio Telemetry*, 2nd ed. Wiley, New York, 1956.

Oswald, J., "The Theory of Analytic Band-Limited Signals Applied to Carrier Systems," *IRE Trans. on Circuit Theory*, **CT-3** (December 1956).

Parry, C. A., "The Equalization of Baseband Noise in Multichannel FM Radio Systems," *Proc. IRE,* **45** (November 1957).

Sanders, R. W., "Communication Efficiency Comparison of Several Communication Systems," *Proc. IRE,* **48** (April 1960).

Slack, M., "The Probability Distribution of Sinusoidal Oscillations Combined in Random Phase," *J. IEE* (London), **93**, pt. 3 (March 1946).

Stiltz, H., *Aerospace Telemetry,* Prentice-Hall, Englewood Cliffs, N. J., 1961.

Watt, A. D., *et al.,* "Performance of Some Radio Systems in the Presence of Thermal and Atmospheric Noise," *Proc. IRE,* **46** (December 1958).

Zadeh, L. A., and K. S. Miller, "Fundamental Aspects of Linear Multiplexing," *Proc. IRE,* **40** (September 1952).

# Chapter Seven

# Time-Division Multiplexing

As the term implies, *time-division* multiplex (TDM) systems accomplish a multichannel transmission capability by representing the continuous input messages in *sampled* form; the samples from individual message channels are transmitted sequentially, so that only one circuit from message source to RF carrier link is completed at any given instant. In TDM, each sampled-message channel occupies the entire baseband bandwidth, rather than only a designated part of it as in FDM. Thus a kind of duality might be considered to exist between FDM and TDM systems. The former combines multiple information channels serially in the frequency domain and transmits them in parallel in the time domain; conversely, the latter combines several message sources serially in the time domain and transmits them in parallel in the frequency domain.

*Commutation,* or *multiplexing,* are terms commonly used to refer to the TDM operation of sequentially sampling multiple channels of continuous input information. Thus the "commutator," or "multiplexer," embraces the dual functions of sampling and time sequencing, whether in a single device or by the interconnection of several distinct circuits. Although we shall not consider physical methods of implementation, Fig. 7.1 shows how, in a simple conceptual TDM system, the continuous waveforms of three message channels undergo commutation.

*Decommutation,* or *demultiplexing,* is the complementary inverse of commutation; it is the process whereby the individual channels

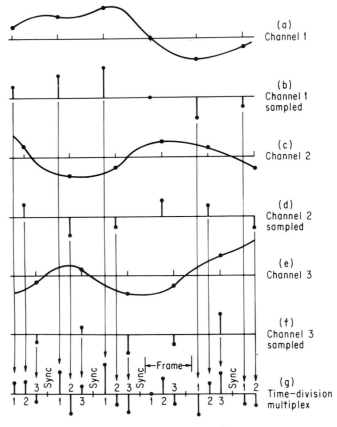

FIGURE 7.1 Commutation.

of TDM sampled information are separated. The composite TDM signal, such as shown in Fig. 7.1(g), is applied to a parallel bank of switches, or *gates*, each of which is closed for short period, the closures occurring in cyclic order so that only one gate circuit is completed at any given instant. If the sequential demultiplexer gate closures are precisely synchronized in time with the message samples applied to their common inputs, then each gate will deliver output pulses representing only one sampled message channel. Figure 7.2 schematically illustrates the decommutation of the TDM signal of Fig. 7.1(g). Although the functional similarity of the commutator and the decommutator is readily apparent, the latter is not ordinarily considered to include the *interpolation* process,

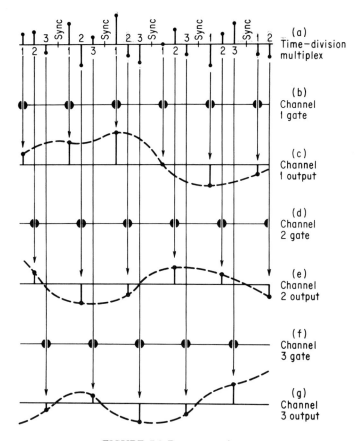

FIGURE 7.2 Decommutation.

whereby a continuous waveform is reconstituted from the samples; interpolation is complementary to *sampling*, and we shall shortly consider both in detail.

A wide variety of message representation schemes can be used for sampled-data TDM transmission. In subsequent articles we shall consider three: *amplitude*, exemplified by pulse-amplitude modulation (PAM); *time*, exemplified by pulse-duration modulation (PDM); and *digital*, exemplified by binary pulse-code modulation (PCM). These are by no means exhaustive, but will serve to instruct the reader in the necessary principles. However, let us first develop some fundamentals which are common to all TDM sampled-data systems.

## 7.1    SAMPLING

It is evident that the sampled versions of Fig. 7.1 (b, d, f) are not continuous representations of the messages shown in Fig. 7.1 (a, c, e) respectively. In fact we preserve only *samples* of the continuous message waveforms, taken at discrete intervals; a TDM signal is usually generated in precisely this way. A switch, or sampling gate, is introduced in series with the continuous message; the switch is normally open, but is closed for short, regularly spaced intervals. The output of the switch is then a sequence of short pulses whose amplitudes and polarities are identical with uniformly spaced instantaneous values of the continuous message.

Since the switch is otherwise open, we may ask whether information is lost, specifically concerning the behavior of the continuous waveform between sampling instants. Certainly information can be lost if the continuous waveform is not sampled frequently enough; however, if the sampling rate exceeds a specifiable minimum value, it can be shown that little or no information is lost. The minimum permissible sampling rate is related to the spectrum of the continuous message, and it can be expressed in a very simple way by idealizing this spectrum. This relationship is known as the *sampling theorem*, and we shall now prove it for ideally band-limited message spectra; subsequently the assumption of ideal bandwidth limitation will be relaxed, and the sampling of physically realizable continuous waveforms will be considered.[†]

*Sampling Theorem:*[‡] If the Fourier transform $X(f)$ (and therefore the power spectrum) of a time function $x(t)$ is identically zero at all frequencies higher than $W$ cps, then $x(t)$ is uniquely determined by specifying its ordinates at a series of points spaced $1/2W$ seconds apart, the series extending throughout the time domain.

To prove the sampling theorem, we first recall the unique relation given by the Fourier transform (see Art. 2.3)

$$x(t) = \int_{-\infty}^{\infty} X(f)e^{j2\pi ft}\,df, \qquad (7.1a)$$

which, since $X(f)$ is postulated to be zero outside the interval $-W \leq f \leq W$, becomes

---

[†] See Bond and Cahn, Linden, Yen, for additional considerations and references on sampling.

[‡] See, for example, Shannon.

$$x(t) = \int_{-W}^{W} x(f)e^{j2\pi ft}\, df. \tag{7.1b}$$

Now, corresponding to the discrete sampling instants, let $t = n/2W$, where $n$ is any positive or negative integer; then (7.1b) becomes

$$x\left(\frac{n}{2W}\right) = \int_{-W}^{W} X(f)e^{j\pi nf/W}\, df. \tag{7.1c}$$

Next expand the transform $X(f)$ in a Fourier series in the interval $-W \leq f \leq W$ (see Art. 2.3):

$$X(f) = \sum_{n=-\infty}^{\infty} C_n e^{j\pi nf/W}, \tag{7.2a}$$

where the coefficients $C_n$ are given by

$$C_n = \frac{1}{2W}\int_{-W}^{W} X(f)e^{-j\pi nf/W}\, df. \tag{7.2b}$$

Comparing (7.1c) and (7.2b) it is evident that

$$x\left(\frac{n}{2W}\right) = 2WC_{-n}; \tag{7.3}$$

thus the set of sample values of $x(t)$ given by $x(n/2W)$ (extending throughout the time domain) determines all the coefficients of the Fourier series expansion of the transform $X(f)$ in the interval $-W \leq f \leq W$, and hence completely specifies $X(f)$ itself within the interval of its existence. Finally, from (7.1a), the transform $X(f)$ uniquely determines the continuous time function $x(t)$; this completes the proof of the sampling theorem.

The sampling theorem formalizes the fact that an ideally band-limited signal of bandwidth $W$ cps cannot have independent values closer together, on the average, than $1/2W$ sec. Thus, sampling such a signal at a rate of at least $2W$ samples per second effectively does preserve all the information contained in the original continuous waveform, and from the discrete samples it is possible to reconstruct its behavior between sample points. We shall now consider the reconstruction problem.

## 7.2  INTERPOLATION

The process of reconstructing a continuous function from a set of sample values is commonly referred to as *interpolation*, for the semantic reason that it involves supplying intermediate values between the discrete ones given. In this article we shall consider interpolation with respect to reconstructing a continuous ideally band-limited function from samples thereof, obtained in accordance with the requirements of the sampling theorem.

Thus we have available only discrete instantaneous samples $x(n/2W)$ of the continuous function $x(t)$, which is ideally band-limited to $W$ cps, and desire to formulate therefrom a continuous function $\hat{x}(t)$ which passes through the sample values $x(n/2W)$, and represents $x(t)$ as accurately as possible in between. We postulate that this can be done by introducing an *interpolation-generating function* $u(t)$ such that

$$\hat{x}(t) = \sum_{n=-\infty}^{\infty} x\left(\frac{n}{2W}\right) u\left(t - \frac{n}{2W}\right). \tag{7.4}$$

In order for $\hat{x}(t)$ to pass through the sample values $x(n/2W)$, it is necessary that

$$u(0) = 1;$$
$$u\left(\frac{n}{2W}\right) = 0, \quad \text{for } n \neq 0. \tag{7.5}$$

Furthermore, if $\hat{x}(t)$ is to be a good representation of $x(t)$ for all values of $t$, it is evident that we must at least require the spectrum of $u(t)$ to be ideally band-limited to $W$ cps, as is that of $x(t)$. Thus for the transform $U(f)$ of $u(t)$, we require that

$$U(f) = 0, \quad \text{for } |f| > W. \tag{7.6}$$

In consequence of (7.6), the Fourier transform relationship for the interpolation-generating function is

$$u(t) = \int_{-W}^{W} U(f) e^{j2\pi ft} \, df. \tag{7.7}$$

Now expand $U(f)$ in a Fourier series in the interval $-W \leq f \leq W$,

$$U(f) = \sum_{k=-\infty}^{\infty} a_k e^{j\pi kf/W}, \quad -W \leq f \leq W, \tag{7.8}$$

and substitute (7.8) into (7.7) with $t = n/2W$ to obtain

$$u\left(\frac{n}{2W}\right) = \sum_{k=-\infty}^{\infty} a_k \int_{-W}^{W} e^{j\pi(n+k)f/W} \, df. \tag{7.9}$$

The integral in (7.9) vanishes except for $n + k = 0$, yielding

$$u\left(\frac{n}{2W}\right) = 2Wa_{-n}, \tag{7.10}$$

and by applying (7.5) to (7.10) we obtain

$$a_0 = \frac{1}{2W};$$
$$a_n = 0, \quad \text{for } n \neq 0. \tag{7.11}$$

Substitution of (7.11) into (7.8) yields

$$U(f) = \frac{1}{2W}, \qquad -W \le f \le W, \qquad (7.12)$$

and using (7.12) in (7.7) we get

$$\begin{aligned} u(t) &= \frac{1}{2W} \int_{-W}^{W} e^{j2\pi ft}\, df \\ &= \frac{\sin 2\pi\, Wt}{2\pi\, Wt}. \end{aligned} \qquad (7.13)$$

Using the interpolation-generating function specified by (7.13) in (7.4) yields finally for the output of the interpolation process

$$\hat{x}(t) = \sum_{n=-\infty}^{\infty} x\left(\frac{n}{2W}\right) \frac{\sin 2\pi\, W(t - n/2W)}{2\pi\, W(t - n/2W)}. \qquad (7.14)$$

By (7.5) we require the continuous function $\hat{x}(t)$ to pass through

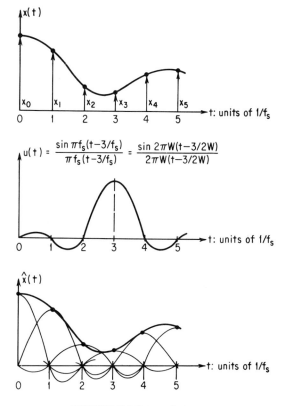

FIGURE 7.3 Interpolation.

the sample values $x(n/2W)$ and by (7.6) require $\hat{x}(t)$ to be ideally band-limited to $W$ cps. By the uniqueness of the sampling theorem it then follows that $\hat{x}(t)$ is the *only* continuous ideally band-limited (to $W$ cps) function which can be the origin of the samples $x(n/2W)$; therefore $\hat{x}(t) = x(t)$. Thus, use of the interpolation-generating function (7.13) enables the *exact* reconstruction of a continuous ideally band-limited function from samples thereof taken in accordance with the minimum requirements of the sampling theorem.

Physically, the interpolation-generating function may be regarded as the impulse response of an *interpolation filter;* (7.13) represents that of a *zonal* filter of bandwidth $W$, and Fig. 7.3 illustrates interpolation accordingly (neglecting delay).

### 7.3  PRACTICAL CONSIDERATIONS

In the foregoing, we have considered sampling and interpolation within the context of functions having ideally band-limited spectra. In practical circumstances, however, the continuous message spectrum is seldom, if ever, ideally band-limited; moreover, it is

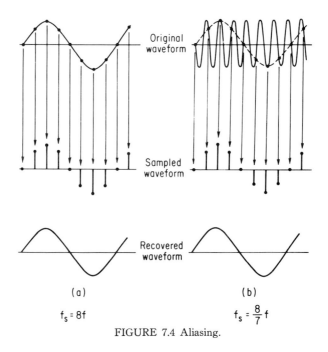

FIGURE 7.4 Aliasing.

impossible to make it is so by introducing a filter prior to the sampling gate, since a zonal filter, which is physically unrealizable, would be required to do this.[†] Thus we must investigate what happens when the spectrum of a continuous waveform which is to be sampled contains some power at frequencies higher than one-half the sampling frequency.[‡]

Figure 7.4 shows the answer. In Fig. 7.4(a), the sampling frequency is eight times that of the sine wave chosen for illustrative purposes to be sampled. The set of sample values bears an obvious resemblance to the continuous waveform, and it is possible therefrom to reconstruct the original signal as accurately as desired. In Fig. 7.4(b), however, the sampling frequency is only 8/7 that of the higher-frequency sine wave shown being sampled. Now the set of sample values does not resemble the continuous waveform; in fact that higher frequency is deliberately chosen so that the samples appear to be derived from the lower-frequency wave of Fig. 7.4(a), and the interpolation process will actually deliver this lower-frequency signal output. Such downward spectral transposition of message power occurs whenever the minimum requirements of the sampling theorem are not satisfied; this phenomenon is known by the descriptive term *aliasing*.

Aliasing is a potential danger in all sampled-data systems. It would be far preferable if the system simply failed to deliver any output corresponding to power in the continuous signal spectrum above the Nyquist frequency. Such, however, is not the case, and a false output component is developed which is indistinguishable from real lower-frequency variations, and which consequently cannot be eliminated by filtering without also distorting the true message spectrum. A detailed analysis of the aliasing effect and of means for its minimization is therefore an important aspect of our consideration of sampled-data TDM systems.

### Aliasing

It is necessary as a first step in the analysis of aliasing to represent the sampling operation mathematically. Thus we shall

---

[†] The zonal interpolation filter required for $u(t) = \sin (2\pi Wt)/2\pi Wt$ (neglecting delay) is also physically unrealizable. In approaching a physical approximation thereto, a progressively longer delay appears which, mathematically, prevents "anticipatory transients"; in the limit the delay becomes infinite.

[‡] One-half the sampling frequency is known as the *Nyquist frequency*; in future we shall adopt this term.

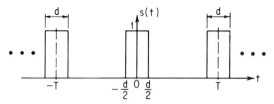

FIGURE 7.5 Sampling function.

consider sampling of a continuous waveform $m(t)$ as equivalent to forming the product $m^{\#}(t) = m(t)s(t)$, where $m^{\#}(t)$ is the sampled version of $m(t)$ and the *sampling function* $s(t)$ is shown in Fig. 7.5. The power spectrum of the sampling function is easily calculated and is given by

$$G_s(f) = \frac{d^2}{T^2} \sum_{k=-\infty}^{\infty} \frac{\sin^2 \pi f d}{(\pi f d)^2} \delta\left(f - \frac{k}{T}\right). \tag{7.15}$$

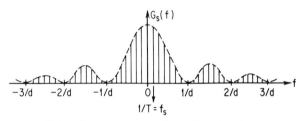

FIGURE 7.6 Spectrum of sampling function.

As shown in Fig. 7.6, this is a discrete spectrum, represented by the delta-functions $\delta(f - k/T)$ at multiples of the sampling frequency $f_s = 1/T$, with magnitudes governed by the spectral envelope $(d/T)^2 \sin^2 \pi f d / (\pi d f)^2$.

If the message $m(t)$ and the sampling function $s(t)$ are independent, then the power spectrum of the sampled message, the product $m^{\#}(t) = m(t)s(t)$, is given by the convolution of the message and sampling function power specta, $G_{m^{\#}}(f) = G_m(f) * G_s(f)$ (see Art. 2.4). As in ordinary AM, sidebands are thus generated about each of the discrete spectral components of the sampling function, and the shapes of the sideband spectra duplicate that of the spectrum of the continuous message. Figure 7.7 illustrates, on an expanded positive-frequency scale, the appearance of the first few components of the power spectrum of the sampled message.

From Fig. 7.7, we can draw a frequency-domain interpretation of the aliasing phenomenon and gain a clue as to how it can be

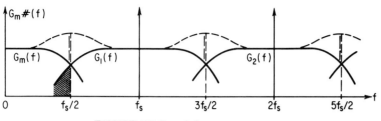

FIGURE 7.7 Sampled message spectrum.

minimized. Because with nonideally band-limited messages the various sideband spectra overlap, as exemplified by the shaded area, it appears as though a continuous message having the composite ideally band-limited spectrum indicated by the dashed curves has actually been sampled. If a "zonal" interpolation filter were used to smooth the sampled message corresponding to the situation shown in Fig. 7.7, then the spectrum of its output would be the lowest-frequency dashed curve. On the other hand, less total error could be achieved if the frequency response of the interpolation filter were chosen so as to de-emphasize the spurious high-frequency peak caused by aliasing. The optimum interpolation filter, then, is one whose frequency response is *not* uniform over the band of frequencies up to $f_s/2$; our next problem is to determine the transfer function of the optimum interpolation filter. Subsequently we shall return to the calculation of the minimum aliasing error using this filter.

### Optimum Interpolation Filter

Disregarding noise and other perturbations which arise in actual operation (to be considered later), the minimization of total error, including aliasing, is a primary function of the interpolation filter, in addition to smoothing the sampled message, i.e., reconstructing a continuous output waveform. In order to derive the optimum interpolation filter, let us first denote the lowest-frequency component (Fig. 7.7) of the sampled-message power spectrum by $G_m(f)$. The higher-order components, $G_1(f), G_2(f), \ldots$ will be collectively designated as $G_n(f)$ in accordance with the relation

$$G_n(f) = \sum_{i=1}^{\infty} G_i(f) \tag{7.16a}$$

$$= \sum_{i=1}^{\infty} G_m(f - if_s), \tag{7.16b}$$

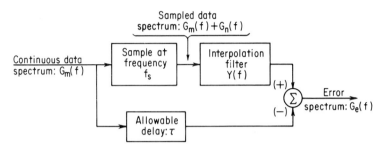

FIGURE 7.8 Interpolation error model.

where we disregard the effect of the spectral envelope of $G_s(f)$. The system model for the analysis is shown in Fig. 7.8. The allowable delay $\tau$ is that which is necessary for the optimum interpolation filter $Y(f)$ to be physically realizable within arbitrarily close tolerances,[†] and is introduced in the reference (lower) channel so that the waveforms being compared by the subtractor are in time synchronism.

By inspection of Fig. 7.8, the power spectrum of the interpolation error $G_e(f)$ is seen to be

$$G_e(f) = |Y(f) - e^{-j2\pi f\tau}|^2 G_m(f) + |Y(f)|^2 G_n(f). \qquad (7.17)$$

Now separate the filter transfer function explicitly into amplitude and phase factors:

$$Y(f) = |Y(f)|e^{-j\theta(f)}. \qquad (7.18)$$

Substitution of (7.18) into (7.17) and use of the trigonometric law of cosines to expand the term $|Y(f) - e^{-j2\pi f\tau}|^2$ yields

$$G_e(f) = \{|Y(f)|^2 + 1 - 2|Y(f)|\cos[\theta(f) - 2\pi f\tau]\}G_m(f)$$
$$+ |Y(f)|^2 G_n(f). \qquad (7.19)$$

The total interpolation error power $P_e$ is given by

$$P_e = \int_0^\infty G_e(f)\, df, \qquad (7.20)$$

and this is the quantity which is to be minimized with respect to the choice of $Y(f)$.

From the calculus of variations, the condition for minimizing a definite integral $\int_a^b G[f; Y(f); Y'(f)]\, df$ is the Euler equation[‡]

[†] See Valley and Wallman, Appendix A.
[‡] See Franklin, chap. XII.

$$\frac{\partial G}{\partial Y(f)} - \frac{d}{df}\left[\frac{\partial G}{\partial Y'(f)}\right] = 0. \tag{7.21}$$

Here, since the integrand $G_e(f) = G[f; Y(f)]$ only, and is not a function of the derivative $Y'(f)$, we have $\partial G/\partial Y'(f) = 0$ and (7.21) reduces to $\partial G/\partial Y(f) = 0$. Expanding this partial derivative in terms of the amplitude and phase components of $Y(f)$, from (7.18), we have

$$\frac{\partial G}{\partial |Y(f)|}\frac{\partial |Y(f)|}{\partial Y(f)} + \frac{\partial G}{\partial \theta(f)}\frac{\partial \theta(f)}{\partial Y(f)} = 0, \tag{7.22a}$$

and carrying out these differentiations using (7.18) and (7.19) yields

$$\{|Y(f)|G_m(f) - G_m(f)\cos[\theta(f) - 2\pi f\tau] + |Y(f)|G_n(f)\}$$
$$+ j\sin[\theta(f) - 2\pi f\tau] = 0. \tag{7.22b}$$

Equating the imaginary part of (7.22b) to zero yields

$$\theta(f) = 2\pi f\tau, \tag{7.23a}$$

and using this in the real part of (7.22b) we obtain

$$|Y(f)| = \frac{G_m(f)}{G_m(f) + G_n(f)}. \tag{7.23b}$$

Thus the transfer function of the optimum interpolation filter, in the sense of minimum error power, is given by

$$Y(f) = \frac{G_m(f)}{G_m(f) + G_n(f)}e^{-j2\pi f\tau}. \tag{7.24}$$

We note two points with respect to the filter specified by (7.24). First, since $Y(f)$ is a voltage transfer function, whereas $G_m(f)$ is a *power* spectral density function, the asymptotic rate of attenuation (in db/octave) of the optimum interpolation filter is twice the spectrum cutoff rate of the continuous message being sampled [where $G_m(f) \ll G_n(f)$ and $G_n(f)$ is approximated by a uniform spectrum]. Second, since at the Nyquist frequency,

$$G_m\left(\frac{f_s}{2}\right) = G_1\left(\frac{f_s}{2}\right) \tag{7.25a}$$

and

$$G_i\left(\frac{f_s}{2}\right) \ll G_1\left(\frac{f_s}{2}\right), \qquad i \geq 2, \tag{7.25b}$$

so that

$$G_n\left(\frac{f_s}{2}\right) \cong G_1\left(\frac{f_s}{2}\right), \tag{7.25c}$$

then $|Y(f_s/2)| \cong \frac{1}{2}$, or the optimum interpolation filter is, to a close approximation, down 6 db at the Nyquist frequency. Practical interpolation filters can be constructed based on the foregoing two observations and knowledge of the message spectrum cutoff rate.

### Minimum Interpolation Error

We now return to the calculation of the minimum interpolation error, including aliasing, using the optimum interpolation filter. By substituting from (7.23a, b) into (7.19), we find for the interpolation error power spectrum

$$G_e(f) = \frac{G_m(f) G_n(f)}{G_m(f) + G_n(f)}, \tag{7.26}$$

and thus the minimum interpolation error power is given by

$$P_{e_{\min}} = \int_0^\infty \frac{G_m(f) G_n(f)}{G_m(f) + G_n(f)} \, df. \tag{7.27}$$

Our task is to evaluate (7.27) as a function of the ratio of sampling frequency to message spectrum bandwidth (suitably defined), with the rate of message spectrum cutoff as a parameter. Unfortunately, a number of approximations are necessary in order to accomplish this mathematically, and the result is somewhat awkward analytically. Nevertheless, the outcome is important, and it will also be presented in graphical form.

We shall choose to represent the message spectrum in a "maximally flat" form

$$G_m(f) = \frac{1}{1 + (f/f_0)^{2k}}, \tag{7.28}$$

where the cutoff rate is $6k$ db/octave and the spectrum bandwidth is defined as equal to the "break frequency" $f_0$, where the power spectral density is down 3 db.

The first approximation consists of truncating the infinite summation (7.16) for $G_n(f)$, after the first term. The first-order component of $G_n(f)$ is actually the principal contributor to the error spectrum, since in (7.26) the higher-order components of $G_n(f)$ are multiplied by $G_m(f > f_0)$, which is small for sharp-cutoff spectra ($k \gg 1$), or high sampling rates ($f_s \gg 2f_0$); these conditions are, in fact, practically representative. Thus we have

$$G_n(f) \cong G_m(f - f_s). \tag{7.29}$$

It was in anticipation of this approximation that we disregarded the spectral envelope of $G_s(f)$ in writing (7.16b).

Combining (7.27), (7.28), and (7.29) yields for the interpolation error power

$$P_{e_{\min}} \cong \int_0^\infty \frac{f_0^{2k}\, df}{f^{2k} + (f - f_s)^{2k} + 2f_0}, \qquad (7.30a)$$

and on defining $y = f/f_s$ and $\gamma = f_s/f_0$ this becomes

$$P_{e_{\min}} \cong \frac{f_0}{\gamma^{2k-1}} \int_0^\infty \frac{dy}{y^{2k} + (y - 1)^{2k} + 2/\gamma^{2k}}. \qquad (7.30b)$$

Two further approximations are required in order to perform the integration for $P_{e_{\min}}$: we shall drop the term $2/\gamma^{2k}$ and extend the lower limit of integration to $-\infty$. Thus

$$P_{e_{\min}} \cong \frac{f_0}{\gamma^{2k-1}} \int_{-\infty}^\infty \frac{dy}{y^{2k} + (y - 1)^{2k}}; \qquad (7.30c)$$

we may easily treat (7.30c) as a contour integral and evaluate it using the theory of residues.†

These last approximations result in the integral of (7.30c) being larger than that of (7.30b); however, this is offset by the opposite effect of the approximation (7.29) where we disregarded the higher-order components of $G_n(f)$. By numercial methods it can be verified that in the worst case, where $\gamma = 2$ and $k = 1$, (7.30c) yields a value less than twice that of (7.30b), and that the discrepancy between the two rapidly vanishes for $k \geq 2$ and/or $\gamma > 2$. As previously noted, these latter conditions are also more representative of actual practice.

The integrand in (7.30c) has $2k$ simple poles symmetrically distributed among the four quadrants of the complex plane at the roots

$$y_0 = \frac{1}{1 - (-1)^{1/2k}} \qquad (7.31)$$

of the equation $y_0^{2k} + (y_0 - 1)^{2k} = 0$, and the corresponding residues are given by

$$\text{Res}\,(y_0) = 1 \Big/ \frac{d}{dy}\,[y^{2k} + (y - 1)^{2k}]_{y=y_0} \qquad (7.32a)$$

$$= \frac{-(-1)^{1/2k}}{2k}\,[1 - (-1)^{1/2k}]^{2k-2} \qquad (7.32b)$$

$$= \frac{-1}{2k}\, e^{j(2q-1)\pi/2k}[1 - e^{j(2q-1)\pi/2k}]^{2k-2}; \qquad (7.32c)$$

$q = 1, 2, \ldots, 2k$, in (7.32c) where we write the $2k$ roots $(-1)^{1/2k}$ in

† See Churchill (II).

polar form. We choose the path of integration so that only the $k$ poles lying in the upper half plane are enclosed, and using the Cauchy integral theorem write the integral as $2\pi j$ times the summation of the residues at these $k$ poles; thus

$$P_{e_{\min}} = \frac{-j\pi f_0}{k\gamma^{2k-1}} \sum_{q=1}^{k} e^{j(2q-1)\pi/2k}[1 - e^{j(2q-1)\pi/2k}]^{2k-2} \qquad (7.33a)$$

$$= \frac{-j\pi f_0}{k\gamma^{2k-1}} \sum_{q=1}^{k} \sum_{p=0}^{2k-2} \binom{2k-2}{p} (-1)^p e^{j(p+1)(2q-1)\pi/2k}, \qquad (7.33b)$$

where in (7.33b) we have used the binominal theorem to expand the term $[1 - e^{j(2q-1)\pi/2k}]^{2k-2}$, and combined the result with the remaining exponential factor. The summation over the index $q$ is a geometric series and yields

$$\sum_{q=1}^{k} e^{j(p+1)(2q-1)\pi/2k} = e^{j(p+1)\pi/2k} \frac{e^{j(p+1)\pi} - 1}{e^{j(p+1)\pi/k} - 1}$$

$$= j \csc \frac{(p+1)\pi}{2k}, \qquad \text{for } p \text{ even}; \qquad (7.34)$$

$$= 0, \qquad\qquad\qquad \text{for } p \text{ odd}.$$

Thus our final result for minimum interpolation error is given by

$$P_{e_{\min}} = \frac{\pi f_0}{k\gamma^{2k-1}} \sum_{\substack{p=0 \\ \text{even}}}^{2k-2} \binom{2k-2}{p} \csc \frac{(p+1)\pi}{2k}. \qquad (7.35)$$

In order to obtain the relative interpolation error, we must normalize (7.35) to the message power $P_m$, which is given by integrating the message power spectrum (7.28a).

$$P_m = \int_0^\infty \frac{df}{1 + (f/f_0)^{2k}}$$

$$= \frac{\pi f_0}{2k} \csc \frac{\pi}{2k}. \qquad (7.36)$$

Thus the minimum relative interpolation error $\overline{E_{\min}^2}$ (on a power basis) is given by

$$\overline{E_{\min}^2} = \frac{P_{e_{\min}}}{P_m} \simeq \frac{2 \sin (\pi/2k)}{\gamma^{2k-1}} \sum_{\substack{p=0 \\ \text{even}}}^{2k-2} \binom{2k-2}{p} \csc \frac{(p+1)\pi}{2k}. \qquad (7.37)$$

It is this expression to which we referred at the outset as being awkward. However, performing the finite summation is not excessively tedious, and in Fig. 7.9 we show the minimum relative rms interpolation error $E_{\min}$, as a function of $\gamma = f_s/f_0$ for various values of the spectrum cutoff constant $k$.

From Fig. 7.9 it is evident that, unless the rate of spectrum

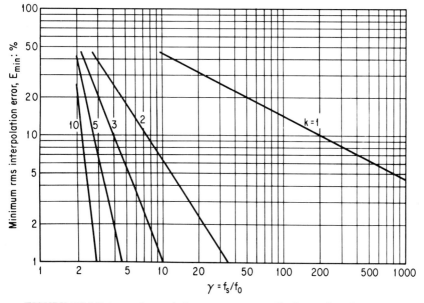

FIGURE 7.9 Minimum interpolation error *vs* normalized sampling frequency.

cutoff is quite high, sampling frequencies greatly in excess of twice the nominal (half-power) bandwidth of the message spectrum are required to maintain the aliasing-plus-interpolation error within tolerable limits of, say, 1 per cent rms; correspondingly, the number of channels that can be time-division multiplexed using a fixed over-all pulse rate is drastically reduced. Conversely, if the spectra of the continuous messages to be transmitted via TDM are sharply restricted to a known frequency band by, say, a 60-db/octave ($k = 10$) cutoff filter, then a sampling frequency only about three times the nominal message bandwidth suffices to insure 1 per cent rms aliasing-plus-interpolation error. Thus in practical systems, where maximum multichannel capability is required, and where greater than a few per cent total error cannot be tolerated, we must have $k \gg 1$ and $\gamma > 2$, so that from a mathematical standpoint the result (7.37) of the approximation (7.30c) becomes quite accurate and is entirely satisfactory for system design purposes.

## 7.4   REPRESENTATIVE ANALOG TDM SYSTEMS

As elsewhere throughout this book, our primary concern is to analyze the effect of additive noise, here in the context of TDM system performance. In particular, it is important to consider how baseband noise passes from the carrier demodulator to and through the demultiplexer to the individual data outputs, and by what means noise contamination of the final recovered messages can be minimized.

Since many channels of information are represented by the baseband TDM signal, the bandwidth of the carrier demodulator output noise spectrum, which is applied to the demultiplexer input, correspondingly may far exceed the bandwidth of any individual sampled message. Visualize a demultiplexer gate as sampling this wideband noise spectrum. The Nyquist frequency associated with this sampling process is in general much lower than the nominal bandwidth of the input noise spectrum; hence, considerable aliasing of high-frequency noise power into the message bandwidth should occur. This is, in fact, the case, and the message-to-noise ratio of each separate demultiplexer output channel is not vastly different from that of the baseband signal applied to its input. (A little thought should convince the reader that the variance of the probability distribution, and the distribution itself, of instantaneous sample amplitudes taken from a stationary continuous random waveform such as a gaussian noise, are the same as the variance and distribution of ordinates of the continuous random waveform itself, independent of the ratio of sampling frequency to the bandwidth of the noise.) Although averaging, in the interpolation filter, over the aperture of noninstantaneous demultiplexer gate-closure time reduces the transmission of noise to an appreciable extent, this effect is not always exploited, nor is it alone generally of sufficient magnitude in a multichannel system for noise reduction purposes; rather, it must be included as a part only of the total picture. Thus the usually large ratio of baseband bandwidth to individual message-channel bandwidth does not, as might at first be expected, directly operate to suppress noise when TDM signals are decommutated; we must more carefully consider what happens.

## The Baseband Filter

It is first necessary to give detailed examination to methods whereby the minimum noise bandwidth necessary to accommodate a TDM signal can be realized. Whatever proportions of the wideband noise spectrum, delivered by the carrier demodulator, are excluded from or passed to the demultiplexer input, are directly determined by a low-pass filter through which the composite TDM signal is passed immediately following the carrier demodulator.

In order to minimize the amount of noise power which thus accompanies the TDM signal to be demultiplexed, the bandwidth of this baseband filter must be as small as possible. However, the transient characteristics of the baseband filter are also important; it must have sufficient bandwidth not to "smear" adjacent pulses into one another, and it cannot exhibit an oscillatory output waveform after being excited by an input pulse. Pulse stretching and lingering transient response cause interchannel crosstalk in TDM systems, and the minimization of this effect primarily governs the best choice of a baseband filter type for noise suppression purposes.

The quality of the transient response characteristics of a filter are closely linked to the constancy of its group delay, or equivalently to the linearity of its phase shift as a function of input frequency. We thus seek a physically realizable *maximally-flat-delay* low-pass filter for use as a baseband filter in TDM systems. As a result of modern network synthesis procedures, it turns out that the transfer function of the maximally-flat-delay, realizable, $N$-pole low-pass filter is given by[†]

$$Y_N(ju) = \frac{(2N)!/2^N N!}{\sum_{k=0}^{N} \frac{(2N-k)!}{2^{N-k}(N-k)!\,k!}(ju)^k}. \tag{7.38a}$$

The transient (step) overshoot of this filter is less than 1 per cent for all values of $N$. In (7.38a) we have absorbed the low-frequency group delay $t_0$ into the normalized real-frequency variable $u = 2\pi f t_0$. The denominator of (7.38a) is identifiable as a *Bessel polynomial*, and for this reason the maximally-flat-delay filter is also often referred to as a *Bessel filter;* in terms of the Bessel functions, the filter transfer function is then given by

$$Y_N(ju) = Ae^{j\theta} = \frac{a_0 e^{-ju}}{u^{N+1}\sqrt{\pi/2u}\,[(-1)^N J_{-N-(1/2)}(u) - jJ_{N+(1/2)}(u)]} \tag{7.38b}$$

where for brevity we write $a_0 = (2N)!/2^N N!$. We shall be directly concerned with calculating the noise bandwidth of circuits including the Bessel filter, and thus note that [see (5.51)]

$$|Y_N(ju)|^2 = |A|^2 = \frac{a_0^2}{u^{2(N+1)}(\pi/2u)[J_{-N-(1/2)}^2(u) + J_{N+(1/2)}^2(u)]}. \tag{7.38c}$$

---

[†] See Storch.

Performing the integration of (5.51) using (7.38c) appears unattractive at best; however the power-spectral response $|A|^2$ approaches the gaussian form

$$|A|^2 = e^{-u^2/(2N-1)} \qquad (7.39)$$

with increasing values of $N$, and the normalized half-power (3-db) bandwidth of the filter is correspondingly given by

$$u_3 = 2\pi f_3 t_0 = \sqrt{(2N-1)\log_e(2)}. \qquad (7.40)$$

The form (7.39) is easily integrated and, if $N \geq 4$, is entirely satisfactory for noise computation purposes. The principal difference between the gaussian approximation (7.39) and the exact form (7.38c) is that the attenuation rate of the latter asymptotically approaches a constant value of $6N$ db/octave (since it represents an $N$-pole low-pass filter), whereas the attenuation rate of the gaussian form continues to increase without limit at progressively higher frequencies. Thus the absolute attenuation introduced at the frequency where the two responses begin to diverge must be sufficiently great that negligible power beyond this point is passed in either case; this requirement clearly is more severe if the power density of the noise spectrum being filtered rises at higher frequencies (as in FM) than it is if the noise spectrum is flat. The gaussian approximation (7.39) generally yields a smaller equivalent noise bandwidth than does the exact form (7.38c). However, even for a parabolic (FM) input noise power spectrum, this difference is less than 3 per cent for $N = 4$, and rapidly vanishes for higher values of $N$.

Using (7.39) in (5.51), the calculation of the equivalent noise bandwidth of the Bessel filter is readily accomplished. Let us assume frequency modulation of the RF carrier and thus represent the input noise power spectral density to the filter in the form $G_n(f) = k^2 f^2 / C$, where for notational convenience we now denote the carrier power by $C$ [see (5.30) using $C = A^2/2$]. Then from (5.51), denoting the equivalent noise bandwidth of the Bessel filter by $B_n$, we have

$$\frac{k^2}{C} \int_0^{B_n} f^2 \, df = \frac{k^2}{C} \int_0^\infty f^2 e^{-(2\pi t_0)^2 f^2/(2N-1)} \, df, \qquad (7.41a)$$

where we also substitute for the normalized frequency variable $u = 2\pi f t_0$. Evaluation of the integrals (using tables for the RHS) and solution for the equivalent noise bandwidth yields

$$B_n = 0.1745\sqrt{(2N-1)}(t_0)^{-1}, \qquad N \geq 4, \qquad (7.41b)$$

for Bessel-filtering of FM baseband noise spectra. It may seem somewhat surprising in (7.41b) that the equivalent noise bandwidth apparently increases with increasing order $N$ of the filter. Actually this is not the case, for from (7.40) we obtain

$$(t_0)^{-1} = \frac{2\pi f_3}{\sqrt{(2N-1)\log_e(2)}};$$

thus in terms of the half-power frequency, the equivalent FM noise bandwidth of the Bessel filter is

$$B_n = 1.317 f_3, \tag{7.41c}$$

irrespective of $N$ if $N \geq 4$. However, for application to TDM system performance analysis, (7.41b) is the more useful equation since the pulse response of the filter is more naturally expressed directly in terms of the delay parameter $t_0$. We are now in a position to consider the noise performance of some representative TDM-FM systems.

### PAM-FM

Ideally, the unfiltered baseband signal at the output of the carrier demodulator of a PAM time-division multiplex system might appear as shown in Fig. 7.10(a). Each successive pulse represents a short sample of the instantaneous amplitude of a different continuous message channel, and the channels are sampled cyclically as discussed at the beginning of this chapter. The *pulse repetition period* $T_p$ of the multiplex is given by $T_p = 1/\nu f_s$, where $f_s$ is the frequency at which each primary message channel is sampled, and $\nu$ is the number of message channels being multiplexed. Typically, the multiplex *duty factor* $d/T_p$ is selected as $d/T_p = \frac{1}{2}$; this results first in the spectrum of the full-wave rectified baseband PAM signal having a strong discrete component at the *pulse repetition frequency* $f_p = 1/T_p$, which can readily be isolated by a narrow bandpass filter and used to sychronize the demultiplexer timing with respect to the incoming PAM signal. Second, the idle interval between pulses allows time for the transient (step) response of the baseband filter to settle, as shown by the shaded areas in Fig. 7.10(b). Although possible, it is considerably more difficult to obtain synchronization information and eliminate crosstalk when $d/T_p = 1$; we shall not consider this system configuration.

In Fig. 7.10(a) we show rectangular pulses with flat tops. Actually, the pulse tops are not quite flat, since we are sampling continuously varying message waveforms. However, the sample

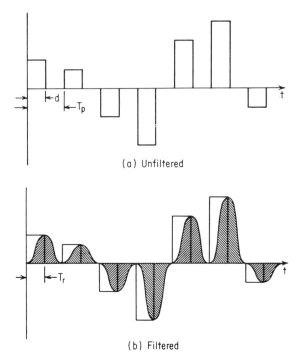

(a) Unfiltered

(b) Filtered

FIGURE 7.10 PAM multiplex waveforms.

duration $d = 1/2vf_s$, and in the usual situation where $v \gg 1$, the samples of any individual message channel are of much shorter duration than the period between which they are taken, and hence than the reciprocal of the message bandwidth. Therefore the slopes of the pulse tops will be very small and essentially negligible. Similarly the pulses are not perfectly rectangular, in practice; bandwidth limitations in the transmitter and in the receiver IF amplifier, and premodulation filtering for the purpose of reducing out-of-band radiation, result in some rounding of the pulse corners and in a noninstantaneous rise time of the PAM multiplex signal delivered by the carrier demodulator. In a well-designed system, however, these factors should be held to a minimum, in order to permit the maximum of baseband noise filtering to be used without introducing excessive interchannel crosstalk due to pulse stretching. Therefore, we shall retain the rectangular-pulse model as a basis for the analysis of PAM-FM system performance.

It is evident from Fig. 7.10(b) that the step-function rise time

$T_r$ of the baseband filter is a quantity of considerable importance from a design standpoint. From published calculations[†] of the transient response of the Bessel filter, we find that the time required to rise from essentially zero to 100 per cent of final response (recall that the Bessel filter overshoot is less than 1 per cent in response to a step input) can be expressed in terms of the delay parameter $t_0$ and the order $N$ of the filter as

$$T_r = 4t_0N^{-0.55}, \qquad N \geq 4. \tag{7.42}$$

In PAM systems where the duty factor $d/T_p = \frac{1}{2}$, the baseband filter rise time may, for example, be taken as $T_r = T_p/2 = 1/2f_p$. Thus the filter responds fully to any individual pulse, and its response thereto decays to zero at and subsequently to the leading edge of the next pulse.[‡] Then, using (7.42), we find for the delay parameter that

$$(t_0)^{-1} = 8f_pN^{-0.55}, \tag{7.43}$$

and using this result in (7.41b) yields for the PAM-FM noise bandwidth of the Bessel filter

$$B_n = 1.4f_p\sqrt{(2N-1)/N^{1.1}}, \qquad N \geq 4. \tag{7.44a}$$

From (7.44a) we see that the noise bandwidth is a very insensitive function of the order $N$ of the baseband filter, and for typical values of $4 \leq N \leq 10$, we can thus write

$$B_n = 1.73f_p \cong \sqrt{3}\, f_p. \tag{7.44b}$$

Correspondingly, the filter output noise power is [see (5.31); a 1-volt-per-cps-deviation discriminator sensitivity is assumed]

$$N_{\text{out}} = \frac{k^2B_n^3}{3C} = \frac{\sqrt{3}\,k^2f_p^3}{C}. \tag{7.45}$$

Note that a fundamental determinant of PAM-FM system performance is the total sample-transmission rate $f_p$, which is related to the number of messages $\nu$, and their individual bandwidths $B_m = f_0$ by $f_p \geq 2\nu B_m$ (recall previous discussion of sampling and aliasing).

In order to calculate the output message-to-noise ratio for PAM-FM, it is necessary to specify the type of operation to be performed by the demultiplexer. Let us first assume that the demultiplexer

---

† See Henderson and Kautz.

‡ Longer rise times, e.g., $T_r = T_p$, can be used for greater noise filtering, without introducing crosstalk, if the timing of an instantaneous-sample demultiplexer is appropriately phased. However, we use the above parameters in order subsequently to show the advantage of area-demultiplexing of PAM.

takes essentially instantaneous samples of the Bessel-filtered base-band signal, at times corresponding to the maxima of the filtered pulses.† Further, let us define output message-to-noise power ratio as the ratio of the sample variance due to message-variation of the pulse amplitudes, to the sample variance due to the additive baseband noise given by (7.45). The output noise variance is actually given by (7.45), in consequence of our opening remarks concerning the variance of an instantaneously sampled continuous stationary time series. Similarly, if the peak (100 per cent modulation) RF carrier-frequency deviation is $f_D$, due to samples of a continuous message or data $m(t)$ of unity peak magnitude, then the output message variance is simply

$$S_{\substack{\text{out, inst} \\ PAM\text{-}FM}} = f_D^2 \overline{m^2(t)}. \tag{7.46}$$

Therefore the output message-to-noise power ratio is

$$(S/N)_{\substack{\text{out, inst} \\ PAM\text{-}FM}} = \frac{2f_D^2 B}{\sqrt{3} f_p^3} \overline{m^2(t)} (S/N)_{\text{in}, FM}. \tag{7.47}$$

In obtaining (7.47) from (7.46) and (7.45) we, as before, multiply numerator and denominator by the half-IF-bandwidth $B$, and recognize the input (IF) noise power as $2k^2B$.

The performance given by (7.47) can be substantially improved by specifying a different type of demultiplexer operation. Instead of taking instantaneous samples at the pulse peaks, let the demultiplexer gates be closed circuits between the baseband filter and a low-pass interpolation filter, for the entire duration $T_p = 1/f_p$ of a filtered pulse. Since the interpolation filter essentially averages the output of its associated demultiplexer gate, this is then equivalent to the finite-time-average operation discussed in Art. 2.4, and found there to introduce an "aperture effect," described in the present instance by the power transfer function

$$|Y_a(f)|^2 = \frac{\sin^2 \pi f T_p}{(\pi f T_p)^2}. \tag{7.48}$$

The aperture operator $|Y_a(f)|^2$ is low-pass in nature and hence contributes additional baseband noise filtering, of substantial magnitude in the common instance where $B \gg f_p$.

The output noise variance is thus determined by integrating the

† A "sample-and-hold" device, which is often used for output presentation in telemetry applications and combines the functions of demultiplexing and "staircase" interpolation, essentially performs this type of operation. As we shall see, this is not a particularly desirable operation from the standpoint of noise suppression capability.

FM baseband noise power spectral density $G_n(f) = k^2 f^2 / C$ over the product of the Bessel filter and aperture-effect power transfer functions. This yields

$$N_{\substack{\text{out} \\ \text{PAM-FM}}} = \frac{k^2}{C} \int_0^\infty f^2 \frac{\sin^2 \pi f T_p}{(\pi f T_p)^2} e^{-(2\pi t_0)^2 f^2/(2N-1)} \, df$$

$$= \frac{k^2 \sqrt{\pi(2N-1)}}{\pi^3 N^{0.55} C} f_p^3 [1 - e^{-16(2N-1)/N^{1.1}}], \tag{7.49a}$$

which, since the exponential term is very small, becomes

$$N_{\substack{\text{out} \\ \text{PAM-FM}}} = \frac{k^2 \sqrt{\pi(2N-1)}}{\pi^3 N^{0.55} C} f_p^3. \tag{7.49b}$$

The integration is performed using tables, and additionally we introduce the relation (7.43) between Bessel filter delay $t_0$ and the total sample-transmission rate $f_p$.

For calculating output message variance we again recall that the interpolation filter essentially averages pulses, and therefore replace $f_D^2$, as used in the instantaneous-sample demultiplexing case, by the quantity

$$\frac{1}{T_p^2} \left[ f_D \int_0^{T_p} p(t) \, dt \right]^2 = \frac{1}{4} f_D^2, \tag{7.50a}$$

where $p(t)$ represents the generic shape of the baseband-filtered pulse. It is not necessary to know the exact form of $p(t)$, since if $p(t)$ is symmetrical about the half-rise-time point, the filtered pulse area is equal to the original rectangular pulse area $f_D T_p/2$; this symmetry requirement on the step response is adequately satisfied by the Bessel filter if $N \geq 4$. Thus the output message variance is given by

$$S_{\substack{\text{out} \\ \text{PAM-FM}}} = \frac{1}{4} f_D^2 \overline{m^2(t)}. \tag{7.50b}$$

Finally, as in obtaining (7.47), the output message-to-noise power ratio is found to be

$$(S/N)_{\substack{\text{out} \\ \text{PAM-FM}}} \frac{\pi^3 N^{0.55}}{2\sqrt{\pi(2N-1)}} \frac{f_D^2 B}{f_p^3} \overline{m^2(t)} (S/N)_{\text{in, FM}}. \tag{7.51}$$

It is interesting to examine the ratio of the performance given by (7.51) and (7.47); this is

$$\frac{(S/N)_{\substack{\text{out} \\ \text{PAM-FM}}}}{(S/N)_{\substack{\text{out, inst} \\ \text{PAM-FM}}}} = \frac{\pi^3 \sqrt{3} \ N^{0.55}}{4\sqrt{\pi(2N-1)}}. \tag{7.52}$$

Substituting a typical Bessel-filter order, say $N = 6$, into (7.52) shows that fully exploiting demultiplexer aperture effect improves PAM-FM system noise performance by a factor or 6.15, or 7.9 db. This is a worthwhile gain over instantaneous-sample demultiplexing.

Indeed, one might conversely inquire whether the baseband Bessel filter is an important system element, if advantage is being taken of demultiplexer aperture effect. We can readily show that it is, i.e., that both a baseband filter and, following it, a noninstantaneous-sample demultiplexer, are necessary to achieve maximum PAM-FM system performance. The FM noise variance at the output of only an aperture-effect filter is given by[†]

$$
\begin{aligned}
N_{\substack{\text{out, aper} \\ PAM\text{-}FM}} &= \frac{k^2}{C} \int_0^B f^2 \frac{\sin^2 \pi f T_p}{(\pi f T_p)^2} \, df \\
&\simeq \frac{k^2 B f_p^2}{2C\pi^2}, \qquad B f_p \gg 1.
\end{aligned}
\tag{7.53}
$$

The output message variance is, of course, still equal to $\frac{1}{4} f_D^2 \overline{m^2(t)}$ [see (7.50a, b)]. Thus, the output message-to-noise power ratio obtained after omitting the baseband filter is

$$
(S/N)_{\substack{\text{out, aper} \\ PAM\text{-}FM}} = \frac{\pi^2 f_D^2}{2 f_p^2} (S/N)_{\text{in}, FM}.
\tag{7.54}
$$

The ratio of (7.51) to (7.54) yields the desired comparison

$$
\frac{(S/N)_{\substack{\text{out} \\ PAM\text{-}FM}}}{(S/N)_{\substack{\text{out, aper} \\ PAM\text{-}FM}}} = \frac{\sqrt{\pi} N^{0.55}}{2\sqrt{(2N-1)}} \frac{B}{f_p}.
\tag{7.55}
$$

If again we typically take $N = 6$, then the RHS of (7.55) yields $0.72 B/f_p$; since, further, it is customary to have $B \gg f_p$, say $B/f_p \geq 4$, then we see that addition of a Bessel-type baseband filter improves PAM-FM system performance by a factor upwards of 2.88 or 4.6 db. This also is a worthwhile gain, compared to a system using aperture-effect noise filtering only.

### PDM-FM

Let us now turn to consideration of a representative time-modulation TDM system: pulse-duration modulation (PDM), also known as pulse-width modulation (PWM). In Fig. 7.11(a) we show how a typical PDM signal might appear, before and after being processed

---

† Here the integration is (as actually it should always be) extended only to the upper limit $B$ of the carrier-demodulator output noise spectrum, instead of to $\infty$ (which introduces negligible error for sharper-cutoff filters), because in this case the improper integral does not converge, but can be evaluated with finite limits.

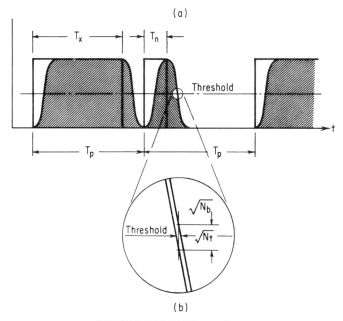

FIGURE. 7.11 PDM waveforms.

by a Bessel-type baseband filter. The leading edges of the pulses occur at a regular rate, equal to the total sample-transmission rate $f_p = 1/T_p$, and the message information is encoded by varying the pulse durations, i.e., the times of occurrence of the trailing edges, in a linear correspondence to message sample amplitudes. Each pulse represents a sample from a different message channel, taken in cyclic sequence. We denote the shortest and longest pulses respectively by

$$T_n = \text{minimum pulse duration},$$

$$T_x = \text{maximum pulse duration},$$

and note that a minimum idle period equal to $T_n$ is allowed between the trailing edge of a maximum-duration pulse and the leading edge of the next pulse.

Commonly in the implementation of PDM receiving equipment, the message information is regarded essentially as residing *directly* in the pulse duration.[†] Therefore the mean pulse duration $T_m$

---

[†] If the pulse amplitudes are constant, one can also regard message information as being represented by the pulse *area*. We shall subsequently find that this is a somewhat superior method of recovering information from PDM signals, compared to direct (time) measurement of pulse duration.

$= \frac{1}{2}(T_x + T_n)$ represents a message sample of zero amplitude, and full-scale (positive or negative) message excursion is represented by the time

$$(T_m - T_n) = (T_x - T_m) = \frac{1}{2}(T_x - T_n).$$

Thus, for direct time-measurement demodulation of PDM signals, the output message variance corresponding to a continuous input message $m(t)$ of unity peak magnitude is given by

$$S_{\substack{\text{out},t \\ PDM}} = \frac{1}{4}(T_x - T_n)^2 \overline{m^2(t)}. \tag{7.56}$$

We must next determine the effect of additive noise on pulse duration, and for this purpose Fig. 7.11(b) shows an enlargement of the trailing edge of a filtered pulse at the point of maximum slope. The standard deviation of the baseband noise is denoted by $\sqrt{N_b}$, and as Fig. 7.11(b) indicates, this noise causes the trailing edge of the pulse to be displaced vertically from its mean position in a random fashion. With respect to a fixed thereshold, a random time jitter then is correspondingly induced, with standard deviation denoted by $\sqrt{N_t}$. Crossing of the fixed threshold, of course, is the event used to effect time measurement. The quantities $N_b$ and $N_t$ are obviously related through the slope of the pulse trailing edge $\lambda$, by $\lambda = \sqrt{N_b/N_t}$, and thus the noise variance associated with time-demodulation of PDM signals is given by

$$N_t = \frac{N_b}{\lambda^2}. \tag{7.57}$$

The ratio of (7.56) to (7.57) yields the output message-to-noise power ratio for time-demodulation of *PDM* signals; thus

$$(S/N)_{\substack{\text{out},t \\ PDM}} = \frac{\lambda^2 (T_x - T_n)^2 \overline{m^2(t)}}{4N_b}. \tag{7.58}$$

Note in obtaining (7.58) that we have included only the time noise on the trailing edge of the duration-modulated pulse; this presupposes that no such noise correspondingly appears on the leading edge. This may appear to be a fundamental oversight—i.e., should not (7.57) be doubled in order to obtain the total duration noise due to uncorrelated time jitter of both the leading and trailing edges? This would be the case if the "leading edges" actually used were noisy. The leading edges, which are not modulated, occur at a regular rate, however, and it is possible in the receiving equipment to exploit knowledge of this fact to derive an essentially noiseless timing reference which is used, instead of the leading edge itself as a basis for the measurement of pulse duration. Hence only trailing-edge time noise is included in (7.58).

The output message-to-noise ratio expressed by (7.58) depends on the ratio $\lambda^2/N_b$, and we must therefore examine a tradeoff between these quantities with respect to baseband noise filtering. Specifically, the maximum slope $\lambda$ of the step response of a low-pass filter of a given type is directly proportional to its bandwidth; hence the presence of $\lambda^2$ in the numerator of (7.58) argues for the widest possible bandwidth, i.e., a minimum of baseband noise filtering. However the total baseband noise power $N_b$ is also a monotonically increasing function of baseband filter bandwidth, and the appearance of this quantity in the denominator of (7.58) weighs in favor of the narrowest possible baseband filter. The resolution of this conflict lies in the form of the baseband noise power spectrum, which governs how rapidly the total noise power $N_b$ increases with increasing filter bandwidth. In FM, this power spectrum is parabolic, and in general the total baseband noise power passed increases as the *cube* of baseband filter bandwidth. Hence it is now clear that in PDM-FM, we require the narrowest possible baseband filter bandwidth for the best performance,[†] and we accordingly proceed to examine the characteristics of the Bessel filter (which is best from the standpoint of "clean" transient response and crosstalk minimization) in the context of application to PDM-FM systems.

First, from Fig. 7.11(a) it is evident that the filter rise time $T_r$ can equal but cannot exceed the minimum pulse duration $T_n$; hence, we have $T_r = T_n$. Then from (7.42) we obtain, in terms of the Bessel filter delay parameter $t_0$ and its order $N$,

$$T_n = 4t_0 N^{-0.55}, \qquad t_0 = \frac{1}{4} T_n N^{0.55}. \qquad (7.59)$$

Next, from published calculations of the Bessel-filter transient response,[‡] we find that the maximum slope of the response to a *unit* step function can be written as

$$\lambda_1 = \frac{5}{12} N^{0.6}(t_0)^{-1}, \qquad N \geq 4. \qquad (7.60a)$$

---

† Conversely, in AM the baseband noise power spectrum is flat, and $N_b$ increases as only the first power of baseband filter bandwidth. Thus the best PDM-AM system would incorporate no baseband filtering whatsoever of the composite TDM signal delivered by the carrier demodulator. The same is true for phase modulation (PM).

‡ See Henderson and Kautz.

Thus, since in PDM-FM the pulse amplitude is equal to the peak RF carrier-frequency deviation $f_D$ (1-volt-per-cps-deviation discriminator sensitivity), we have, also using (7.59), for the maximum pulse slope

$$\lambda = \frac{5}{3} N^{0.05} \frac{f_D}{T_n}, \qquad N \geq 4. \tag{7.60b}$$

Third, using (7.59) in (7.41b), the PDM-FM noise bandwidth of the Bessel filter is $B_n = 0.698\sqrt{(2N-1)}/T_n N^{0.55}$, and using this result in $N_b = k^2 B_n^2/3C$ [see (7.45)], we find for the baseband noise power

$$N_b = 0.1133 \frac{(2N-1)^{3/2}k^2}{T_n^3 N^{1.65} C}. \tag{7.61}$$

Finally, substituting (7.60b) and (7.61) into (7.58) yields

$$(S/N)_{\substack{\text{out},t \\ PDM\text{-}FM}} = 12.25 \frac{(T_x - T_n)^2 T_n N^{1.75} f_D^2 B}{(2N-1)^{3/2}} \overline{m^2(t)} (S/N)_{\text{in, } FM} \tag{7.62a}$$

with the usual manipulation involving introducing $N_{\text{in}, FM} = 2k^2 B$. The factor $N^{1.75}/(2N-1)^{3/2}$ is a relatively insensitive function of $N$, and for typical values $4 \leq N \leq 10$, we can write within 5 per cent that

$$(S/N)_{\substack{\text{out},t \\ PDM\text{-}FM}} = 7.74 \left(\frac{T_x}{T_n} - 1\right)^2 T_n^3 f_D^2 B \overline{m^2(t)} (S/N)_{\text{in}, FM}. \tag{7.62b}$$

In (7.62b) we have also substituted $(T_x - T_n)^2 = [(T_x/T_n) - 1]^2 T_n^2$ in order to show explicitly the role of the pulse duration ratio $T_x/T_n$; also for a fixed pulse duration ratio, the total sample-transmission rate $f_p$, and $T_n$ are in inverse proportion, again demonstrating the characteristic of TDM-FM systems (and FM techniques in general) that the output message-to-noise ratio is inversely proportional to the cube of the total message or data bandwidth capacity, other parameters held constant.

Direct time-demodulation of PDM signals is analogous to instantaneous-sample demultiplexing of PAM, in that an instantaneous sample of the baseband noise operates to determine the ultimate output message-to-noise ratio. As in PAM, another alternative is available: to measure the pulse area, which in PDM is proportional to the pulse duration if the pulse amplitudes are constant. This procedure introduces additional demultiplexer aperture-effect filtering of the baseband noise spectrum, but does not take advantage of time-noise suppression by the slope of the pulse trailing edge. However, we shall show that pulse-area measurement is nevertheless somewhat superior to direct time-demodulation of PDM signals.

Thus, we shall allow the PDM demultiplexer gates to be closed circuits for the time $T_p = T_x + T_n$, now between the baseband filter and a low-pass interpolation filter, instead of a threshold-type time-measuring device. The low-pass interpolation filter essentially averages pulses delivered by its associated demultiplexer gate, and yields an output message response proportional to pulse area divided by the observation interval $T_p$. In particular, the output message variance now becomes

$$S_{\underset{PDM\text{-}FM}{\text{out}}} \frac{(T_x - T_n)^2 f_D^2}{4T_p^2} \overline{m^2(t)} \tag{7.63}$$

[see (7.50a) and remarks thereon]. The aperture operator corresponding to averaging over the interval $T_p$ is given by (7.48), and the output noise variance for this in cascade with the Bessel-type baseband filter is calculated from the same integral as was used in obtaining (7.49a, b). Thus, also using (7.59), the output noise variance for area-demodulation of PDM-FM is

$$N_{\underset{PDM\text{-}FM}{\text{out}}} = \frac{\sqrt{\pi(2N-1)}k^2}{2\pi^3 T_p^2 T_n N^{0.55} C}. \tag{7.64}$$

From (7.63) and (7.64), in the usual fashion, we obtain the output message-to-noise power ratio for area-demodulation of PDM-FM as

$$(S/N)_{\underset{PDM\text{-}FM}{\text{out}}} = \frac{\pi^3 (T_x - T_n)^2 T_n N^{0.55} f_D^2 B}{\sqrt{\pi(2N-1)}} \overline{m^2(t)} (S/N)_{\text{in},FM}. \tag{7.65}$$

The ratio of (7.65) to (7.62a) yields the comparison between area- and time-demodulation of PDM-FM; thus

$$\frac{(S/N)_{\underset{PDM\text{-}FM}{\text{out}}}}{(S/N)_{\underset{PDM\text{-}FM}{\text{out},t}}} = \frac{\pi^3 (2N-1)}{12.25 N^{1.2} \sqrt{\pi}} \tag{7.66}$$

and for a typical value, $N = 6$, this yields 2.6 db superiority for area-demodulation, retaining the Bessel-type baseband filter. With respect to noise performance alone, this is not an overwhelming advantage; however, the substitution of a low-pass interpolation filter for the considerably more complex threshold and pulse-regeneration circuits ordinarily used for direct time-demodulation is a substantial equipment simplification, where a continuous-waveform output message format is suitable. Conversely, some applications of PDM, notably in radio-telemetry, also involve special output presentation requirements, with which time-demodulation is more directly compatible.

Finally, if the Bessel-type baseband filter were to be eliminated in area-demodulation of PDM-FM, then the output noise variance would be calculated from the same integral as used in (7.53); thus we have

$$N_{\substack{\text{out, aper}\\PDM\text{-}FM}} \simeq \frac{k^2 B}{2C\pi^2 T_p^2}. \qquad (7.67)$$

The output message variance is still given by (7.63), and thus the output message-to-noise power ratio is

$$(S/N)_{\substack{\text{out, aper}\\PDM\text{-}FM}} = \pi^2 (T_x - T_n)^2 f_D^2 \overline{m^2(t)} (S/N)_{\text{in}, FM}. \qquad (7.68)$$

Comparison of (7.68) with (7.65) yields a quantitative measure of the effectiveness of the baseband filter in area-demodulation of PDM-FM; thus

$$\frac{(S/N)_{\substack{\text{out}\\PDM\text{-}FM}}}{(S/N)_{\substack{\text{out, aper}\\PDM\text{-}FM}}} = \frac{\pi T_n N^{0.55} B}{\sqrt{\pi(2N-1)}} = 1.43 BT_n, \quad (N = 6). \quad (7.69)$$

Since for the rectangular-pulse model of a well-designed PDM-FM system, we have $B \gg T_n^{-1}$, then (7.69) shows a positive recommendation for the inclusion of a Bessel-type baseband filter in PDM-FM systems even when area-demodulation is used.

### 7.5    DIGITAL MESSAGE REPRESENTATION†

In the preceding article, we considered two analog methods of representing sampled messages or data: amplitude (PAM) and time (PDM). It is also common practice to represent the samples of a continuous message in a *digital* form, and it is our purpose in this article to consider some of the aspects of digital message representation in the context of analog carrier-modulation techniques.

Digital message representation is used for two principal reasons. First, one can thereby secure higher resolution of the full scale of message or data variation than can be achieved even under conditions of high message-to-noise ratio using direct analog representations. Second, greater immunity to the effect of additive noise can be attained, particularly in situations where a communication system consists of a number of individual links in cascade, such as in transcontinental microwave relay networks. This immunity

---

† See Oliver, Pierce, Shannon.

is achieved through the regeneration, at each repeater, of easily recognized pulses which individually represent only a part of each message sample.

Naturally, a price is paid for these advantages, in terms of baseband bandwidth and inherent, though specifiable, deleterious effects on recovered message quality. Similarly, the role of additive noise must be viewed differently than has been done heretofore with respect to analog transmission methods. In this article we shall consider the special problems of digital-representation-analog-transmission techniques; the following chapter will deal with exclusively digital systems.

### Quantizing

In order to represent a continuous message (continuous both in time and in ordinate distribution) in digital form, it is necessary, in addition to sampling it at discrete intervals, to *quantize* it so that only a finite number of amplitude levels are distinguishable. In essence, one divides the total expected range of excursion into a number of discrete amplitude intervals, and at each sampling instant transmits only one of a finite set of numbers, indexed upon the corresponding set of amplitude increments. Thus associated with each digitized sample amplitude is an irreducible uncertainty as to *precisely* where, within a quantizing interval, the continuous-in-distribution (analog) sample amplitude actually fell. Thus, quantizing or digitizing an analog waveform introduces *quantizing*

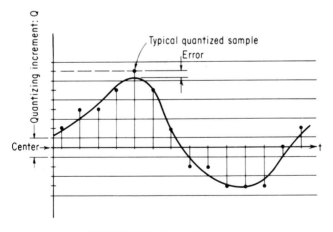

FIGURE 7.12 Quantizing error.

*noise,* in the sense that the mean-squared difference between the digitized message and its analog ancestor is not zero. Figure 7.12 is a conceptual illustration of this situation; it is, of course, possible to reduce the quantizing noise to arbitrarily small proportions by increasing the number of quantizing increments chosen within the expected range waveform excursion.

For purposes of calculating the magnitude of quantizing noise, it is reasonable to assume that an instantaneous message sample amplitude is uniformly likely to fall anywhere within the quantizing increment within which it is found. Thus the probability density function for the quantizing error $q$ is, with respect to the center of a quantizing interval, given by

$$p_q(u) = \frac{1}{Q}, \qquad \frac{-Q}{2} \leq u \leq \frac{Q}{2}, \qquad (7.70)$$

where $Q$ is the width of the quantizing increment in amplitude. Therefore, the mean-squared quantizing error, or quantizing noise power, is given by

$$N_q = \overline{q^2} = \int_{-Q/2}^{Q/2} u^2 p_q(u) \, du = \frac{1}{Q} \int_{-Q/2}^{Q/2} u^2 \, du = \frac{Q^2}{12}. \qquad (7.71)$$

If the peak message-waveform excursion is normalized to $\pm 1$ (as we have done throughout), then the width of a quantizing increment is $Q = 2/\nu_q$, where $\nu_q$ is the number of discrete amplitude levels distinguishable after digitizing. Thus the power ratio of message-to-quantizing noise is given by

$$(S/N)_q = \frac{\overline{m^2(t)}}{N_q} = 3\overline{m^2(t)}\nu_q^2. \qquad (7.72)$$

In the foregoing, we have implicitly assumed uniform partitioning of the message-amplitude range into equal quantizing increments. It is often suggested that a more satisfactory digital system might be realized by "tapering" of the quantizing increments, i.e., proportioning of the width of the quantizing increments to the amplitude level at which their centers are situated.[†] Such a system could be realized by logarithmically compressing the continuous message waveform in amplitude before sampling and digitizing, and exponentially expanding the recovered information prior to presentation. The motivation for such schemes is to maintain uniform "instantaneous" message-to-quantizing noise ratio, throughout the message amplitude range. Except, however, where special

---

† See Panter and Dite; also Spang and Schultheiss.

factors such as psychoacoustical perception attend the ultimate message receptor, it is usually the absolute magnitude of message recovery error, irrespective of instantaneous message amplitude, that is important. We shall therefore restrict our attention to the equal-increment quantizing case.

### Digitizing

After amplitude-quantizing the time-samples of a continuous analog message waveform, it is necessary to choose some arithmetic scheme to represent the sequence of numbers so obtained. The most common of such arithmetic devices is the *binary* system, which involves only two digits, ordinarily designated as "0" and "1," in contrast to the decimal number system which uses the digits "0" through "9." The reason for this nearly universal preference for the binary arithmetic system in digital coding is that it requires only a simple "yes-no" decision on the part of the electronic circuitry concerned.[†] Thus when one, in the context of digital TDM communication systems, speaks of pulse-code-modulation (PCM), almost invariably it is meant that binary arithmetic is used to encode digitized, or quantized, message samples.

Binary arithmetic, quite simply, uses the symbols "0" and "1" to designate whether or not a power of two (hence the term *binary*), corresponding to the digit position in a binary *word*, should be included in a sum which yields the equivalent decimal number. Figure 7.13 illustrates this scheme, by translating the decimal numbers "0" through "7" into binary notation. Of course, any decimal number is expressible in binary terms by simply using a longer binary word, and correspondingly allowing higher powers $2^n$; thus

| Decimal Number | Binary Number $n = 0\,1\,2$ | Equivalence |
|:---:|:---:|:---|
| 0 | 0 0 0 | $0(2^n) = 0$ |
| 1 | 1 0 0 | $2^0 = 1$ |
| 2 | 0 1 0 | $2^1 = 2$ |
| 3 | 1 1 0 | $2^0 + 2^1 = 3$ |
| 4 | 0 0 1 | $2^2 = 4$ |
| 5 | 1 0 1 | $2^0 + 2^2 = 5$ |
| 6 | 0 1 1 | $2^1 + 2^2 = 6$ |
| 7 | 1 1 1 | $2^0 + 2^1 + 2^2 = 7$ |

FIGURE 7.13 Binary coding.

† See B. D. Smith.

the decimal number 1234 becomes the eleven-digit binary number 01001011001, and eleven binary digits can be used to express any decimal number up to $2047 = 2^{11} - 1$. The individual digits comprising a binary word are often known as *bits*, and it is evident that an $N$-bit word is capable of expressing $2^N$ decimal numbers, or in our application, $2^N$ discrete message amplitude levels.

### Digital Errors

As a consequence of additive noise, the receiver in a PCM communication system will occasionally decide incorrectly that a "0" digit is a "1," or vice versa. Thus the binary word in which such an error is committed is incorrectly decoded, and an equivalent analog error arises with respect to the message sample amplitude concerned. We can easily determine the relative magnitude of this equivalent analog error, due to digital errors in PCM transmission.

Note first that a full-scale (positive or negative) message sample corresponds to the number $2^{N-1}$, where $N$ is the number of bits per binary word used to digitize the message samples.[†] Then the weight of the $n$th bit in an $N$-bit word, relative to full-scale, is $2^n/2^{N-1}$, where $0 \leq n \leq N - 1$. It is reasonable to assume that any bit in a word, from the least to the most significant, is *equally* likely to be in error, with *binary error probability $P_b$* governed by signal-to-noise ratio conditions.[‡] Then the mean-squared error (error variance) due to *single* bit errors within a word is, relative to full-scale,

$$\overline{e^2} = \frac{P_b}{2^{2(N-1)}} \sum_{N=0}^{N-1} 2^{2n} = \frac{4P_b(4^N - 1)}{3(4^N)}, \qquad (7.73a)$$

obtained by summing the geometric series. Since $2^N = \nu_q$, the number of quantizing increments, (7.73a) becomes

$$\overline{e^2} = \frac{4P_b(\nu_q^2 - 1)}{3\nu_q^2}. \qquad (7.73b)$$

We do not consider multiple-bit errors within a word, since these occur with extremely small and essentially negligible probability if, as usually is the case, $P_b$ is small, typically less than $10^{-4}$. The

---

† Our previous use of the symbol $N$ to denote the order of a Bessel-type baseband filter should cause no confusion. Unfortunately, we have only a finite symbol alphabet at our disposal.

‡ A power-weighting scheme has been described [Bedrosian (I)] which yields some improvement over the following conditions. See also Bellman and Kalaba.

message power relative to full-scale is simply $\overline{m^2(t)}$. Thus the equivalent analog message-to-noise ratio due to digital errors is

$$(S/N)_b = \frac{3\overline{m^2(t)}v_q^2}{4P_b(v_q^2 - 1)}. \tag{7.74}$$

Since quantizing noise and noise due to digital transmission errors are independent, the over-all message-to-noise ratio for binary PCM systems is

$$(S/N)_{PCM} = \frac{\overline{m^2(t)}}{N_q + e^2} = \frac{3\overline{m^2(t)}v_q^2}{4P_b(v_q^2 - 1) + 1}, \tag{7.75}$$

where we have used the result of (7.71).

The total binary error probability can be made essentially additive in the situation where a number $L$ of PCM communication links operate in cascade as a relay network. To show this, we note first that a bit which experiences an *even* number of errors in traversing the network actually emerges correct. Therefore the network error probability $P_{b,L}$ is the probability that any *odd* number of link errors occurs. Thus,

$$P_{b,L} = \binom{L}{1}P_b(1 - P_b)^{L-1} + \binom{L}{3}P_b^3(1 - P_b)^{L-3}$$
$$+ \binom{L}{5}P_b^5(1 - P_b)^{L-5} + \cdots, \tag{7.76}$$

where, for example, the binominal coefficient $\binom{L}{5}$ gives the number of ways in which 5 links of the $L$-link network can be in error. This series can be summed as follows: the probability of an even number of link errors, and hence of *no* network error, is
$Q_{b,L} = 1 - P_{b,L}$

$$= \binom{L}{0}(1 - P_b)^L + \binom{L}{2}P_b^2(1 - P_b)^{L-2} + \binom{L}{4}(1 - P_b)^{L-4} + \cdots. \tag{7.77}$$

From the form of the series (7.76) and (7.77), it appears logical to examine the quantity

$$(1 - 2P_b)^L = [(1 - P_b) - P_b]^L$$
$$= \binom{L}{0}(1 - P_b)^L - \binom{L}{1}P_b(1 - P_b)^{L-1}$$
$$+ \binom{L}{2}P_b^2(1 - P_b)^{L-2} - \cdots \tag{7.78}$$
$$= Q_{b,L} - P_{b,L}$$
$$= 1 - 2P_{b,L},$$

where in obtaining the latter forms of (7.78) we use (7.76) and (7.77). Thus from (7.78) we obtain for the over-all network error probability

$$P_{b,L} = \frac{1}{2}\,[1 - (1 - 2P_b)^L];\qquad\qquad(7.79a)$$

for $P_b \ll \frac{1}{2}$, as is usually the case, (7.79a) becomes approximately

$$P_{b,L} \cong LP_b.\qquad\qquad(7.79b)$$

These results presume that a decision process and bit regeneration are performed at the receiving terminal of each PCM link in the network. Otherwise, the per-link noise power would accumulate additively, and a single decision process at the final receiving terminal would be required to combat this accumulated noise level. However, it is characteristic of binary decision processes that the error probability increases exponentially with noise level; thus individual link decision and bit regeneration has the decided advantage of substituting a linear increase in binary error probability with the number of links, for a much more rapid exponential relationship, were accumulated network noise allowed to confront a single final decision process.

### PCM-FM

As was mentioned at the outset, message samples are often represented in digital form in order to secure higher scale resolution and immunity to noise-induced uncertainty than is generally attainable by analog representations such as PAM and PDM. As a matter of convenience, it is also common practice to transmit digital signals by analog modulation methods, such as FM. Thus PCM-FM has found widespread application in the field of telemetry and, under the nomenclature *frequency-shift keying* (FSK), in the transmission of teletype messages. We shall briefly consider PCM-FM as the final topic in this chapter on TDM systems.

The basic problem is to calculate the binary error probability $P_b$ as a function of the system modulation parameters and information transmission rate. In order to do this, one might begin as with other analog TDM-FM systems by calculating a per-bit output signal-to-noise ratio; then, postulating that the output noise is statistically gaussian, determine the probability that it will cause the binary decision process to commit an error. The difficuty with this approach is that it yields a binary error probability which is several orders of magnitude less than what can be shown to be optimum, without qualification.[†]

Two reasons can broadly be given for the failure of formerly successful analysis techniques to yield a credible answer for the PCM-FM error probability. First, although the discriminator output noise *power* confronting the decision process can be quite accurately calculated, it turns out that the actual output noise variate is grossly nongaussian with respect to the "tails" of its probability density function; a relatively much higher probability of large excursions from the mean exists than is the case for a gaussian variate of the same variance. Thus a much higher probability of (actually infrequent) errors exists than is predicted under the postulate of gaussian output noise statistics. Second, the "signal" output, which establishes a decision threshold against the probability density of the output noise, is strongly dependent upon nonlinear waveform distortion encountered in transmission through a restrictive-bandwidth FM link (see Art. 5.1). Thus, even knowing the actual probability density function of the output noise, it is difficult to estabish a generally valid threshold for analysis of the decision process.[‡]

We shall attempt to make the foregoing comments somewhat more explicit with respect to a specific PCM-FM reception system model, shown in Fig. 7.14. Let the sum of signal and noise applied to the limiter-discriminator be represented in envelope-and-phase form

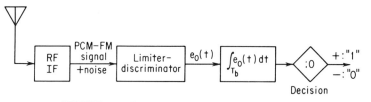

FIGURE 7.14 PCM-FM reception system model.

[†] In the next two chapters (see Art. 8.3) we shall show, using optimization techniques and statistical decision theory, that the minimum error probability for reception of orthogonal binary signalling (which PCM-FM or FSK essentially is) is given by $P_b = P[N(0,1) > \sqrt{E/2N_0}]$, where $N(0,1)$ denotes a (standardized) normal random variable having zero mean and unit standard deviation, $E$ is the signal *energy* per bit, and $N_0$ is the *two-sided* power spectral density of ambient white gaussian noise. An asymptotic expansion yields $P[N(0,1) > T] \cong (1/\sqrt{2\pi}T)e^{-T^2/2}$, within 10 per cent for $T \geq 3$. This also demonstrates the exponential behavior of the error probability with signal-to-noise ratio, as previously noted.

[‡] See McCoy, Ormsby.

$$s(t) + n(t) = V(t)e^{j\phi(t)}, \tag{7.80a}$$

where the instantaneous phase

$$\phi(t) = 2\pi \left[ f_c t + \int^t \Delta f(\tau)\, d\tau \right] + \theta(t) \tag{7.80b}$$

includes terms $2\pi \int^t \Delta f(\tau)\, d\tau$ and $\theta(t)$ relative to the unmodulated carrier due respectively to the apparent PCM-FM signal frequency deviation $\Delta f(t)$ (after IF bandwidth-limiting) and to the additive noise. Thus the output of a balanced discriminator, for 1-volt-per-cps-deviation sensitivity, is

$$e_0(t) = \frac{1}{2\pi} \phi'(t) - f_c = \Delta f(t) + \frac{1}{2\pi} \theta'(t). \tag{7.81}$$

The operation of the keyed integrator over the bit duration $T_b$ is assumed to be properly synchronized with the bit stream; thus an output is generated:

$$\int_{T_b} e_0(t)\, dt = \int_{T_b} \Delta f(t)\, dt + \frac{1}{2\pi} \int_{T_b} \theta'(t)\, dt$$

$$= \int_{T_b} \Delta f(t)\, dt + \frac{1}{2\pi} [\theta(t + T_b) - \theta(t)]. \tag{7.82}$$

Assuming equal and opposite ($\pm$) frequency deviations from the center frequency $f_c$ respectively for the transmission of the symbols "1" and "0," this output is then examined for polarity by the decision circuit, i.e., $+ \to$ "1" and $- \to$ "0." The binary error probability can thus be written

$$P_b = P\left\{ \frac{1}{2\pi} [\theta(t + T_b) - \theta(t)] > \int_{T_b} \Delta f(t)\, dt \right\}, \tag{7.83}$$

where we assume equal a priori probability of $\frac{1}{2}$ of transmitting the symbols "1" and "0," and even symmetry with respect to a mean of zero for the probability density function of the random variate $[\theta(t + T_b) - \theta(t)]$. It is thus evident that we must determine the statistics of this variate, and evaluate the threshold quantity $\int_{T_b} \Delta f(t)\, dt$, in order to calculate the PCM-FM binary error probability.

The quantities $\theta(t)$ and $\theta(t + T_b)$ are the phases of carrier-plus-noise relative to a noiseless carrier, respectively at the beginning and end of the keyed integration period $T_b$. Thus, we have

$$\theta(t) = \tan^{-1}\left[ \frac{x_c(t)}{A - x_s(t)} \right] \tag{7.84a}$$

and

$$\theta(t + T_b) = \tan^{-1}\left[\frac{x_c(t + T_b)}{A - x_s(t + T_b)}\right], \tag{7.84b}$$

where the carrier amplitude is $A$, and $x_s$ and $x_c$ denote respectively the in-phase and quadrature components of narrow-band gaussian noise [see (3.45)]. If we associate a zonal positive-frequency bandwidth of $B$ cps each with $x_s$ and $x_c$, then their autocovariance functions are given by

$$R_{x_s, x_c}(\tau) = \sigma_x^2 \frac{\sin 2\pi B\tau}{2\pi B\tau}. \tag{7.85}$$

In particular, if $\tau = T_b = n/2B$, $(n = 1, 2, \ldots)$, then $R_{x_s, x_c}(T_b) = 0$ and since $x_s$ and $x_c$ are gaussian variates this uncorrelation means that $x_{s,c}(t)$ and $x_{s,c}[t + (T_b = n/2B)]$ are statistically independent (see Art. 2.1). We may therefore infer that $\theta(t)$ and $\theta[t + (T_b = n/2B)]$ are also statistically independent, and thus determine the probability density function of the variate $[\theta(t + T_b) - \theta(t)]$ by convolving the density function $p(\theta)$ given by (3.37c) with itself, in accordance with (1.37).

The condition $T_b = 1/2B = 1/B_{IF}$ is commonly used in PCM-FM, in conjunction with a non-return-to-zero (NRZ) pulse format, wherein no idle interval is allowed between adjacent bits. The use of the NRZ format is feasible in PCM (unlike PAM and PDM where crosstalk considerations recommend a guard interval), because of less critical synchronization and recognition requirements for digital signals. Preference for NRZ operation is based on maximizing the information rate that can be accommodated by a given bandwidth, and minimizing the threshold carrier power requirement. However, the condition $T_b = 1/B_{IF}$ represents a very restrictive link bandwidth, and the output pulses delivered by the FM discriminator will be drastically distorted by comparison with the original rectangular pulses representing the digital message.

We see at this point that calculating the binary error probability of an analog-modulation PCM-FM system is not an attractive problem. One first faces the tedious task of computing the density function $p(\theta)$ given by (3.37c), then convolving this with itself, for several signal-to-noise ratios, in order to determine a set of probability density functions for $[\theta(t + T_b) - \theta(t)]$. Next, one must somehow evaluate the nonlinear distortion encountered in FM pulse transmission through the restrictive bandwidth $B_{IF} = 1/T_b$, in order to establish the threshold $2\pi \int_{T_b} \Delta f(t) \, dt$. Finally, analysis of the decision process requires integrating the probability density functions of $[\theta(t + T_b) - \theta(t)]$ upward from the threshold $2\pi \int_{T_b} \Delta f(t) \, dt$, in order to determine the error probability as a function of signal-to-noise ratio.

The urgency of this problem is not sufficient to have resulted in its solution "by hand," exactly as outlined above; neither is it really of sufficient length or complexity to warrant programming effort toward a digital computer solution. Suffice it to state that more approximate analyses, and careful laboratory measurements, confirm that error-rate performance not significantly poorer than the optimum, given by

$$P_b = P\left[N(0, 1) > \sqrt{\frac{E}{2N_0}}\right] \tag{7.86}$$

for orthogonal binary signalling, can be attained in practical analog-modulation PCM-FM systems.[†] We note finally that the quantity $E/2N_0$ (see footnote on p. 171) can be written as

$$\frac{E}{2N_0} = \frac{EB_{IF}}{2N_0 B_{IF}} = \frac{E/T_b}{k^2 B_{IF}} = (S/N)_{in, FM} \tag{7.87}$$

where the input noise power $N$ is calculated in the bandwidth $B_{IF} = 1/T_b = f_b$, the system bit rate.

In the foregoing rather lengthy chapter we have been able to introduce only three (of a great many) TDM techniques, and to cover some basic principles of analysis and design. However the reader should now be sufficiently well prepared to cope with the many other analog-modulation TDM systems.

## REFERENCES

Aeronutronic Division, Ford Motor Co., Technical Report No. U-743, *Telemetry System Study*, Newport Beach, Calif. December 1959.

Bedrosian, E.
(I) "Weighted PCM," *IRE Trans. on Information Theory*, **IT-4** (March 1958).

Bellman, R., and R. Kalaba, "On Weighted PCM and Mean-Square Deviation," *IRE Trans. on Information Theory*, **IT-4** (March 1958).

Bennett, W. R.
(II) "Time-Division Multiplex Systems," *Bell Sys. Tech. J.*, **20** (April 1941).

Black, H. S. *Modulation Theory*. Van Nostrand, Princeton, N. J., 1953.

† See Aeronutronic Report U-743, Smith, Ormsby.

Bond, F. E., and C. R. Cahn, "On Sampling the Zeros of Bandwidth Limited Signals," *IRE Trans. on Information Theory*, **IT-4** (September 1958).

Brogle, A. P., "A New Transmission Method for Pulse-Code Modulation Communication Systems," *IRE Trans. on Communication Systems*, **CS-8** (September 1960).

Childers, D. G., "Study and Experimental Investigation on Sampling Rate and Aliasing in Time-Division Telemetry Systems," *IRE Trans. on Space Electronics and Telemetry*, **SET-8** (December 1962).

Churchill, R. V.
(II) *Introduction to Complex Variables and Applications*. McGraw, New York, 1948.

Franklin, P., *Methods of Advanced Calculus*. McGraw-Hill, New York, 1944.

Glomb, W. L., "Practical Considerations in the Design of Minimum Bandwidth Digital Frequency Modulation Systems Using Gaussian Filtering," *IRE Trans. on Communication Systems*, **CS-7** (December 1959).

Goldman, H. D., and R. C. Sommer, "An Analysis of Cascaded Binary Communication Links," *IRE Trans. on Communication Systems*, **CS-10** (September 1962).

Henderson, K. W., and W. H. Kautz, "Transient Responses of Conventional Filters," *IRE Trans. on Circuit Theory*, **CT-5** (December 1958). [See also corrections: Beck, G. A., "Comments on 'Transient Responses of Conventional Filters'," *IRE Trans. on Circuit Theory*, **CT-8** (June 1961).]

Lees, A. B., "Interpolation and Extrapolation of Sampled Data," *IRE Trans. on Information Theory*, **IT-2** (March 1956).

Linden, D. A., "A Discussion of Sampling Theorems," *Proc. IRE*, **47** (July 1959).

McCoy, R. E., "FM Transient Response of Band Pass Circuits," *Proc. IRE*, **42** (March 1954).

Montgomery, G. F., "A Comparison of Amplitude and Angle Modulation for Narrow-Band Communication of Binary-Coded Messages in Fluctuation Noise," *Proc. IRE*, **42** (February 1954).

Moskowitz, S., L. Diven, and L. Feit, "Cross-Talk Consideration in Time-Division Multiplex Systems," *Proc. IRE* **38** (November 1950).

Nichols, M. H., and A. T. Bublitz, "The Effect of Different Types of Video Filters on PDM-FM and PCM-FM Radio Telemetry," *IRE Trans. on Space Electronics and Telemetry*, **SET-6** (June 1960).

Nichols, M. H., and L. L. Rauch, *Radio Telemetry*, 2nd ed. Wiley, New York, 1956.

Oliver, B. M., J. R. Pierce, and C. E. Shannon, "The Philosophy of PCM," *Proc. IRE*, **36** (November 1948).

Ormsby, R. D., "PCM-FM Telemetry Signal Analysis and Bandwidth Effects," *IRE Trans. on Space Electronics and Telemetry*, **SET-6** (September-December, 1960)

Oxford, A. J., "Pulse-Code Modulation Systems," *Proc. IRE*, **41** (July 1953).

Panter, P. F., and W. Dite, "Quantization Distortion in Pulse-Count Modulation with Nonuniform Spacing of Levels," *Proc. IRE*, **39** (January 1951).

Schwartz, M., *Information Transmission, Modulation, and Noise*. McGraw-Hill, New York, 1959.

Shannon, C. E., "Communication in the Presence of Noise," *Proc. IRE*, **37** (January 1959).

Smith, B. D., "Coding By Feedback Methods," *Proc. IRE*, **41** (August 1953).

Smith, E. F., "Attainable Error Probabilities in Demodulation of Random Binary PCM-FM Waveforms," *IRE Trans. on Space Electronics and Telemetry*, **SET-8** (December 1962).

Spang, H. A., III, and P. M. Schultheiss, "Reduction of Quantizing Noise by Use of Feedback," *IRE Trans. on Communications Systems*, **CS-10** (December 1962).

Spilker, J. J., Jr., "Theoretical Bounds on the Performance of Sampled Data Communications Systems," *IRE Trans. on Circuit Theory*, **CT-7** (September 1960).

Stewart, R. M., "Statistical Design and Evaluation of Filters for the Restoration of Sampled Data," *Proc. IRE*, **44** (February 1956).

Stiltz, H., *Aerospace Telemetry*. Prentice-Hall, Englewood Cliffs, N. J., 1961.

Storch, L., "Synthesis of Constant-Time-Delay Ladder Networks Using Bessel Polynomials," *Proc. IRE*, **42** (November 1954).

Straube, H. M., "Dependency of Crosstalk on Upper and Lower Cutoff Frequencies in PAM Time-Multiplexed Transmission Paths," *IRE Trans. on Communication Systems*, **CS-10** (September 1962).

Valley, G. E., Jr., and H. Wallman, *Vacuum Tube Amplifiers*, MIT Rad. Lab. Series, vol. 18. McGraw-Hill, New York, 1948.

Viterbi, A. J.
(I) "Classification and Evaluation of Coherent Synchronous Sampled-Data Telemetry Systems," *IRE Trans. on Space Electronics and Telemetry*, **SET-8** (March 1962).

Widrow, B., "A Study of Rough Amplitude Quantization by Means of Nyquist Sampling Theory," *IRE Trans. on Circuit Theory*, **CT-3** (December 1956).

Yen, J. L., "On Nonuniform Sampling of Bandwidth-Limited Signals," *IRE Trans. on Circuit Theory*, **CT-3** (December 1956).

Zadeh, L. A., and K. S. Miller, "Fundamental Aspects of Linear Multiplexing," *Proc. IRE*, **40** (September 1952).

# Chapter Eight

# Coherent Digital Signalling

In preceding chapters we have, with the exception of PCM, been concerned with systems intended to recover the analog form of a signal in the presence of noise. However, in digital signalling the form of the received signal is not of direct consequence; rather we are interested only in establishing the *presence* of one or another transmitted symbol. Further, since we use a finite symbol alphabet, it is possible to arrange for the transmitted waveforms to be known in advance at the receiver, i. e., to provide the receiver with a noise-free "dictionary." The availability and use of such a priori information in the receiver is generically known as *coherent* detection, and the synchronous AM demodulator discussed in Chapter 4 is an elementary example of this technique; in general, coherent detection schemes do not suffer threshold effects in the same sense that we have found for incoherent analog demodulators. Let us first develop the concept of coherent detection in greater generality, by introducing the *matched filter*.

## 8.1   THE MATCHED FILTER†

With respect to digital signalling, the specification of a filter (receiver) so as to have maximum output signal-to-noise ratio is appealing, even though the output "signal" may constitute only

† See Turin (I). Our development follows Davenport and Root, Art. 11.7.

the basis for a binary decision. Our previous discussion of PCM should establish the relevance of signal-to-noise ratio concepts within the context of digital signalling. Thus we desire to specify a linear filter to process the input signal-plus-noise, $s(t) + n(t)$, in such a way that the output signal-to-noise ratio

$$(S/N)_{\text{out}} = \frac{s_0^2(t_1)}{n_0^2(t_1)} \tag{8.1}$$

is a maximum at some chosen time $t_1$.

Let the impulse response of the optimum filter sought be denoted by $h(\tau)$, and let it operate on its input for a finite period $T$. Then from an alternate form of the convolution (superposition) integral (2.72) we have

$$s_0(t_1) = \int_0^T h(\tau)s(t_1 - \tau)\, d\tau, \tag{8.2a}$$

$$n_0(t_1) = \int_0^T h(\tau)n(t_1 - \tau)\, d\tau, \tag{8.2b}$$

and

$$\overline{n_0^2(t_1)} = \overline{\int_0^T \int_0^T h(\mu)h(\tau)n(t_1 - \mu)n(t_1 - \tau)\, d\mu\, d\tau} \tag{8.3a}$$

$$= \int_0^T \int_0^T h(\mu)h(\tau)R_n(\mu - \tau)\, d\mu\, d\tau, \tag{8.3b}$$

where $R_n$ denotes the covariance function of the noise, $R_n(\mu - \tau) = \overline{n(\mu)n(\tau)}$, and is introduced in (8.3b) by interchanging the order of integration and averaging in (8.3a). If the maximum output signal-to-noise ratio is denoted by $1/\lambda$, then for any filter we must have

$$\overline{n_0^2(t_1)} - \lambda s_0^2(t_1) \geq 0, \tag{8.4}$$

where equality holds only for the optimum filter. Further, multiplying the filter impulse response by a constant does not alter the output signal-to-noise ratio, and we may thus let the filter gain be normalized so that $s_0(t_1) = 1$. We can now derive the impulse response $h(\tau)$ of the optimum filter.

Let $g(\tau)$ be any real function such that

$$\int_0^T g(\tau)s(t_1 - \tau)\, d\tau = 0. \tag{8.5}$$

Then for any number $\epsilon$, the normalization

$$\int_0^T [h(\tau) + \epsilon g(\tau)]s(t_1 - \tau)\, d\tau = 1 \tag{8.6}$$

also holds, where we recall (8.2a). Further, introducing the notation

$\sigma^2(h) = \overline{n_0^2(t_1)}$ when the filter impulse response is $h(\tau)$, then (8.4) yields

$$\sigma^2(h) - \lambda = 0, \tag{8.7a}$$

$$\sigma^2(h + \epsilon g) - \lambda \geq 0, \tag{8.7b}$$

for any $g(\tau)$ satisfying (8.5). Subtracting (8.7a) from (8.7b) yields

$$\sigma^2(h + \epsilon g) - \sigma^2(h) \geq 0, \tag{8.8a}$$

and expanding this with the help of (8.3b) we obtain

$$\epsilon^2 \sigma^2(g) + 2\epsilon \int_0^T \int_0^T h(\mu)g(\tau)R_n(\mu - \tau) \, d\mu \, d\tau \geq 0. \tag{8.8b}$$

However, the inequality (8.8b) is satisfied for all values of $\epsilon$ only if the integral vanishes:

$$\int_0^T \int_0^T h(\mu)g(\tau)R_n(\mu - \tau) \, d\mu \, d\tau = 0. \tag{8.9}$$

To find the conditions under which this is the case, let

$$\int_0^T h(\mu)R_n(\mu - \tau) \, d\mu = a(\tau), \tag{8.10}$$

where $a(\tau)$ is any function, and select

$$g(\tau) = a(\tau) - \frac{s(t_1 - \tau)}{\int_0^T s^2(t_1 - u) \, du} \int_0^T a(u)s(t_1 - u) \, du. \tag{8.11}$$

Direct substitution from (8.10) and (8.11) shows that (8.5) is satisfied by $g(\tau)$ so defined, but from (8.9) we obtain the condition

$$a(\tau) \int_0^T s^2(t_1 - u) \, du = \int_0^T a(u)s(t_1 - u)s(t_1 - \tau) \, du, \tag{8.12}$$

which evidently is satisfied if

$$a(\tau) = \int_0^T h(\mu)R_n(\mu - \tau) \, d\mu = as(t_1 - \tau). \tag{8.13}$$

The value of the constant $\alpha$ is immaterial with respect to the signal-to-noise ratio, and affects only the normalization. By substituting $s(t_1 - \tau)$ from (8.13) into (8.2a) and (8.3b), we find that $\alpha = \overline{n_0^2(t_1)}/s_0(t_1)$.

An important special case arises where the noise power spectral density is uniform, i. e., we have "white" noise. Then $R_n(\tau) = N_0\delta(\tau)$, where $N_0$ is the two-sided noise power spectral density, and from (8.13) we obtain

$$N_0 \int_0^T h(\mu)\delta(\mu - \tau) \, d\mu = N_0 h(\tau) = as(t_1 - \tau). \tag{8.14}$$

Thus for white noise, the optimum filter impulse response has the form of the anticipated signal run backwards in time from the chosen time $t_1$ at which the output signal-to-noise ratio is to be maximized. Such a filter is known as a *matched filter*. Ordinarily, the time $t_1$ is the end of the observation interval $T$, which also usually is equal to the signal (symbol) duration; thus the matched filter impulse response generally assumes the form $h(\tau) = s(T - \tau)$. Similarly, the form of a matched filter for "colored" noise, i. e., nonuniform noise power spectral density, is easily seen. One first provides a filter to "whiten" the noise spectrum, then constructs a matched filter for the expected signal as it is altered in form by the noise-whitening filter. However, the noise-whitening filter may not in general be physically realizable, and we shall not consider further the detection of signals in colored noise.

## 8.2   CORRELATION DETECTION†

From the foregoing results, we can easily develop the form of the *correlation detector*, which is optimum for the detection of signals in the presence of white noise. Specifically, substitute $h(\tau) = s(T - \tau)$ into (8.2a); then

$$s_0(T) = \int_0^T s^2(T - \tau)\, d\tau = \int_T s^2(t)\, dt. \qquad (8.15)$$

Thus we multiply the incoming signal by a locally available replica and integrate the product over the signal duration $T$; the result is the signal energy, and the identification with correlation is obvious. The locally available replica is commonly known as the *reference signal*.

## 8.3   COHERENT BINARY SIGNALLING

For purposes of binary signalling, let us represent the two symbols "1" and "0" by transmitted waveforms $s_1(t)$ and $s_0(t)$, respectively, where these are presumed to have equal power $S$ and duration $T$. Then by definition

$$\int_T s_1(t)s_0(t)\, dt = \rho TS, \qquad (8.16)$$

where $\rho$ is the correlation coefficient of $s_1(t)$ and $s_0(t)$. For purposes

† See Green, Lee *et al.*, Mayo and Cheng.

of correlation detection, let the reference signal be $r(t) = s_1(t) - s_0(t)$ with energy given by

$$TS_r = \int_T [s_1(t) - s_0(t)]^2 \, dt \tag{8.17}$$

$$= 2TS(1 - \rho).$$

Then the result of correlating $r(t)$ with an input signal-plus-noise $y(t) = s_{1,0}(t) + n(t)$ yields an output signal component

$$S_{\text{out}}(T) = \int_T s_{1,0}(t)[s_1(t) - s_0(t)] \, dt \tag{8.18}$$

$$= \pm TS(1 - \rho).$$

The output noise component is defined as the variance

$$N_{\text{out}} = \overline{\left[\int_T r(t)n(t) \, dt\right]^2}$$

which is conveniently evaluated by first recalling that the power spectrum of the product $r(t)n(t)$ is the convolution of the individual spectra; thus

$$G_{r \cdot n}(f) = N_0 \int_{-\infty}^{\infty} G_r(f - u) \, du = N_0 S_r, \tag{8.19}$$

where we assume white noise with two-sided power spectral density $N_0$ watts per cps. Since integrating over the aperture $T$ has the power transfer function $(1/\pi f)^2 \sin^2 \pi f T$, we then have

$$N_{\text{out}} = N_0 S_r \int_{-\infty}^{\infty} \frac{\sin^2 \pi f T}{(\pi f)^2} \, df \tag{8.20}$$

$$= N_0 S_r T = 2N_0 TS(1 - \rho),$$

where we use (8.17).

Since the correlation-detection operation (essentially a matched-filter) is linear, if the input noise is gaussian, so is the output noise. Thus the binary error probability is[†]

$$P_b = \frac{1}{2} P\{N[TS(1 - \rho), \sqrt{2N_0 TS(1 - \rho)}] < 0\} \tag{8.21a}$$

$$+ \frac{1}{2} P\{N[-TS(1 - \rho), \sqrt{2N_0 TS(1 - \rho)}] > 0\}$$

$$= P\{N[0, \sqrt{2N_0 TS(1 - \rho)}] > TS(1 - \rho)\} \tag{8.21b}$$

$$= P\left[N(0, 1) > \sqrt{\frac{E(1 - \rho)}{2N_0}}\right], \tag{8.21c}$$

[†] Here, $N(m, \sigma)$ denotes a gaussian random variable having mean $m$, and standard deviation $\sigma$.

where in obtaining (8.21b) we use the symmetry of the normal probability density function, and in (8.21c) standardize the gaussian random variable and introduce the signal energy $E = TS$. The above demonstrates an important property of coherent signalling: that the error probability depends on the ratio of signal *energy* to noise power spectral *density*, with no threshold effects introduced by the detection process. Also from (8.21b) we see the role of the correlation coefficient $\rho$; specifically, in order to obtain the largest threshold, i. e., the smallest error probability, we should have $\rho = -1$, which corresponds to $s_1(t) = -s_0(t)$ or vice versa. Thus such coherent polarity-reversal binary signalling enjoys a 3-db power advantage over a system which uses orthogonal, i. e., uncorrelated, waveforms to transmit the symbols "1" and "0." In a sense, polarity-reversal signalling takes maximum advantage of a priori knowledge which can be provided the receiver concerning the transmitted symbols.

## 8.4   COHERENT PHASE-REVERSAL KEYING

Coherent phase-reversal keying (CPRK) is a particulary simple way of implementing a coherent binary signalling system. Here we simply transmit alternate phases of a sinusoid to represent the symbols "1" and "0," i. e.,

$$s_1(t) = A \cos \omega_c t \quad \text{and} \quad s_0(t) = -A \cos \omega_c t.$$

Thus the intersymbol correlation coefficient $\rho = -1$ and the binary error probability is

$$P_{b,CPRK} = P\left[ N(0,1) > \sqrt{\frac{E}{N_0}} \right] \tag{8.22a}$$

$$= \frac{1}{2}\left[ 1 - \mathscr{N}\left( \sqrt{\frac{E}{N_0}} \right) \right], \tag{8.22b}$$

where in (8.22b) we introduce the normal probability function explicitly as

$$\mathscr{N}\left( \sqrt{\frac{E}{N_0}} \right) = \int_{-\sqrt{E/N_0}}^{\sqrt{E/N_0}} e^{-x^2/2}\, dx;$$

this is the form in which it is usually tabulated. It is not particularly difficult to recover the needed reference signal $r(t) = \cos \omega_c t$ from the incoming signal, and to establish synchronization of the periodic integration over the symbol duration $T$.

There is an alternate method of treating CPRK, based on the

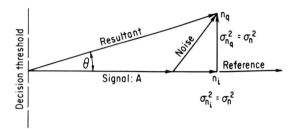

FIGURE 8.1 CPRK phasor diagram.

use of sinusoidal symbol waveforms, which we shall need as a basis for the next article.[†] Thus in Fig. 8.1 is shown a sine-wave phasor $A$ along with in-phase and quadrature gaussian noise components $n_i$ and $n_q$, each having variance $\sigma_n^2$, such as are used in the quadrature-carrier representation of a narrow-band gaussian random process having variance $\sigma_n^2$. With regard to CPRK errors, it seems natural to consider the probability of a noise-induced phase reversal of the in-phase component of the resultant:

$$P\left(|\theta| \geq \frac{\pi}{2}\right) = P(n_i \leq -A) = P(n_i \geq A).$$

Thus we have

$$P\left(|\theta| \geq \frac{\pi}{2}\right) = \frac{1}{2} - \frac{1}{\sqrt{2\pi}\,\sigma_n} \int_0^A e^{-x^2/2\sigma_n^2}\, dx$$

$$= \frac{1}{2}[1 - \mathcal{H}((\sqrt{2R})],$$

(8.23)

where the signal-to-noise ratio $R = A^2/2\sigma_n^2$. Comparing (8.23) with (8.22b) we see that the same result for the error probability is obtained if we set $R = E/2N_0$, and thus that the CPRK error probability can also be expressed as

$$P_{b,CPRK} = 1 - \int_{-\pi/2}^{\pi/2} p_{R=E/2N_0}(\theta)\, d\theta,$$

(8.24)

where $p_R(\theta)$ denotes the probability density function of the phase of the sum of a sine wave and narrow-band gaussian noise at signal-to-noise ratio $R$, as given by (3.37c). The foregoing may seem an unnecessary complication; as noted above, however, this line of reasoning is needed as a basis for the analysis to be undertaken in the next article.

† See Cahn (II).

## 8.5   DIFFERENTIALLY COHERENT PHASE-REVERSAL KEYING

Instead of correlating each received symbol waveform with a locally stored reference signal, it is entirely feasible in phase-reversal keying to use the previous symbol waveform as a reference against which to correlate the one presently being received. This technique is known as *differentially coherent* phase-reversal keying (DCPRK); a delay line one symbol duration long serves to store the previous symbol for current use as a reference signal. One might at first expect that DCPRK entails a 3-db penalty in signal-to-noise ratio required to attain a given error probability, compared with CPRK, since in DCPRK *both* input channels to the correlation process are equally noisy. This would indeed be the case if one were to calculate the error probability for *each* symbol *independently*, using a fixed decision threshold. However, in DCPRK the errors do not arise on such a completely independent basis, and it turns out that DCPRK is considerably less than 3 db inferior to CPRK in most practical circumstances. An analysis similar to the foregoing alternate treatment of CPRK serves to show this behavior.

Thus in Fig. 8.2 we show the presently received symbol phasor $A$, with noise resolved into in-phase and quadrature components $n_i'$ and $n_q'$ with respect to the previous noisy symbol $s_1$. Then the conditional probability of error, given the phase $\theta$ of the first (reference) noisy symbol $s_1$, is the probability that the second presently received symbol $s_2$ crosses the decision threshold shown, because of noise perturbation of the phasor $A$. The decision thresh-

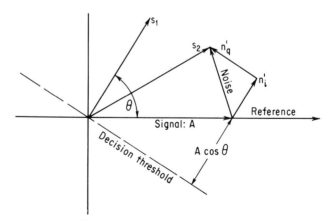

FIGURE 8.2 DCPRK phasor diagram.

old is perpendicular to the first noisy symbol $s_1$, as in CPRK it is perpendicular to the noiseless horizontal reference axis. Evidently, only the noise component $n_i'$ of the second symbol, which is parallel to the first noisy symbol $s_1$, can cause such an error, and the conditional error probability is thus the probability that the gaussian random variable $n_i'$ exceeds $A \cos \theta$, as indicated in Fig. 8.2.

Mathematically we have, for the conditional (on $\theta$) error probability,

$$(P_b | \theta) = P[N(0, \sigma_n) > A \cos \theta], \qquad (8.25a)$$

which becomes, on standardizing the gaussian random variable and introducing the signal-to-noise ratio $R = A^2/2\sigma_n^2 = E/2N_0$ (as in the analysis of CPRK),

$$(P_b | \theta) = P\left[N(0, 1) > \sqrt{\frac{E}{N_0}} \cos \theta\right]. \qquad (8.25b)$$

The total error probability is then obtained by averaging the conditional probability (8.25b) over all values of $\theta$, i.e., by integrating the joint probability density function $p(\theta)(P_b|\theta)$ over the interval $-\pi \leq \theta \leq \pi$. Thus

$$P_b = \int_{-\pi}^{\pi} p(\theta) P\left[N(0, 1) > \sqrt{\frac{E}{N_0}} \cos \theta\right] d\theta, \qquad (8.26)$$

where the probability density function (3.37c) for the phase of the sum of a sine wave and gaussian noise is rewritten for present purposes as

$$p(\theta) = \frac{1}{2\pi} e^{-E/2N_0} + \sqrt{\frac{E}{2\pi N_0}} \cos \theta \, e^{-(E/2N_0)\sin^2\theta}$$
$$\times \left\{1 - P\left[N(0, 1) > \sqrt{\frac{E}{N_0}} \cos \theta\right]\right\}. \qquad (8.27)$$

Undertaking the integration of (8.26) after substituting from (8.27) does not appear to be an appealing task; actually the desired result is fairly easily obtained. We first expand the normal distribution function as a (uniformly and absolutely convergent) power series in $\sqrt{E/N_0} \cos \theta$; thus

$$P\left[N(0, 1) > \sqrt{\frac{E}{N_0}} \cos \theta\right] = \frac{1}{2} - \frac{1}{\sqrt{2\pi}} \int_0^{\sqrt{E/N_0}\cos\theta} e^{-x^2/2} \, dx$$
$$= \frac{1}{2} - \frac{1}{\sqrt{2\pi}} \int_0^{\sqrt{E/N_0}\cos\theta} \sum_{n=0}^{\infty} (-1)^n \frac{x^{2n}}{2^n n!} \, dx \qquad (8.28)$$
$$= \frac{1}{2} - \frac{1}{\sqrt{2\pi}} \sum_{n=0}^{\infty} \frac{(-1)^n}{2^n n!(2n+1)} \left(\sqrt{\frac{E}{N_0}} \cos \theta\right)^{2n+1}.$$

We see that the terms in $\cos \theta$ are all raised to an odd power, and hence will integrate to zero over the full cycle $-\pi \leq \theta \leq \pi$. Thus in (8.26), after substituting from (8.27) and (8.28), we first have the form

$$\frac{1}{2\pi} e^{-E/2N_0} \int_{-\pi}^{\pi} \underbrace{\left[\frac{1}{2} - \sum_{n=0}^{\infty} a_n \left(\sqrt{\frac{E}{N_0}} \cos \theta\right)^{2n+1}\right]}_{\text{Integrates to zero}} d\theta = \frac{1}{2} e^{-E/2N_0}, \quad (8.29a)$$

where for brevity we write $a_n = (-1)^n/\sqrt{2\pi}\, 2^n n!(2n + 1)$. The second form arising in (8.26) is

$$\sqrt{\frac{E}{2\pi N_0}} \int_{-\pi}^{\pi} \cos \theta e^{-(E/2N_0)\sin^2\theta} \left\{\frac{1}{2} - \sum_{n=0}^{\infty} a_n \left(\sqrt{\frac{E}{N_0}} \cos \theta\right)^{2n+1}\right.$$

$$\left. - \left[\frac{1}{2} - \sum_{n=0}^{\infty} a_n \left(\sqrt{\frac{E}{N_0}} \cos \theta\right)^{2n+1}\right]^2\right\} d\theta$$

$$= \sqrt{\frac{E}{2\pi N_0}} \int_{-\pi}^{\pi} \cos \theta e^{-(E/2N_0)\sin^2\theta} \left[\frac{1}{4} - \sum_{m=0}^{\infty} \sum_{n=0}^{\infty} a_m a_n \left(\sqrt{\frac{E}{N_0}} \cos \theta\right)^{2(m+n+1)}\right] d\theta$$

$$= 0. \quad (8.29b)$$

This vanishes, since again only odd powers of $\cos \theta$ appear, and the term $e^{-(E/2N_0)\sin^2\theta}$ is an even function with respect to all integer multiples of $\pi/2$ (and has periodicity $\pi$ in the variable $\theta$). Hence the net result of integrating (8.26) yields for the binary error probability of DCPRK

$$P_{b,DCPRK} = \frac{1}{2} e^{-E/2N_0}. \quad (8.30)$$

It is somewhat surprising that the performance obtainable from DCPRK is so simply expressible, whereas the binary errror probability for CPRK, a more straightforward technique than DCPRK, involves the nonelementary normal probability distribution function. In Fig. 8.3, we plot (8.22b) and (8.30) for comparison purposes; note that at error probabilities less than about $5 \times 10^{-4}$, less than 1 db greater signal energy is required by DCPRK to attain the same error probability as in CPRK.

## REFERENCES

Arthurs, E., and H. Dym, "On the Optimum Detection of Digital Signals in the Presence of White Gaussian Noise—A Geometric Interpretation and a Study of Three Basic Data Transmission Systems," *IRE Trans. on Communications Systems* **CS–10** (December 1962).

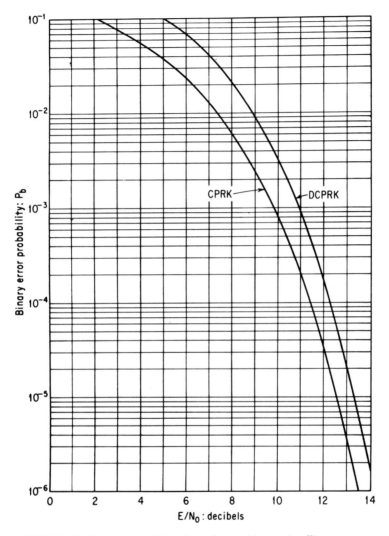

FIGURE 8.3 Error probabilities for coherent binary signalling.

Baghdady, E. J., ed.
   (V) *Lectures on Communication System Theory*. McGraw-Hill, New York, 1961.

Bendat, J. S., *Principles and Applications of Random Noise Theory*. Wiley, New York, 1958.

Cahn, C. R.
   (II) "Performance of Digital Phase-Modulation Communication Systems," *IRE Trans. on Communication Systems,* **CS-7** (May 1959).

Costas, J. P., "Phase-Shift Radio Teletype," *Proc. IRE,* **45** (January 1957).

Davenport, W. B., Jr., and W. L. Root, *An Introduction to the Theory of Random Signals and Noise.* McGraw-Hill, New York, 1958.

Glenn, A. B., "Comparison of PSK vs. FSK and PSK-AM vs. FSK-AM Binary-Coded Transmission Systems," *IRE Trans. on Communication Systems,* **CS-8** (June 1960).

Green, P. E., Jr., "The Output Signal-to-Noise Ratio of Correlation Detectors," *IRE Trans. on Information Theory,* **IT-3** (March 1957); also corrections **IT-4** (June 1958).

Kotel'nikov, V. A. (trans. R. A. Silverman), *The Theory of Optimum Noise Immunity.* McGraw-Hill, New York, 1959.

Lee, Y. W., T. P. Cheatam, Jr., and J. B. Wiesner, "Application of Correlation Analysis to the Detection of Periodic Signals in Noise," *Proc. IRE,* **38** (October 1950).

Mayo, B. R., and D. K. Cheng, "Analysis of Correlator Signal-to-Noise Characteristics," *IRE Trans. on Communication Systems,* **CS-10** (September 1962).

Middleton, D.
   (I) *An Introduction to Statistical Communication Theory.* McGraw-Hill, New York, 1960.

Price, R., and P. E. Green, Jr., "A Communication Technique for Multipath Channels" (RAKE), *Proc. IRE,* **46** (March 1958).

Turin, G. L.
   (I) "An Introduction to Matched Filters," *IRE Trans. on Information Theory,* **IT-6** (June 1960) (matched-filter issue).
   (II) "Error Probabilities for Binary Symmetric Ideal Reception Through Nonselective Slow Fading and Noise," *Proc. IRE,* **46** September 1958).

Viterbi, A. J.
   (II) "On Coded Phase-Coherent Communications," *IRE Trans. on Space Electronics and Telemetry,* **SET-7** (March 1961).

Wainstein, L. A., and V. D. Zubakov (trans. R. A. Silverman), *Extraction of Signals from Noise.* Prentice-Hall, Englewood Cliffs, N. J., 1962.

Yaglom, A. M. (trans. R. A. Silverman), *An Introduction to the Theory of Stationary Random Function.* Prentice-Hall, Englewood Cliffs, N. J., 1962.

Zadeh, L. A., and J. R. Ragazzini, "Optimum Filters for the Detection of Signals in Noise," *Proc. IRE* **40** (October 1952).

# Chapter Nine

## Optimum Signal Detection
## and Decision Theory

"Optimization" is a universally sought objective in communication systems engineering, and "optimum signal detection" is a topic having many meanings in as many different contexts, among which we can broadly distinguish two categories:

1. "Signal detection" in the sense of *processing* an available signal so as to recover the message conveyed, in a form best suited to the requirements of the ultimate receptor; and

2. "Signal detection" in the sense of most effectively *separating* a desired signal from the background of noise which inevitably accompanies it.

Throughout this book we have predominantly treated problems of the first kind: of demodulating a given signal in the presence of relatively small noise perturbations. The analysis of such problems is an important facet of communication systems engineering, and it has been our primary purpose to develop appropriate mathematical models and methods in some detail, and to present typical solutions. However, problems of the second type are also important, and indeed in a real sense represent the more fundamental aspects of modern communication system theory. In this final chapter, therefore, we shall attempt to provide some insight into the topic of optimum signal detection, and to introduce appropriate analytical philosophies. Let the reader quite clearly understand, however, that we make no pretense of exploring these subjects deeply; rather what we give here, believing it worthwhile, is an elementary "popular" account.

## 9.1   NATURE OF THE PROBLEM

Let us first consider four factors which largely circumscribe any system optimization problem. These are:

*1.* The purpose of the system;
*2.* The nature of the inputs thereto;
*3.* The performance criteria to be satisfied;
*4.* The latitude of system design allowed.

*1.* The intended system function is generally to separate a desired signal from accompanying noise in some "optimum" fashion with respect to the third factor, the system performance criteria. For the moment let us defer a more explicit discussion of this point.

*2.* It is necessary to specify, or characterize on some *ad hoc* basis, the nature of the system signal and noise inputs. Obviously, no problem exists if the noise itself is exactly known a priori or can be developed in real time; one then simply subtracts this known perturbation from the input. Further, no need for a system even exists, if the expected signal can be specified with 100 per cent certainty. Conversely, if absolutely no a priori information of any kind is available or can be gained concerning either the input signal or noise, then one would do as well to turn his equipment off and "communicate" by means of any arbitrary guesswork procedure he chooses. The significant cases, then, are those in which some, but not total, uncertainty exists concerning the system inputs. Thus the type of carrier used and the modulation format generally are known, or the signal might be a member of a finite prearranged signalling alphabet; similarly, the noise usually can be represented by a random process having known statistics.

*3.* The performance criteria are basically dictated by the intended system function but, even so, may be largely arbitrary, depending on the judgment and past experience of the user. Suppose that the system input is $x(t)$, the desired output is $s(t)$, and the actual output is $z(t)$; then, for example, we might choose as measures of performance quality

(a) $\overline{|z(t) - s(t)|}$,

(b) $\overline{|z(t) - s(t)|^2}$

(c) $P[z(t) = s(t) \,|\, x(t - \tau)]$,

(d) $P[|z(t) - s(t)| > \epsilon]$.

In (a) we weight the significance of system output discrepancies proportionately to their magnitudes, and in (b) we further emphasize the seriousness of large errors in comparison with small ones. These criteria are intuitively appealing and, indeed, the system designer might elect to use any increasing *loss function* of $|z(t) - s(t)|$; for example, $\log[1 + |z(t) - s(t)|]$. However, the mean-square criterion (b) is by far the most widely used loss function of this type, because it frequently provides the most or the only mathematically tractable basis for analysis; further, it directly yields a measure of error or output noise power which, as we have seen, is in many instances a meaningful quantity. The performance criterion (c) specifies the system whose output has the highest conditional probability of being exactly correct, given the appropriate past history of the system input. This type of criterion is especially applicable to digital systems such as were considered in Chapter 8; however, to be used directly as a basis for system optimization, a complete statistical description of the inputs is required. Criterion (d) in essence regards all errors greater than the threshold $\epsilon$ to be equally unacceptable, but tolerates errors smaller than $\epsilon$. Thus the best system under this condition is the one which minimizes the probability (d); "go-no-go" decision situations suggest the area of applicability of such performance criteria.

*4.* With regard to the latitude allowed in system design: first, we seldom are so rash as to attempt the analysis or optimization of anything but a *linear* system, or one so represented. The near-universality of this restriction arises not because linear systems are in general best, but because the difficulties involved in nonlinear systems analysis are of formidable magnitude; the isolated successes which have been achieved in this area are the consequence both of a wise choice of the problem, and of the perceptive application of mathematical wizardry. Further, we usually require physically realizable systems as a matter of practical value, divorced from considerations of analytical simplification; quite conversely, the condition of physical realizability generally demands a more sophisticated analysis.

Finally, a few words about these factors and analytical limitations in relation to the physical communications world. One may well ask whether it is possible at all to cope effectively with nature on any realistic basis. Refreshingly, the answer is yes for a large class of important problems. The class is that involving additive gaussian noise, which is precisely the perturbation by which nature more-or-less ultimately bounds the performance of any communication system. Let us enumerate some reasons why this circumstance is fortunate. First, the gaussian probability distribution is (assuming zero mean) uniquely specified by its variance $\sigma^2$; thus the mean-square performance criterion (b), in addition to fostering analytical tractability, yields a physically meaningful measure of the severity of normally distributed error factors in communication systems. Second, a normally distributed quantity, e.g., a noise current, remains unaltered statistically after passing through *any* *linear* system. Third, linear systems *are* in general best for combating gaussian noise; in particular, correlation or matched-filter detection schemes represent the optimum linear system in this context. Fourth, linear regression (correlation) yields all the relevant information concerning the possible dependence of two gaussian random variables, and if two such are uncorrelated they also are statistically independent. And so on; it is one of nature's rare gifts that the omnipresent problem involving gaussian noise is amenable to analysis and real reduction by the relatively limited techniques that we are generally able to formulate.

## 9.2   OPTIMIZATION TECHNIQUES

The theory of the optimum separation of signals from noise divides broadly into two approaches: *filter theory* and *decision theory*. To the extent that we intend to treat the first topic, it has already been presented in our discussion of the optimum interpolation filter in Art. 7.3; here, therefore, we shall only restate the problem and some of the results of its solution.

The central problem of decision theory is to establish probabilistic rules for deciding which is the more credible of alternate outcomes. The application of this discipline to the signal-detection problem is a relatively recent innovation in communication theory, and we shall give an explicit although elementary account of it in the context of the detection schemes developed in Chapter 8.†

### Filter Theory

Suppose that we are seeking a signal $s(t)$ in a background of additive noise $n(t)$; let the filter input thus be $x(t) = s(t) + n(t)$,

† See Middleton, Peterson *et al.*, Wainstein and Zubakov, Woodward, Youla.

and the filter output be $z(t)$. We propose to separate $s(t)$ from $n(t)$ by means of a *linear* filter, described by its (voltage) transfer function $Y(f)$, such that the *mean-square* difference $\overline{[z(t) - s(t)]^2}$ between the actual and desired outputs is minimized. We presume that $s(t)$ and $n(t)$ are uncorrelated sample functions of *stationary* random processes, and interpret use of the mean-square performance criterion with respect to the common situation where $n(t)$ derives from a gaussian random process (having zero mean). A solution of this optimization problem is given by the filter transfer function

$$Y(f) = \frac{G_s(f)}{G_s(f) + G_n(f)} \, e^{-j2\pi f\tau}, \qquad (9.1)$$

where $G_s(f)$ and $G_n(f)$ are respectively the power spectra of the signal and of the noise. In general this filter is not physically realizable, but it can be physically approximated within arbitrarily close tolerances by allowing a sufficiently long delay $\tau$. Thus (9.1) specifies the optimum *infinite-lag* smoothing filter, actually a fairly trivial solution of the general optimum physically-realizable smoothing and prediction problem considered in Wiener's classic work.[†] Nevertheless, the solution (9.1) does have practical value: it specifies a near-optimum filter for situations in which a "long" but finite delay is of no consequence, and in addition it is related mathematically to the optimum *realizable* filter. Equation (9.1) also has an intuitively satisfying interpretation: the best smoothing filter results when the input signal-plus-noise spectrum is more heavily weighted where the signal-to-noise spectral density ratio is large, i.e., the spectral regions which contain largely signal power are treated favorably and those containing mostly noise power unfavorably.

### Decision Theory

We shall treat decision theory from the elementary standpoint of making binary decisions in the presence of white gaussian noise. The general formulation of this problem in essence involves assigning to each possible input waveform, $x(t) = s_{1,0}(t) + n(t)$, one of two possible outputs: "1" or "0," YES or NO, etc. It is often useful to visualize this dichotomy in the following way. By the sampling theorem, each input waveform of bandwidth $W$ and duration $T$ can be uniquely represented by a set of $2TW$ sample amplitudes taken at uniformly spaced times $1/2W$ sec apart through-

---

† See Bode and Shannon, Wiener (I), Zadeh and Ragazzini.

out the interval $0 \leq t < T$. These samples can in turn be regarded as the coordinates of a point in a $2TW$-dimensional space, where each point in the space represents a different input waveform.[†] A decision rule is then constructed by assigning one or the other of the two possible outputs to each point in the space; this is equivalent to dividing the whole $2TW$-dimensional signal space into two disjoint volumes, respectively identified by "declare $s_1(t)$" and "declare $s_0(t)$" to have been the transmitted symbol.

Suppose now that two volumes, $V_1$ and $V_0$, have thus been established and that a particular input waveform $x(t)$ falls in $V_1$; thus we declare that $s_1(t)$ was transmitted, although in fact $s_0(t)$ may have been sent and the noise $n(t)$ is responsible for an error being committed. If we visualize $s_1(t)$ and $s_0(t)$ as vectors from the origin of the signal space respectively to the centroids of the volumes $V_1$ and $V_0$, then the vector corresponding to the noise must, to cause an error, carry the resultant $\mathbf{x} = \mathbf{s}_0 + \mathbf{n}$ into $V_1$ or vice versa. However, $\mathbf{x}$ is the only information available, and we cannot distinguish with certainty whether such an event has actually occurred. Thus, in order to minimize the average number of errors committed, we should for each actual input signal $x(t)$ compute the conditional probabilities[‡] $P(x\,|\,s_1)$ and $P(x\,|\,s_0)$ of receiving this waveform, under the separate assumptions that $s_1(t)$ or $s_0(t)$ was transmitted; then declare "1" or "0" depending on which probability is larger. Symbolically, this decision rule becomes: compute the *likelihood ratio*

$$\Lambda = \frac{P(x\,|\,s_1)}{P(x\,|\,s_0)} \tag{9.2}$$

and compare it with unity, declaring "1" if $\Lambda > 1$ and "0" if $\Lambda < 1$. This is an example of *Bayes' solution* of the *canonic decision problem.*

A variety of decision rules depend on the likelihood ratio. For example, after a particular signal $x(t)$ is received, all that can be known about the corresponding state of the transmitter are the conditional a posteriori probabilities $P(s_1\,|\,x)$ and $P(s_0\,|\,x)$; however, since either $s_1(t)$ or $s_0(t)$ *must* have been sent (discounting an inoperative transmitter), the sum of these disjoint probabilities is unity, and knowledge of either alone is thus sufficient. Now from Bayes' rule [see (1.14) and (1.15)] we have

---

† See Shannon.

‡ These probabilities are actually probability densities (but are not written as such), defined on a probability space whose points correspond to all the possible received waveforms $x(t)$.

$$P(s_1, x) = P(s_1 \mid x)P(x) = P(x \mid s_1)P(s_1), \qquad (9.3a)$$

$$P(s_0, x) = P(s_0 \mid x)P(x) = P(x \mid s_0)P(s_0). \qquad (9.3b)$$

Addition of (9.3a) and (9.3b), using the fact $P(s_1 \mid x) + P(s_0 \mid x)$ = 1, yields

$$P(x) = P(x \mid s_1)P(s_1) + P(x \mid s_0)P(s_0);$$

substituting this result in (9.3a), we have

$$P(s_1 \mid x) = \frac{P(x \mid s_1)P(s_1)}{P(x \mid s_1)P(s_1) + P(x \mid s_0)P(s_0)}, \qquad (9.4a)$$

which becomes, on dividing both numerator and denominator by $P(x \mid s_0) P(s_0)$ and using (9.2):

$$P(s_1 \mid x) = \frac{\Lambda \dfrac{P(s_1)}{P(s_0)}}{1 + \Lambda \dfrac{P(s_1)}{P(s_0)}}. \qquad (9.4b)$$

The quantities $P(s_1)$ and $P(s_0)$ are the a priori probabilities with which the symbols $s_1(t)$ and $s_0(t)$ can be expected to be sent, independently of what signal $x(t)$ is received; the received waveform $x(t)$ then influences the a posteriori probabilities $P(s_1 \mid x)$ and $P(s_0 \mid x)$ = $1 - P(s_1 \mid x)$ only through the likelihood ratio $\Lambda$. Thus $\Lambda$ has the property of being a *sufficient statistic*, since it per se represents all the information in $x(t)$ which is relevant to making a decision whether $s_1(s)$ or $s_0(t)$ was transmitted. For example, if $s_1(t)$ and $s_0(t)$ are equally likely a priori, then the particular Bayes' solution "compare $\Lambda$ with unity, declaring '1' if $\Lambda > 1$ and '0' if $\Lambda < 1$," is seen from (9.4b) to be equivalent to choosing the symbol with the highest a posteriori probability of having been sent.

The foregoing decision-theoretic considerations fundamentally regard system optimization in terms of *directly* minimizing the output error probability, whereas the coherent binary detection schemes of Chapter 8 were developed on the more familiar basis of maximizing an output signal-to-noise ratio. Despite the apparent logic of this latter approach, there actually is *no* guarantee that so optimizing a *linear* system constitutes an absolute optimization in the decision-theoretic sense. However, we can now show, for the case of white gaussian noise, that correlation or matched-filter detection actually is a physical mechanization of the decision rule "compare $\Lambda$ with unity."[†]

To do this we first note that the conditional probability $P(x \mid s_1)$ is simply the probability that white gaussian noise will assume

---

† See Slepian for some qualification of the following.

the waveform $n(t) = x(t) - s_1(t)$, and similarly for $P(x|s_0)$. Now from the sampling and interpolation theorems (Arts. 7.1 and 7.2) we can (neglecting end effects) represent band-limited (to $-W \leq f \leq W$) white gaussian noise in the interval $0 \leq t < T$ in the form

$$n(t) = \sum_{k=1}^{2TW} n(t_k) \frac{\sin 2\pi W(t - t_k)}{2\pi W(t - t_k)} \qquad (9.5)$$

where $t_k = k/2W$ and the samples $n(t_k)$ are independent gaussian random variables each having zero mean and variance $2WN_0$ (two-sided noise spectrum). The probability that $n(t) = x(t) - s_1(t)$ is then simply the joint probability that each of the samples $n(t_k)$ equals the corresponding $x(t_k) - s_1(t_k)$; thus

$$P(x|s_1) = \frac{1}{(4\pi N_0 W)^{TW}} \exp\left\{ -\frac{1}{4WN_0} \sum_{k=1}^{2TW} [x(t_k) - s_1(t_k)]^2 \right\} \qquad (9.6)$$

and the likelihood ratio becomes

$$\Lambda = \exp\left( -\frac{1}{4WN_0} \sum_{k=1}^{2TW} \{[x(t_k) - s_1(t_k)]^2 - [x(t_k) - s_0(t_k)]^2\} \right). \qquad (9.7a)$$

Denoting the interval between samples by $\Delta t = 1/2W$ and passing to the limit $W \to \infty$ yields

$$\Lambda = \exp\left( -\frac{1}{2N_0} \int_0^T \{[x(t) - s_1(t)]^2 - [x(t) - s_0(t)]^2\} \, dt \right). \qquad (9.7b)$$

If now the symbol energies are equal, $\int_0^T s_1^2(t)dt = \int_0^T s_0^2(t)dt$, this becomes

$$\Lambda = \exp\left\{ \frac{1}{N_0} \int_0^T x(t)[s_1(t) - s_0(t)]dt \right\}, \qquad (9.7c)$$

and since comparing $\Lambda$ with unity is equivalent to comparing $\log_e \Lambda$ with zero, we see that the Bayes' solution of the decision problem becomes: "compare $\int_0^T x(t)[s_1(t) - s_0(t)] \, dt$ with zero, declaring '1' if positive and '0' if negative." However, this is precisely the decision rule implicitly obtained in Art. 8.3 [see (8.18)] for the detection of coherent binary signals, on the basis of maximizing the output signal-to-noise ratio.[†] Thus for the canonic decision problem in the presence of white gaussian noise, correlation or matched-filter detection is indeed an optimum technique, with no qualification necessary of what is meant by "optimum."

---

[†] It is not difficult to show that use of the reference signal $r(t) = s_1(t) - s_0(t)$ to form $\int_0^T x(t)[s_1(t) - s_0(t)] \, dt$ maximizes the difference between the two possible signal outputs relative to the output noise variance (zero mean).

However, this is an unusually unequivocal result; more generally, a priori probabilities and arbitrary a posteriori judgments influence the form of the "optimum" decision system.

## 9.3   DISCUSSION OF OPTIMIZATION METHODS

The foregoing examples are similar in one respect: in both, a mean-square error or perturbation effect is fundamentally minimized. However, major differences also exist, and a comparison of filtering with decision-theory methods is an appropriate concluding topic. Possibly the most basic difference is that the filtering approach specifies the form of the signal-processing system, e.g., a linear filter, and accepts whatever output signal there results as an optimized product. Conversely, the decision-theory approach specifies the form of the output, e.g., a minimum-error sequence of binary decisions, and seeks the optimum receiving system, whatever may be its form.

This distinction profoundly affects the character of the system errors. Filtering techniques tend to discriminate against large errors, at the penalty of allowing a persistent small one. Often this represents reasonable behavior, as in conventional analog-modulation systems. It is interesting to note, in this context, that the ideal receiver treated by Kotel'nikov[†] performs identically in the presence of weak noise to the actual AM and FM receiver models analyzed in Chapters 4 and 5. Here by "ideal" is meant that receiver which *exactly* reproduces the modulating message in the absence of noise, and which produces a minimum mean-square error approximation to the message in the presence of weak noise. The mathematical manipulations necessary to show this are relatively lengthy and therefore are not given here; however, it is reassuring to note that everyday practice, intuitively conceived years ago, is consistent with contemporary theoretical predictions.[‡]

[†] See Kotel'nikov, pt. IV.

[‡] We observe that Kotel'nikov's analysis of the "ideal" receiver implicitly prohibits *any* change in its form, depending whether the received signal is noisy or noise-free. Thus the first postulate of *exact* message recovery under noiseless conditions precludes the use of a Wiener post-detection filter in the presence of noise, and the "ideal" receiver is not "optimum" in Wiener's message-distortion-plus-noise sense of minimum mean-square error. However it is possible mathematically to formulate AM and FM demodulation schemes which effect exact message recovery in the absence of noise, but which completely fail in the presence of any arbitrarily small amount of noise; in the sense then that the "ideal", and actual receivers do not behave in this fashion, they accomplish minimum mean-square error (distortionless) message recovery.

Conversely, the minimum mean-square error philosophy may not be directly applicable, as in a binary data-transmission system where an output between "0" and "1" is meaningless; here a decision-theory approach is more appropriate. When a decision system commits an error, it is a total falsehood; however, most of the time, the output is precisely correct.

The choice of a reception technique clearly depends on the nature of the desired signal. If it is analog in form, then a filtering approach is generally preferable; if digital, then a decision system may be more appropriate. However, the design of decision systems requires extensive beforehand knowledge of the signals sought and of the statistical character of the noise, whereas the implementation of an optimum filter requires only knowledge of the power spectra involved. Thus the type of a priori information that can be made available to the receiver is really the factor that governs the choice of a system and its performance.

## 9.4 CONCLUSION

In this final chapter we have attempted to give the reader a glimpse of some relevant contemporary trends of thought in modern statistical communication theory, within the context of foregoing detailed discussions. Although the surface has been left virtually intact, the author hopes he may have stimulated the reader toward deeper researches.

### REFERENCES

Baghdady, E. J., ed.
  (V) *Lectures on Communication System Theory*. McGraw-Hill, New York, 1961.

Bendat, J. S., *Principles and Applications of Random Noise Theory*. Wiley, New York, 1958.

Bode, H. W., and C. E. Shannon, "A Simplified Derivation of Linear Least-Square Smoothing and Prediction Theory," *Proc. IRE*, **38** (April 1950).

Davenport, W. B., Jr., and W. L. Root, *An Introduction to the Theory of Random Signals and Noise*. McGraw-Hill, New York, 1958.

Kotel'nikov, V. A. (trans. R. A. Silverman), *The Theory of Optimum Noise Immunity*. McGraw-Hill, New York, 1959.

Middleton, D.
(I) *An Introduction to Statistical Communication Theory*. McGraw-Hill, New York, 1960.
(II) ———, and D. Van Meter, "Detection and Extraction of Signals in Noise from the Point of View of Statistical Decision Theory," *J. Soc. Industrial and Appl. Math.*, pt. I, **3** (December 1955); pt. II, **4** (June 1956).
(III) "Statistical Theory of Signal Detection," *IRE Trans. on Information Theory*, **PGIT-3** (March 1954).

Peterson, W. W., T. G. Birdsall, and W. C. Fox, "The Theory of Signal Detectability," *IRE Trans. on Information Theory*, **PGIT-4**; (September 1954).

Shannon, C. E., "Communication in the Presence of Noise," *Proc. IRE*, **37** (January 1949).

Slepian, D., "Some Comments on the Detection of Gaussian Signals in Gaussian Noise," *IRE Trans. on Information Theory*, **IT-4**; (June 1958).

Valley, G. E., Jr., and H. Wallman, *Vacuum Tube Amplifiers*, MIT Rad. Lab. Series, vol. **18**. McGraw-Hill, New York, 1948.

Wainstein, L. A., and V. D. Zubakov (trans. R. A. Silverman), *Extraction of Signals from Noise*. Prentice-Hall, Englewood Cliffs, N. J., 1962.

Wiener, N.
(I) *Extrapolation, Interpolation, and Smoothing of Stationary Time Series*. Wiley, New York, 1949.

Woodward, P. M., *Probability and Information Theory, with Applications to Radar*. McGraw-Hill, New York, 1955.

Yaglom, A. M. (trans. R. A. Silverman), *An Introduction to the Theory of Stationary Random Functions*. Prentice-Hall, Englewood Cliffs, N. J., 1962.

Youla, D. C., "The Use of the Method of Maximum Likelihood in Estimating Continuous-Modulated Intelligence Which Has Been Corrupted by Noise," *IRE Trans. on Information Theory*, **PGIT-3** (March 1954).

Zadeh, L. A., and J. R. Ragazzini, "Optimum Filters for the Detection of Signals in Noise," *Proc. IRE*, **40** (October 1952).

# Bibliography

(Alphabetical Listing of Chapter References)

Aeronutronic, Division of Ford Motor Co., *Telemetry System Study*. Report No. U-743, Newport Beach, California, 1959.

Arthurs, E., and H. Dym, "On the Optimum Detection of Digital Signals in the Presence of White Gaussian Noise—A Geometric Interpretation and a Study of Three Basic Data Transmission Systems," *IRE Trans. on Communcations Systems*, **CS–10** (December 1962).

Assadourian, F., "Distortion of a Frequency-Modulated Signal by Small Loss and Phase Variations, *Proc. IRE*, **40** (February 1952).

Baghdady, E. J.
(I) "Frequency-Modulation Interference Rejection with Narrow-Band Limiters," *Proc. IRE*, **43** (January 1955).
(II) "Theory of Low-Distortion Reproduction of FM Signals in Linear Systems," *IRE Trans. on Circuit Theory*, **CT–5** (September 1958).
(III) "FM Demodulator Time - Constant Requirements for Interference Rejection," *Proc. IRE*, **46** (February 1958).
(IV) "Theory of Stronger-Signal Capture in FM Reception," *Proc. IRE*, **46** (April 1958).
(V) ed., *Lectures on Communication System Theory*. McGraw-Hill, New York, 1961.

Bedrosian, E.
(I) "Weighted PCM," *IRE Trans. on Information Theory*, **IT–4** (March 1958).

(II) "The Analytic Signal Representation of Modulated Waveforms," *Proc.* IRE, **50** (October 1962).

Bellman, R., and R. Kalaba, "On Weighted PCM and Mean-Square Deviation," *IRE Trans. on Information Theory*, **IT**-4 (March 1958).

Bendat, J. S., *Principles and Applications of Random Noise Theory*. Wiley, New York, 1958.

Bennett, W. R.
   (I) "Methods of Solving Noise Problems," *Proc. IRE*, **44** (May 1956).
   (II) "Time-Division Multiplex Systems," *Bell Sys. Tech. J.*, **20** (April 1941).
   (III) ———, H. E. Curtis, and S. O. Rice, "Interchannel Interference in FM and PM Systems," *Bell Sys. Tech. J.*, **34** (May 1955).

Blachman, N. M.
   (I) "The Output Signal-to-Noise Ratio of a Power-Law Device," *J. Appl. Phys.*, **24** (June 1953).
   (II) "The Demodulation of an FM Carrier and Random Noise by a Limiter and Discriminator," *J. Appl. Phys.*, **20** (January 1949).

Black, H. S., *Modulation Theory*. Van Nostrand, Princeton, N. J., 1953.

Blackman, R. B., and J. W. Tukey, "The Measurement of Power Spectra from the Point of View of Communication Engineering," *Bell Sys. Tech. J.*, **37** (January and March 1958) also Dover, New York.

Bode, H. W., and C. E., Shannon, "A Simplified Derivation of Linear Least-Square Smoothing and Prediction Theory," *Proc. IRE* **38** (April 1950).

Bond, F. E., and C. R. Cahn, "On Sampling the Zeros of Bandwidth Limited Signals," *IRE Trans. on Information Theory*, **IT**-4 (September 1958).

Brock, R. L., and R. C. McCarty, "On the Modulation Levels in a Frequency-Multiplexed Communication System by Statistical Methods," *IRE Trans. on Information Theory*, **IT**-1 (March 1955).

Brogle, A. P., "A New Transmission Method for Pulse-Code Modulation Communication Systems," *IRE Trans. on Communication Systems*, **CS**-8 (September 1960).

Brown, J. L., "A Property of the Generalized Envelope," *IRE Trans. on Circuit Theory*, **CT**-6 (September 1959).

Bruene, W. B., "Comments on 'Compatible Single Sideband,'" *Proc. IRE*, **50** (March 1962).

Cahn, C. R.
   (I) "A Note on Signal-to-Noise Ratio in Band-Pass Limiters," *IRE Trans. on Information Theory*, **IT**-7 (January 1961).
   (II) "Performance of Digital Phase-Modulation Communication Systems," *IRE Trans. on Communication Systems*, **CS**-7 (May 1959).

Carson, J. R., and T. C. Fry, "Variable-Frequency Electric Circuit Theory," *Bell Sys. Tech. J.*, **16** (October 1937).

Chessin, P. L., "A Bibliography on Noise," *IRE Trans. on Information Theory*, **IT-1** (September 1955).

Childers, D. G., "Study and Experimental Investigation on Sampling Rate and Aliasing in Time-Division Telemetry Systems," *IRE Trans. on Space Electronics and Telemetry*, **SET-8** (December 1962).

Churchill, R. V.
(I) *Fourier-series and Boundary-value Problems*. McGraw-Hill, New York, 1941.
(II) *Introduction to Complex Variables and Applications*. McGraw-Hill, New York, 1948.

Combellick, T., "Synchronization of Single-Sideband Carrier Systems for High-Speed Data Transmission," *IRE Trans. on Comunication Systems*, **CS-7** (June 1959).

Corrington, M. S.
(I) "Variation of Bandwidth with Modulation Index in Frequency Modulation," *Proc. IRE*, **35** (October 1947).
(II) "Frequency-Modulation Distortion Caused by Multipath Transmission," *Proc. IRE*, **33** (December 1945).

Costas, J. P., "Phase-Shift Radio Teletype," *Proc. IRE*, **45** (January 1957).

Cramér, H., *Mathematical Methods of Statistics*. Princeton U. P., Princeton, N. J., 1946.

Crosby, M. G., "Frequency Modulation Noise Characteristics," *Proc. IRE*, **25** (April 1937).

Davenport, W. B., Jr., and W. L. Root, *An Introduction to the Theory of Random Signals and Noise*. McGraw-Hill, New York, 1958.

Develet, J. A., Jr.
(I) "Coherent FDM/FM Telephone Communication," *Proc. IRE*, **50** (September 1962).
(II) "Threshold Criterion for Phase-Lock Demodulation," *Proc. IEEE*, **51** (February 1963).

Doob, J. L., *Stochastic Processes*. Wiley, New York, 1953.

Dugundji, J., "Envelopes and Pre-Envelopes of Real Waveforms," *IRE Trans. on Information Theory*, **IT-4** (March 1958).

Elias, P., A. Gill, R. Price, P. Swerling, L. Zadeh, and N. Abramson, "Progress in Information Theory in the U. S. A. 1957–1960," *IRE Trans. on Information Theory*, **IT-7** (July 1961).

Enloe, L. H., "Decreasing the Threshold in FM by Frequency Feedback," *Proc. IRE*, **50** (January 1962).

Feller, W., *Probability Theory and its Applications*. Wiley, New York, 1950.

Franklin, P., *Methods of Advanced Calculus*. McGraw-Hill, New York, 1944.

Fubini, E. G., and D. C. Johnson, "Signal-to-Noise Ratios in AM Receivers," *Proc. IRE*, **36** (December 1948).

Gerlach, A. A., "Distortion-Band-Pass Considerations in Angular Modulation," *Proc. IRE*, **38** (October 1950).

Glenn, A. B., "Comparison of PSK vs. FSK and PSK-AM vs. FSK-AM Binary-Coded Transmission Systems," *IRE Trans. on Communication Systems*, **CS–8** (June 1960).

Glomb, W. L., "Practical Considerations in the Design of Minimum Bandwidth Digital Frequency Modulation Systems Using Gaussian Filtering," *IRE Trans. on Communication Systems*, **CS–7** (December 1959).

Goldman, H. D., and R. C. Sommer, "An Analysis of Cascaded Binary Communication Links," *IRE Trans. on Communication Systems*, **CS–10** (September 1962).

Goldman, S.
(I) *Transformation Calculus and Electrical Transients*. Prentice-Hall, Englewood Cliffs, N. J., 1949.
(II) *Frequency Analysis, Modulation, and Noise*. McGraw-Hill, New York, 1948.

Green, P. E., Jr., "The Output Signal-to-Noise Ratio of Correlation Detectors," *IRE Trans. on Information Theory*, **IT–3** (March 1957) [corrected **IT–4** (June 1958)].

Grumet, A., "Demodulation Effect of an Envelope Detector at Low Signal-to-Noise Ratios," *Proc. IRE*, **50** (October 1962).

Heitzman, R. E., "A Study of the Threshold Power Requirements of FMFB Receivers," *IRE Trans. on Space Electronics and Telemetry*, **SET–8** (December 1962).

Henderson, K. W., and W. H. Kautz, "Transient Responses of Conventional Filters," *IRE Trans. on Circuit Theory*, **CT–5** (December 1958) [corrections by G. A. Beck, **CT–8** (June 1961)].

Holbrook, B. D., and J. T. Dixon, "Load Rating Theory for Multi-Channel Amplifiers," *Bell Sys. Tech. J.*, **18** (October 1939).

Hupert, J. J., "Normalized Phase and Gain Derivatives as an Aid in Evaluation of FM Distortion," *Proc. IRE*, **42** (February 1954).

Jaffee, R., and R. Rechtin, "Design and Performance of Phase-Lock Circuits Capable of Near-Optimum Performance over a Wide Range of Input Signal and Noise Levels," *IRE Trans. on Information Theory*, **IT–1** (March 1955).

Jahnke, E., and F. Emde, *Tables of Functions*. 4th ed. Dover, New York, 1945.

Kahn, L. R.
> (I) "Single-Sideband Transmission by Envelope Elimination and Restoration," *Proc. IRE*, **40** (July 1952).
> (II) "Compatible Single Sideband," *Proc. IRE*, **49** (October 1961).

Kallman, H. E., and R. E. Spencer, "Transient Response of Single-Sideband Systems," *Proc. IRE*, **28** (December 1940).

Kotel'nikov, V. A. (trans. R. A. Silverman), *The Theory of Optimum Noise Immunity*. McGraw-Hill, New York, 1959.

Lampard, D. G., "Definitions of 'Bandwidth' and 'Time Duration' of Signals Which are Connected by an Identity," *IRE Trans. on Circuit Theory*, **CT-3** (December 1956).

Landon, V. D.
> (I) "Impulse Noise in FM Reception," *Electronics*, **14** (February 1941).
> (II) "Theoretical Analysis of Various Systems of Multiplex Transmission," *RCA Review*, **9** (June-September 1948).

Lawson, J. L., and G. E. Uhlenbeck, *Threshold Signals*, MIT Rad. Lab. Series, vol. 24. McGraw-Hill, New York, 1950.

Lee, Y. W., T. P. Cheatam, Jr., and J. B. Wiesner, "Application of Correlation Analysis to the Detection of Periodic Signals in Noise," *Proc. IRE*, **38** (October 1950).

Lees, A. B., "Interpolation and Extrapolation of Sampled Data," *IRE Trans. on Information Theory*, **IT-2** (March 1956).

Linden, D. A., "A Discussion of Sampling Theorems," *Proc. IRE*, **47** (July 1959).

Lindgren, B. W., *Statistical Theory*. Macmillan, New York, 1962.

Loéve, M., *Probability Theory*. Van Nostrand, Princeton, N. J., 1955.

Loughlin, B. D., "The Theory of Amplitude-Modulation Rejection in the Ratio Detector," *Proc. IRE*, **40** (March 1952).

Margolis, S. G., "The Response of a Phase-Locked Loop to a Sinusoid Plus Noise," *IRE Trans. on Information Theory*, **IT-3** (June 1957).

Mayo, B. R., and D. K. Cheng, "Analysis of Correlator Signal-to-Noise Characteristics," *IRE Trans. on Communication Systems*, **CS-10** (September 1962).

McCoy, R. E., "FM Transient Response of Band-Pass Circuits," *Proc. IRE*, **42** (March 1954).

Medhurst, R. G.
> (I) "RF Bandwidth of Frequency-Division Multiplex Systems Using Frequency Modulation," *Proc. IRE*, **44** (February 1956).

(II) "RF Spectra and Interfering Carrier Distortion in FM Trunk Radio Systems with Low Modulation Ratios," *IRE Trans. on Communication Systems*, **CS-9** (June 1961).

Meyers, S. T., "Nonlinearity of Frequency Modulation Radio Systems Due to Multipath Propagation," *Proc. IRE*, **34** (May 1946).

Middleton, D.
(I) *An Introduction to Statistical Communication Theory*. McGraw-Hill, New York, 1960.

(II) ———, and D. Van Meter, "Detection and Extraction of Signals in Noise from the Point of View of Statistical Decision Theory," *J. Soc. Industrial and Appl. Math.*, pt. I, **3** (December 1955); pt. II, **4** (June 1956).

(III) Statistical Theory of Signal Detection," *IRE Trans. on Information Theory*, **PGIT-3** (March 1954).

(IV) "Rectification of a Sinusoidally Modulated Carrier in the Presence of Noise," *Proc. IRE*, **36** (December 1948).

Montgomery, G. F., "A Comparison of Amplitude and Angle Modulation for Narrow-Band Communication of Binary-Coded Messages in Fluctuation Noise," *Proc. IRE*, **42** (February 1954).

Moskowitz, S., L. Diven, and L. Feit, "Cross-Talk Considerations in Time-Division Multiplex Systems," *Proc. IRE*, **38** (November 1950).

Mullen, J. A., and D. Middleton, "Limiting Forms of FM Noise Spectra," *Proc. IRE*, **45** (June 1957).

National Bureau of Standards, *Tables of Normal Probability Functions*, Table 23, NBS Appl. Math. Series. Washington, D. C., U. S. Government Printing Office, 1953.

Nichols, M. H., and A. T. Bublitz, "The Effect of Different Types of Video Filters on PDM-FM and PCM-FM Radio Telemetry," *IRE Trans. on Space Electronics and Telemetry*, **SET-6** (June 1960).

Nichols, M. H., and L. L. Rauch, *Radio Telemetry*, 2nd ed. Wiley, New York, 1956.

Oliver, B. M., J. R. Pierce, and C. E. Shannon, "The Philosophy of PCM," *Proc. IRE*, **36** (November 1948).

Ormsby, R. D., "PCM-FM Telemetry Signal Analysis and Bandwidth Effects," *IRE Trans. on Space Electronics and Telemetry*, **SET-6** (September-December 1960).

Oswald, J., "The Theory of Analytic Band-Limited Signals Applied to Carrier Systems," *IRE Trans. on Circuit Theory*, **CT-3** (December 1956).

Oxford, A. J., "Pulse-Code Modulation Systems," *Proc. IRE*, **41** (July 1953).

Panter, P. F., and W. Dite, "Quantization Distortion in Pulse-Count Modulation with Nonuniform Spacing of Levels," *Proc. IRE*, **39** (January 1951).

Parry, C. A., "The Equalization of Base-Band Noise in Multichannel FM Radio Systems," *Proc. IRE*, **45** (November 1957).

Peterson, W. W., T. G. Birdsall, and W. C. Fox, "The Theory of Signal Detectability," *IRE Trans. on Information Theory*, **PGIT**-4 (September 1954).

Powers, K. H., "The Compatibility Problem in Single-Sideband Transmission," *Proc. IRE*, **48** (August 1960).

Price, R.
(I) "A Note on the Envelope and Phase-Modulated Components of Narrow-Band Gaussian Noise," *IRE Trans. on Information Theory*, **IT**-1 (September 1955).
(II)———, and P. E. Green, Jr., "A Communication Technique for Multipath Channels," *Proc. IRE*, **46** (March 1958) (RAKE).
(III) "A Useful Theorem for Nonlinear Devices Having Gaussian Inputs," *IRE Trans. on Information Theory*, **IT**-4 (June 1958).

*Proc. IRE*, **42** (January 1954) (second color television issue; special amplitude-modulation techniques).

*Proc. IRE*, **44** (December 1956) (single-sideband issue); also discussion, *Proc. IRE*, **45** (April 1957).

Raemer, H. R., and R. Blyth, "The Probability Density of the Phase Difference of a Narrow-Band Gaussian Noise with Sinusoidal Signal," *IRE Trans. on Information Theory*, **IT**-7 (October 1961).

Ragazzini, J. R. "The Effect of Fluctuation Voltages on the Linear Detector," *Proc. IRE*, **30** (June 1942).

Rice, S. O.
(I) "Mathematical Analysis of Random Noise," *Bell Sys. Tech. J.*, **23** (July 1944); **24** (January 1945). Also reprinted in Wax, N., *Selected Papers on Noise and Stochastic Processes*. Dover, New York, 1954.
(II) "Statistical Properties of a Sine-Wave Plus Random Noise," *Bell Sys. Tech. J.*, **27** (January 1948).
(III) "Noise in FM Receivers," *Proc. Symposium on Time Series Analysis*, M. Rosenblatt, ed. Wiley, 1963.

Rowe, H. E., "Distortion of Angle-Modulated Waves by Linear Networks," *IRE Trans. on Circuit Theory*, **CT**-9 (September 1962).

Ruthroff, C. L., and W. F. Bodtmann, "Design and Performance of a Broad-Band FM Demodulator with Frequency Compression," *Proc. IRE*, **50** (December 1962).

Sanders, R. W., "Communication Efficiency Comparison of Several Communication Systems," *Proc. IRE*, **48** (April 1960).

Schwartz, M., *Information Transmission, Modulation, and Noise*. McGraw-Hill, New York, 1959.

Shannon, C. E., "Communication in the Presence of Noise," *Proc. IRE*, **37** (January 1949).

Slack, M., "The Probability Distribution of Sinusoidal Oscillations Combined in Random Phase," *J. IEE* (London), **93**, pt. 3 (March 1946).

Slepian, D., "Some Comments on the Detection of Gaussian Signals in Gaussian Noise," *IRE Trans. on Information Theory*, **IT**-4 (June 1958).

Smith, B. D., "Coding by Feedback Methods," *Proc. IRE*, **41** (August 1953).

Smith, E. F., "Attainable Error Probabilities in Demodulation of Random Binary PCM-FM Waveforms," *IRE Trans. on Space Electronics and Telemetry*, **SET**-8 (December 1962).

Spang, H. A., III, and P. M. Schultheiss, "Reduction of Quantizing Noise by Use of Feedback," *IRE Trans. on Communications Systems*, **CS**-10 (December 1962).

Spilker, J. J., Jr., "Theoretical Bounds on the Performance of Sampled Data Communications Systems," *IRE Trans. on Circuit Theory*, **CT**-7 (September 1960).

Stewart, J. L., "The Power Spectrum of a Carrier Frequency Modulated by Gaussian Noise," *Proc. IRE*, **42** (October 1954).

Stewart, R. M., "Statistical Design and Evaluation of Filters for the Restoration of Sampled Data," *Proc. IRE*, **44** (February 1956).

Stiltz, H., *Aerospace Telemetry*. Prentice-Hall, Englewood Cliffs, N. J., 1961.

Storch, L., "Synthesis of Constant-Time-Delay Ladder Networks Using Bessel Polynomials," *Proc. IRE*, **42** (November 1954).

Straube, H. M., "Dependency of Crosstalk on Upper and Lower Cutoff Frequencies in PAM Time-Multiplexed Transmission Paths," *IRE Trans. on Communication Systems*, **CS**-10 (September 1962).

Stumpers, F. L. H. M.
(I) "Theory of Frequency-Modulation Noise," *Proc. IRE*, **36** (September 1948).
(II) "Distortion of Frequency-Modulated Signals in Electrical Networks," *Communication News*, **9** (April 1948).
(III) "A Bibliography of Information Theory," *IRE Trans. on Information Theory*, **PGIT**-2 (November 1953); 1st Supplement, *IRE Trans. on Information Theory*, **IT**-1 (September 1955); 2nd Supplement, **IT**-3 (June 1957); 3rd Supplement, **IT**-6 (March 1960).

Thaler, S., and S. A. Meltzer, "The Amplitude Distribution and False Alarm Rate of Noise After Post-Detection Filtering," *Proc. IRE,* **49** (February 1961).

Turin, G. L.
(I) "An Introduction to Matched Filters," *IRE Trans. on Information Theory,* **IT-6** (June 1960) (matched-filter issue).
(II) "Error Probabilities for Binary Symmetric Ideal Reception through Nonselective Slow Fading and Noise," *Proc. IRE,* **46** (September 1958).

Valley, G. E., Jr., and H. Wallman, *Vacuum Tube Amplifiers,* MIT Rad. Lab. Series, vol. 18. McGraw-Hill, New York, 1948.

Van der Pol, B., "The Fundamental Principles of Frequency Modulation," *J. IEE* (London), **93**, pt. 3 (May 1946).

Van Kessel, T. J., F. L. H. M. Stumpers, and J. M. A. Uyen, "A Method for Obtaining Compatible Single-Sideband Modulation," *Proc. IRE,* **50** (September 1962).

Viterbi, A. J.
(I) "Classification and Evaluation of Coherent Synchronous Sampled-Data Telemetry Systems," *IRE Trans. on Space Electronics and Telemetry,* **SET-8** (March 1962).
(II) "On Coded Phase-Coherent Communications," *IRE Trans. on Space Electronics and Telemetry,* **SET-7** (March 1961).

Wainstein, L. A., and V. D. Zubakov (trans. R. A. Silverman), *Extraction of Signals from Noise.* Prentice-Hall, Englewood Cliffs, N. J., 1962.

Ward, R. C., "FM Noise Spectra," *Proc. IRE,* **45** (December 1957).

Watt, A. D., R. M. Coon, E. Maxwell, and R. Plush, "Performance of Some Radio Systems in the Presence of Thermal and Atmospheric Noise, *Proc. IRE,* **46** (December 1958).

Wax, N., *Selected Papers on Noise and Stochastic Process.* Dover, New York, 1954.

Widrow, B., "A Study of Rough Amplitude Quantization by Means of Nyquist Sampling Theory," *IRE Trans. on Circuit Theory,* **CT-3** (December 1956).

Wiener, N.
(I) *Extrapolation, Interpolation, and Smoothing of Stationary Time Series.* Wiley, New York, 1949.
(II) *The Fourier Integral and Certain of Its Applications.* Cambridge University Press, New York, 1933; also Dover, New York.

Wilmotte, R. M., "Reduction of Interference in FM Receivers by Feedback Across the Limiter," *Proc. IRE,* **40** (January 1952).

Woodward, P. M., *Probability and Information Theory, with Applications to Radar.* McGraw-Hill, New York, 1955.

Yaglom, A. M. (trans. R. A. Silverman), *An Introduction to the Theory of Stationary Random Functions.*" Prentice-Hall, Englewood Cliffs, N. J., 1962.

Yen, J. L., "On Nonuniform Sampling of Bandwidth-Limited Signals," *IRE Trans. on Circuit Theory,* **CT**-3 (December 1956).

Youla, D. C., "The Use of the Method of Maximum Likelihood in Estimating Continuous-Modulated Intelligence Which Has Been Corrupted by Noise," *IRE Trans. on Information Theory,* **PGIT**-3 (March 1954).

Zadeh, L. A., ed., "Report on Progress in Information Theory in the U.S.A. 1960–1963," *IEEE Trans. on Information Theory,* **IT**-9 (October 1963).

Zadeh, L. A., and K. S. Miller, "Fundamental Aspects of Linear Multiplexing," *Proc. IRE,* **40** (September 1952).

Zadeh, L. A., and J. R. Ragazzini, "Optimum Filters for the Detection of Signals in Noise," *Proc. IRE,* **40** (October 1952).

Zweig, F., P. M. Schulthesis, and C. A. Wogrin, "On The Response of Linear Systems to Signals Modulated in Both Amplitude and Frequency," *IRE Trans. on Circuit Theory,* **CT**-2 (December 1955).

# Index

## A

Aliasing, 141–43
Amplitude modulation (AM), 65–83
Analog TDM systems, 149–64
    Baseband filter, 150–53
    PAM-FM, 153–58
    PDM-FM, 158–64
Angle modulation, 86–111
Aperture effect, 47–48
Arithmetic weighting, 128
Autocorrelation function, 25
Autocovariance function, 25–31
    Normalized, 25
    Properties, 25–26
    Time, 30
Average, 9–11

## B

Bandwidth considerations in FM, 89–93
Bayes' rule, 7, 194
Bessel filter, 151–53, 155, 161–62
Binary arithmetic, 167–68
    Bit, 168
Binary signalling, coherent, 180–82

Binomial coefficient, 6
Binomial distribution, 5–6
Boxcar function, 26–30

## C

Canonic decision problem, 193–94
Capture effect in FM, 109
Central limit theorem, 16–19
Characteristic function, 14–15
Chebyshev inequality, 20–21
Coherent binary signalling, 180–82
Coherent digital signalling, 177–87
    Binary, 180–82
    Coherent phase-reversal keying,
        182–83
    Correlation detection, 180
    Differentially-coherent phase-reversal
        keying, 184–87
    Matched filter, 177–80
Coherent phase-reversal keying
    (CPRK), 182–83
Commutation, 133–34
Convergence-in-the-mean, 32
Convolution, 15, 42

Correlation, 22–31
  Coefficient, 22–25
  Function, 25
Correlation detection, 180
Covariance function, 25
  Relations among, 48–49

**D**

Decision theory, 193–97
Decommutation, 133–35
Delay, 41
Derived distributions, 13
Deviation ratio, 88
Differentially-coherent phase-reversal
    keying (DCPRK), 184–87
Differentiation, 45–46
Digital errors, 168–70
  Multiple-link, 169–70
Digital message representation, 164–74
  Digitizing, 167–68
  Errors, 168–70
  PCM-FM, 170–74
  Quantizing, 165–67
Digital signalling, coherent, 177–87
Digitizing, 167–68
Dirac delta-function, 27–28
  Representations, 34, 36
  Sifting property, 27
Disjoint events, 4
Distribution, 3–4, 13, 14
  Derived, 13
  Function, 3–4
  Sum, 14
Double-sideband   suppressed-carrier
    (DSSC), 72–73

**E**

Ensemble, 11
Envelope demodulation, 69–71
Envelope function, 53
Envelope noise, 59–60
Ergodicity, 10–11, 12, 29–30
Euler equation, 145
Expectation, 11
Exponential modulation, 86–111

**F**

Filtering, 43–45
Finite-time average, 47–48
Fourier series, 31–32
Fourier transform, 32–33
Frequency-division multiplexing
    (FDM), 114–31
  FM-FM, 121–31
  SSSC-FM, 116–21
Frequency modulation (FM), 87–111
  Bandwidth considerations, 89–93
  Capture effect, 109
  Deviation ratio, 88
  Improvement, 100
  Interference, 106–109
  Limiter, 93
  Modulation index, 88
  Noise 93–106 (see Noise in FM)
  Spectrum, 87–89
  Threshold effects, 102–106
FM-FM, 121–31
  Arithmetic weighting, 127–28
  Constant-bandwidth subcarriers,
    125–27
  Peaking factor, 128
  Proportional-bandwidth subcarriers,
    123–25
  RF carrier modulation, 127–31
  Statistical weighting, 129–31
Frequency noise, 60–61

**G**

Gaussian distribution, 16–19
  Joint, 49

**H**

Histogram, 4
Harmonic conjugate, 79

**I**

Integration, 46–47
Interference in FM, 106–109

Interpolation, 137–40, 143–49
   Error, 144, 146–49
   Filter, 140
   Generating function, 138–39
   Optimum filter, 143–46

## L

Law of large numbers, 10
Likelihood ratio, 194–95
Limiter, FM, 93
Limit-in-the-mean, 32
Linear addition, 39–40
Linear independence, 24
Linear modulation, 65–83
Linear regression, 22–25

## M

Matched filter, 177–80
Mean, 11
Modulation, 41–42
Modulation index, 88
Moment, 11
   Central, 11
   Generation, 14
Multiplexing, 113–74
   Frequency-division, 115–31
   Time-division, 133–74
Multiplication, 42–43
Mutually exclusive events, 4

## N

Noise in FM, 93–106
   Baseband filter, 100–102
   Effect of modulation, 96–98
   Output noise spectrum, 95–96
   Threshold effects, 102–106
   Total output noise, 94–95
   Wideband improvement, 99–100
Noise representations, narrow-band,
   51–61
   Envelope-and-phase, 53
   Plus sine wave, 56–59
   Quadrature-carrier, 51–53
   Relationships between, 53–56

Normal distribution, 16–19
Normalized covariance, 24
Nyquist frequency, 141

## O

Optimum signal detection, 189–92
Optimization techniques, 192–98
   Decision theory, 193–97
   Discussion of methods, 197–98
   Filter theory, 192–93

## P

PAM-FM, 153–58
   Area demultiplexing, 156–58
   Instantaneous-sample demultiplexing,
     155–56
Parseval's theorem, 33
Partition, 41
PCM-FM, 170–74
PDM-FM, 158–64
   Area demodulation, 162–64
   Time demodulation, 159–62
Peaking factor in FM-FM, 128
Phase function, 53
Phase modulation, 86–87
Phase noise, 59–60
Phase-reversal keying, 182–87
   Coherent, 182–83
   Differentially-coherent, 184–87
Phasor, 60
Plancherel's theorem, 32
Power spectral density, 31, 33–39
   Periodic function, 32–36
Power spectrum, 33–39
   Arbitrary function, 38–39
   Cumulative, 33, 34
   Periodic random process, 36–37
Price's theorem, 48–49
Probability, 3–21
   Conditional, 6–7
   Density function, 3–4
   Distribution function, 3–4
   Joint, 6–7
   Space, 5, 11

# Q

Quantizing, 165–67
  Noise, 166–67

# R

Random process, 11–12
Random variable, 3–5
Rayleigh distribution, 55
Regression line, 23–24

# S

Sample function, 11, 12
Sampling theorem, 136–37
Scale change, 40–41
Scatter diagram, 22–23
Sifting property, 27–28
Single-sideband suppressed-carrier
    (SSSC), 73–77
  Outphasing, 79
Spectral analysis, 31–48
SSSC-FM, 116–21
  Preemphasis, 118–21
Standard deviation, 11
Stationarity, 12–13
  Strict-sense, 12
  Wide-sense, 12
Statistical independence, 7–9
Statistical weighting, 129–31
Suppressed-carrier techniques, 71–82
  DSSC, 72–73
  Peak power considerations, 77–82
  SSSC, 73–77
Synchronous demodulation, 68–69

# T

Threshold effects in FM, 102–106
Time-division multiplexing (TDM),
    114, 133–74
  Aliasing, 141–43
  Commutation, 133–34
  Decommutation, 133–35
  Interpolation, 137–40, 143–49
  Sampling, 136–37
  Systems, 149–74
Transform properties, 39–48
  Delay, 41
  Differentiation, 45–46
  Filtering, 43–45
  Finite-time average, 47–48
  Integration, 46–47
  Linear addition, 39–40
  Modulation, 41–42
  Multiplication, 42–43
  Partition, 41
  Scale change, 40–41

# U

Unstable transmission media, 82–83

# V

Variance, 11
Variate, 53

# W

Wiener-Kinchine relation, 37–38
Wideband improvement in FM, 99–100